ALGEBRAIC GEOMETRY

PRINCETON MATHEMATICAL SERIES

Editors: MARSTON MORSE and A. W. TUCKER

1. The Classical Groups. By HERMANN WEYL.
2. Topological Groups. By L. PONTRJAGIN. Translated by EMMA LEHMER.
3. An Introduction to Differential Geometry. By LUTHER PFAHLER EISENHART.
4. Dimension Theory. By WITOLD HUREWICZ and HENRY WALLMAN.
5. Analytical Foundations of Celestial Mechanics. By AUREL WINTNER.
6. The Laplace Transform. By DAVID VERNON WIDDER.
7. Integration. By EDWARD J. McSHANE.
8. Theory of Lie Groups. By CLAUDE CHEVALLEY.
9. Mathematical Methods of Statistics. By HARALD CRAMÉR.
10. Several Complex Variables. By S. BOCHNER and W. T. MARTIN.
11. Introduction to Topology. By SOLOMON LEFSCHETZ.
12. The Topology of Surfaces and their Transformations. By JAKOB NIELSEN and WERNER FENCHEL.
13. Algebraic Curves. By ROBERT J. WALKER.
14. The Topology of Fibre Bundles. By NORMAN STEENROD.
15. Foundations of Algebraic Topology. By S. EILENBERG and N. STEENROD.
16. Functionals of Finite Riemann Surfaces. By M. SCHIFFER and D. C. SPENCER.
17. Introduction to Mathematical Logic, Vol. I. By ALONZO CHURCH.
18. Algebraic Geometry. By SOLOMON LEFSCHETZ.
19. Homological Algebra. By HENRI CARTAN and SAMUEL EILENBERG.

ALGEBRAIC GEOMETRY

By

SOLOMON LEFSCHETZ

GEOFFREY CUMBERLEGE
OXFORD UNIVERSITY PRESS
LONDON
1953

Published : 1953 by Princeton University Press
London : Geoffrey Cumberlege, Oxford University Press

L.C. CARD 52—13158

PRINTED BY THE PITMAN PRESS, BATH, ENGLAND

Preface

The present volume grew out of a set of lithoprinted Lecture Notes issued in two parts in 1935–38 and long since out of print. The material of the Notes has been amplified considerably in places, and Chapters II and IV in parts, Chapters III and IX are new. In the main however the general program of the Notes has been preserved. In Chapters II, III, IV, on algebraic varieties the groundfield is generally merely taken infinite. In Chapters V to IX, which except for Chapter IX, are devoted to the classical study of algebraic curves, the groundfield is prudently taken to be algebraically closed and especially of characteristic zero.

It is no secret that the literature on algebraic geometry, now nearly a century old, is as indigestible as it is vast. This field is now undergoing an extensive process of recasting and reorganization in which the most advanced arsenal of modern algebra is playing a fundamental role. At all events one cannot write on algebraic geometry today outside of the general framework of algebra. On the other hand many have come to algebraic geometry and have been attracted to it through analysis, and it would seem most desirable to preserve this attraction and this contact. A common ground for algebra and analysis is found in the method of formal power series which was adopted in the earlier Lecture Notes and is utilized here again to the full. This method has made it possible for example to operate with a general groundfield of characteristic zero, and yet to provide for algebraic curves a treatment surprisingly close to the classical treatment of Émile Picard's *Traité d'Analyse*, vol. 2, or of Severi's *Vorlesungen über algebraische Geometrie*. It is not too much to say that the whole of the classical theory in which the periods play no role may be dealt with by means of formal power series.

By way of preparation it is assumed that the reader is in possession of the rudiments of modern algebra (rings, fields, ideals, polynomials and their factorization) such as are amply developed for our purpose in any recent text. On the geometric side he should also possess elementary information on affine and projective spaces. In point of fact, the topics required along these lines in the book have been summarized in the first chapter and the first few pages of the second.

We wish especially to give our thanks to Ernst Snapper, who read most carefully the whole manuscript and made many exceedingly valuable suggestions for improvement and corrections. We could scarcely exaggerate our debt to him.

S. Lefschetz

Princeton, New Jersey

Contents

ALGEBRAIC GEOMETRY

I. Algebraic Foundations

§ 1. PRELIMINARIES

1. The reader is expected to be familiar with the elementary concepts of modern algebra: groups, rings, ideals, fields, and likewise with the customary notations of the subject. Multiplication is supposed to be commutative throughout. To avoid certain awkward points appeal is made to the well known device of an all embracing field Ω which includes all the elements of rings, $\cdots$, under consideration.

(1.1) *Notations.* Aggregates such as $x_0, \cdots, x_n$ or $\alpha_1, \cdots, \alpha_m$ will often be written x or α, the range being generally clear from the context. Accordingly the ring or field extensions $K[x_0, \cdots, x_n]$ or $K(\alpha_1, \cdots, \alpha_m)$ will be written $K[x]$ or $K(\alpha)$, with evident variants of these designations. Similarly for example for the functional notations: $f(x)$ or $\varphi(\alpha)$ for $f(x_0, \cdots, x_n)$, or $\varphi(\alpha_1, \cdots, \alpha_m)$. In this connection the "partial" extensions $K[x_0, \cdots, x_r]$, $K(\alpha_1, \cdots, \alpha_s)$, will also be written $K^r[x]$, $K^s(\alpha)$, with meaning generally clear from the context.

The following symbols of point-set theory will also be utilized throughout:

$\subset$: is contained in; $\supset$: contains; $\cap$: intersection, $\cup$ union; $\in$: is an element of.

(1.2) *The groundfield.* Very soon a certain fundamental field K, the *groundfield* will dominate the situation and all rings and fields will then be extensions of K. When K is of characteristic p the universal field Ω is also supposed to be of the same characteristic. The groundfield is always assumed to be *infinite* and *perfect* (irreducible polynomials have no multiple roots in an algebraic extension of K). Often also K is supposed to be *algebraically closed* (polynomials with coefficients in K have all their roots in K). The unique algebraic closure of a field Φ is denoted by $\overline{\Phi}$.

All rings will have a unit element and will always be *integral domains* (without zero divisors) and with unity element.

(1.3) *Noetherian rings.* This all important class of rings includes all those considered in the book. Consider the following two properties of a ring $\mathfrak{R}$:

(a) *Every sequence of distinct increasing ideals of* $\mathfrak{R}$: $\mathfrak{a}_1 \subset \mathfrak{a}_2 \cdots$, *is necessarily finite.*

(b) *Every ideal* $\mathfrak{a}$ *of* $\mathfrak{R}$ *has a finite base.*

That is to say there is a finite set $\{\alpha_1, \cdots, \alpha_n\}$ of elements of $\mathfrak{a}$, the *base* of the ideal, such that every $\alpha \in \mathfrak{a}$ satisfies a relation:

$$\alpha = \Sigma\lambda_i\alpha_i, \ \lambda_i \in \mathfrak{R}.$$

One refers to (a) as the *ascending chain* property, and to (b) as the *Hilbert base* property. And now:

(1.4) *The ascending chain property and the Hilbert base property are equivalent.*

A Noetherian ring is a ring which possesses one or the other of the two properties, and therefore both.

(1.5) *The polynomial ring* $K[x]$ *is Noetherian.*

(1.6) *Every ideal* $\mathfrak{a}$ *of a Noetherian ring and hence of* $K[x]$ *admits a canonical decomposition* $\mathfrak{a} = \mathfrak{q}_1 \cap \cdots \cap \mathfrak{q}_s$ *where the* $\mathfrak{q}_i$ *are primary ideals. If* $\mathfrak{p}_i$ *is the prime ideal associated with* $\mathfrak{q}_i$, *then the* $\mathfrak{p}_i$ *are all distinct and unique.*

For a detailed treatment of the above properties see van der Waerden [1], II, Ch. XII.

(1.7) *Homogeneous rings, ideals, and fields.* By a *form* $f(x_0, x_1, \cdots, x_n)$ is meant a homogeneous polynomial. Let the quantities $x_0, \cdots, x_n$ be such that the only relations between them are of type $f_\alpha(x_0, \cdots, x_n) = 0$, where the f_α are forms with coefficients in K. Consider now a collection $\mathfrak{R}_H$ of forms $g \in K[x_0, \cdots, x_n]$ such that if $g, g' \in \mathfrak{R}_H$ then: (a) $gg' \in \mathfrak{R}_H$; (b) if moreover g and g' have the same degree then $g + g' \in \mathfrak{R}_H$ also. In other words $\mathfrak{R}_H$ behaves like a ring save that addition is restricted to forms of the same degree. We refer to $\mathfrak{R}_H$ as a *homogeneous ring* and denote it by $K_H[x_0, \cdots, x_n]$. *Homogeneous ideals* $\mathfrak{a}_H$ of $\mathfrak{R}_H$ are defined in the usual way save that addition is again restricted to forms of equal degree. Homogeneous integral domains, Noetherian rings, prime ideals, primary ideals, are also defined in the usual way and properties (1.4), (1.5), (1.6) hold with all ideals homogeneous. The quotients of forms of $\mathfrak{R}_H$ of the same degree make up a subfield of $K(x_0, \cdots, x_n)$, called a *homogeneous field* and written $K_H(x_0, \cdots, x_n)$.

The extension to *multiforms* $f(\cdots; x_i; \cdots)$ homogeneous separately in say n sets of variables $\cdots; x_i; \cdots$ is quite automatic. The rings and fields are written $K_H^n[\cdots; x_i; \cdots]$ and $K_H^n(\cdots; x_i; \cdots)$.

2. We shall now recall a certain number of properties of polynomials in indeterminates x_i, referring mainly to their factorization.

(2.1) *If* $f(x) = f(x_1, \cdots, x_n) \in K[x_1, \cdots, x_n]$ *and* $f \neq 0$, *there exists an infinite number of sets* $\alpha = (\alpha_1, \cdots, \alpha_n)$, $\alpha_i \in K$, *such that* $f(\alpha) \neq 0$.

(2.2) *Factorization in the ring* $K[x_1, \cdots, x_n]$ *is unique to within a factor in* K.

(2.3) *Let* $f, g \in K[x_1, \cdots, x_n, y] = K[x; y]$. *If* f *is divisible by* g *in* $K(x_1, \cdots, x_n)[y] = K(x)[y]$, i.e., *when both are considered as polynomials in* y *with coefficients in* $K(x)$, *and if* g *has no factor free from* y (*i.e. in* $K[x]$) *then* f *is divisible by* g *in* $K[x; y]$, *or* $f = gh$, $h \in K[x; y]$.

(2.4) *Forms.* The following properties may be stated: Let us describe the sets $(\alpha_0, \cdots, \alpha_n)$ and $(\beta_0, \cdots, \beta_n)$ of numbers of K as *essentially distinct* whenever not all the α_i, nor all the β_i are zero and there is no number $\rho \in K$ such that $\beta_i = \rho\alpha_i$, $i = 0, 1, \cdots, n$. Then:

(2.5) *Property* (2.1) *for* $n > 1$ *holds for forms when the infinite sets* $(\alpha_0, \cdots, \alpha_n)$ *under consideration are restricted to sets essentially distinct in pairs.*

(2.6) *The factorization properties* (2.2) *and* (2.3) *hold when all the polynomials are forms.*

A polynomial or form $f(x_1, \cdots, x_n)$ of degree s is said to be *regular* in x_i if it contains a term in x_i^s.

(2.7) *Given a polynomial or form* $f(x_0, \cdots, x_n) \in K[x_0, \cdots, x_n]$ *it is always possible to find a non-singular linear transformation*

$$x_i = \Sigma a_{ij} y_j, \quad a_{ij} \in K, \left| a_{ij} \right| \neq 0$$

which changes f *into a new polynomial or form* $g(y_0, \cdots, y_n)$ *regular in some or all the variables* y_j.

§ 2. Resultants and Elimination

3. We shall recall some elementary properties of resultants and elimination theory. For further elaboration and proofs the reader is referred to treatises on algebra, and notably to van der Waerden, [1], II, Chapter XI, and E. Netto, [1], II.

Consider first two polynomials in one variable x:

$$f = a_0 x^m + a_1 x^{m-1} + \cdots + a_m, \quad g = b_0 x^n + \cdots + b_n$$

where the a_i, b_j are indeterminates. The resultant $R(f, g)$ is a doubly homogeneous form in the a_i, b_j, whose coefficients are integers and whose explicit expression is well known but will not be required here. Let $\mathfrak{R}$ be the rational field, $\mathfrak{L}$ any finite algebraic extension of $\mathfrak{R}$ and let $\mathfrak{R}_H^2[a; b]$ and $\mathfrak{L}_H^2[a; b]$ be the associated doubly homogeneous rings of the a_i, b_i. Then the only pertinent facts as to the resultant are:

(3.1) $R(f, g)$ *is of degree* n *in the* a_i *and* m *in the* b_j. *One of its terms is* $a_0^n b_n^m$.

(3.2) $R(f, g)$ *is irreducible in every ring* $\mathfrak{L}_H^2[a; b]$. (This is so-called "absolute irreducibility.")

(3.3) *There exist unique polynomials* A *and* B *of degrees at most* $n - 1$ *and* $m - 1$ *in* x, *with coefficients in* $\mathfrak{R}_H^2[a; b]$, *such that*

$$Af + Bg = R. \qquad (3.3a)$$

(3.4) *Let the coefficients* a_i, b_j *and the roots* ξ_i *of* f *and* η_j *of* g *be elements of a field* K. *Then*

$$R(f, g) = a_0^n b_0^m \Pi(\xi_i - \eta_j) = a_0^n \Pi g(\xi_i) = (-1)^{mn} b_0^m \Pi f(\eta_j).$$

(3.5) *Let* f *and* g *have their coefficients in a field* K. *If they have a common factor* $\in \bar{K}[x]$ *then* $R = 0$. *Conversely if* $R = 0$ *and* a_0 *or* $b_0 \neq 0$ *then* f *and* g *have a common factor* $\in \bar{K}[x]$.

Let now f, g be forms of degrees m, n in $x_0, \cdots, x_r$. Let $R(f; g; x_i)$ denote the resultant as to x_i, i.e. as if f and g were polynomials in x_i. Then:

(3.6) *Let* f *or* g *have indeterminate coefficients. Then* $R(f, g; x_r)$ *is a form of degree* mn *in* $x_0, \cdots, x_{r-1}$, *and in* (3.3a) A *and* B *are forms in all the* x_i *and of degrees* $\leq n - 1$ *and* $m - 1$ *in* x_r. *Moreover a n.a.s.c. in order that* $f, g \in K_H[x_0, \cdots, x_r]$ *both containing* x_r *and one of them regular in* x_r *have a common factor containing* x_r *is that* $R(f, g; x_r) = 0$. *When it exists the common factor is in* $K_H[x_0, \cdots, x_r]$.

Consider now $r + 1$ forms in $x_0, \cdots, x_r$ with indeterminate coefficients and let m_i be the degree of f_i and $m = \Pi m_i$. There exists a multiform $R_H(f_0, \cdots, f_r)$ in the sets of coefficients of the f_i, whose coefficients are integers, the *resultant* of the f_i, and with the following properties:

(3.7) R_H *is of degree* m/m_i *in the coefficients of* f_i.

(3.8) R_H *is absolutely irreducible in the ring of multiforms with integral coefficients.*

(3.9) *There take place identities*

$$\Sigma A_j^i f_j = x_i^{s_i} R_H, \quad i = 0, 1, \cdots, r$$

where the A_j^i *are multiforms with integral coefficients in the coefficients of the* f_j *and in the* x_i.

(3.10) *If one takes for the* f_i *forms of* $K_H[x_0, \cdots, x_r]$ *then* $R_H = 0$ *is a n.a.s.c. in order that the system*

$$f_0 = \cdots = f_r = 0$$

admit a solution with the x_i *not all zero and in* $\bar{K}$.

(3.11) *If* $a_i x_i^{m_i}$ *is the highest degree term in* x_i *of* f_i *then* R_H *contains a term* $\Pi a_i^{m/m_i}$.

More generally given any set of forms $f_0, \cdots, f_p$ with indeterminate coefficients there exists a resultant system $R_H^i(f_0, \cdots, f_p)$, $i = 1, 2, \cdots, q$ where each R_H^i is an irreducible multiform such as R_H above and now:

(3.12) *Same as* (3.10) *with* $R_H^i = 0$, $i = 1, 2, \cdots, q$ *as the n.a.s.c.*

§ 3. ALGEBRAIC DEPENDENCE. TRANSCENDENCY

4. Let Φ be a field over K. The elements $\alpha_1, \cdots, \alpha_p$ of Φ are said to be *algebraically dependent over* K whenever they satisfy a relation $P(\alpha_1, \cdots, \alpha_p) = 0$, $P(\alpha_1, \cdots, \alpha_p) \in K[\alpha_1, \cdots, \alpha_p]$. If the term α_1 is actually present in P we say that α_1 is *algebraically dependent on* $\alpha_2, \cdots, \alpha_p$ *over* K. As the groundfield K is generally clear from the context the mention "over K" is usually omitted.

A *transcendence base* $\{\alpha_i\}$ *for* Φ *over* K is a set of elements of Φ such that: (a) no finite subset of the α_i is algebraically dependent; (b) every element $\alpha \in \Phi$ is algebraically dependent upon some finite subset of $\{\alpha_i\}$.

(4.1) *If the number* p *of elements in one transcendence base is finite (only such cases arise in the sequel) then it is the same for all other such bases.*

The number p of elements in a transcendence base is called the *transcendency* of Φ *over* K, written $\operatorname{transc}_K \Phi$, or merely $\operatorname{transc} \Phi$ when the particular K is clear from the context.

One may manifestly define the transcendency ρ over K of any set $\{\alpha_1, \cdots, \alpha_s\}$ of elements of Φ as the maximum number of elements which are algebraically independent over K. Let $\Psi = K(\alpha_1, \cdots, \alpha_s)$, so that Ψ is a field between K and Φ. It is readily shown that $\operatorname{transc} \Psi = \rho$.

(4.2) *If* $K \subset L \subset \Phi$, *where all three are fields then* $\operatorname{transc}_K \Phi = \operatorname{transc}_L \Phi + \operatorname{transc}_K L$.

(4.3) *Rational and homogeneous bases.* These two concepts will be found very convenient later. Given a field L over K we will say that a set $\{\alpha_1, \cdots, \alpha_n\}$ of elements of L is a *rational base* for L over K whenever $L = K(\alpha_1, \cdots, \alpha_n)$. A set of elements $\{\beta_0, \cdots, \beta_r\}$ of some field Ψ over L is known as a *homogeneous base* for L over K whenever

$$L = K(\{\beta_i/\beta_j\}), \ \beta_j \neq 0.$$

If $\beta_h \neq 0$ then this condition is equivalent to $L = K(\{\beta_i/\beta_h\})$ where β_h is now fixed.

(4.4) *If* L *has a finite rational base then* $r = \operatorname{transc}_K L$ *is finite.*

Another noteworthy property is:

(4.5) *Let* K *have zero characteristic. Then if* $\{\alpha_1, \cdots, \alpha_r\}$ *is a transcendence base for* L *over* K *and* L *is a finite extension of* $K(\alpha_1, \cdots, \alpha_r)$ *there exists an element* β *of* L *such that* $\{\alpha_1, \cdots, \alpha_r, \beta\}$ *is a rational base for* L. *Hence if* M *is a field over* L *and* $\alpha_0, \cdots, \alpha_r \in M$ *are such that* $\{\alpha_i/\alpha_0\}$ *is a transcendence base for* L *and* L *is a finite extension of* $K(\{\alpha_i/\alpha_0\})$, *there exists an* $\alpha_{r+1} \in M$ *with* $\alpha_{r+1}/\alpha_0 \in L$ *such that* $\{\alpha_0, \cdots, \alpha_{r+1}\}$ *is a homogeneous base for* L.

§ 4. Extension of the Groundfield

5. In many questions arising naturally in the study of algebraic varieties it is necessary to replace the groundfield K by a finite *pure* transcendental extension, that is to say by an extension $K(u_1, \cdots, u_r)$ by a finite number of indeterminates.

We are particularly interested in what happens then to the polynomial ideals and their mutual relations. Since all questions are trivial for the ideal $\mathfrak{a} = 1$, consisting of all polynomials of the ring $K[x] = K[x_1, \cdots, x_n]$, we assume throughout $\mathfrak{a} \neq 1$.

Let us suppose that the ideal $\mathfrak{a}$ has the base $\{f_1(x), \cdots, f_r(x)\}$. Upon replacing K by any field $L \supset K$ the f_i will span in $L[x]$ a new ideal $\mathfrak{a}^*$ referred to as the *extension* of $\mathfrak{a}$. Let in particular $L = K(u_1, \cdots, u_s)$ be an extension by indeterminates u_j. If $f(x; u_1, \cdots, u_s) \in L[x]$ and disregarding a common denominator $\in L$, we may write

$$f(x; u_1, \cdots, u_s) = \Sigma f_{\alpha \cdots \beta}(x) u_1^{\alpha} \cdots u_s^{\beta}, f_{\alpha \cdots \beta} \in K[x].$$

Then $f \in \mathfrak{a}^*$ is equivalent to: every $f_{\alpha \cdots \beta} \in \mathfrak{a}$. If the extension is by a single variable u we will write

$$(5.1) \qquad f(x; u) = f_0(x)u^n + f_1(x)u^{n-1} + \cdots, f_i \in K[x].$$

The extension operation $\mathfrak{a} \to \mathfrak{a}^*$ has the following properties:

(5.2) *It preserves the relations of inclusion, sum, intersection and product.*

(5.3) *If* $\mathfrak{p}$, $\mathfrak{q}$ *are a prime and a primary ideal then so are* $\mathfrak{p}^*$, $\mathfrak{q}^*$.

(5.4) *If* $\mathfrak{p}$ *is the prime ideal of* $\mathfrak{q}$ *then* $\mathfrak{p}^*$ *is the prime ideal of* $\mathfrak{q}^*$ *and if* $\mathfrak{p}^\rho \subset \mathfrak{q}$ *then* $\mathfrak{p}^{*\rho} \subset \mathfrak{q}^*$.

(5.5) *The factorization into primary ideals is preserved.*

Observe at the outset that it is sufficient to consider a simple extension $K(u)$. Moreover since elements of the groundfield may be multiplied in without affecting our arguments we may always assume our polynomials to be polynomials in u also. Finally (5.2) and the derivation of (5.4), (5.5) from (5.2), (5.3) are elementary. Thus we only need to take up the proof of (5.3). The case of prime ideals is simple and indeed it reduces essentially to Eisenstein's classical lemma. We consider it first.

Suppose then $\mathfrak{p}$ prime and let

$$(5.6) \qquad \begin{cases} a(x; u) = a_0(x)u^m + a_1(x)u^{m-1} + \cdots + a_m(x) \\ b(x; u) = b_0(x)u^n + \cdots + b_n(x), \end{cases}$$

where $a_i, b_j \in K[x]$. Suppose now that $ab \in \mathfrak{p}^*$. We may manifestly suppress in a and b the terms whose coefficients $a_i, b_j \in \mathfrak{p}$. If as a consequence say a reduces to zero then it was initially in $\mathfrak{p}^*$. Suppose that neither a nor b reduces to zero. Thus we will have (5.6) with a_0, b_0 not in $\mathfrak{p}$. Since $ab \in \mathfrak{p}^*$ all the coefficients of the powers of u in ab must be in $\mathfrak{p}$. Hence $a_0 b_0 \in \mathfrak{p}$ and since $\mathfrak{p}$ is prime one of the factors say $a_0 \in \mathfrak{p}$. This contradiction proves that, say in a, all the coefficients are in $\mathfrak{p}^*$. Hence $a \in \mathfrak{p}^*$ and $\mathfrak{p}^*$ is prime.

6. The case of the primary ideal $\mathfrak{q}$ is much more difficult. Following E. Snapper, its treatment will be made to rest upon a noteworthy lemma due to Dedekind.

(6.1) **Lemma.** *Let a, b be as in* (5.6) *and let*

$$ab = c(x; u) = c_0(x)u^{m+n} + \cdots + c_{m+n}(x).$$

If $\mathfrak{a}$, $\mathfrak{b}$, $\mathfrak{c}$ are the ideals of $K[x]$ spanned respectively by the a_i, b_j, c_k then $\mathfrak{a}^{n+1}\mathfrak{b} = \mathfrak{c}\mathfrak{a}^n$.

We follow Dedekind's own proof as given in: Gesammelte Werke, pp. 36–38. It is clear that $\mathfrak{c} \subset \mathfrak{a}\mathfrak{b}$ hence $\mathfrak{c}\mathfrak{a}^n \subset \mathfrak{a}^{n+1}\mathfrak{b}$. All that is necessary then is to show that the inclusion may be reversed.

Consider first the ideal $\mathfrak{a}^{n+1}$. A finite base for $\mathfrak{a}^{n+1}$ consists of all the products α_j of any $n + 1$ of the coefficients a_h. Now $\alpha_j = a_{r_0}a_{r_1-1} \cdots a_{r_n-n}$, $r_0 < r_1 < \cdots < r_n$. Let all the products α_j be ordered lexicographically, and let us agree to set $a_i = 0$ wherever $i > m$. Suppose also the elements of the base $\alpha_0, \alpha_1, \cdots, \alpha_s$ written in increasing order.

Now corresponding to α_j above we may introduce the determinant

$$\delta_j = \left| a_{r_i}, a_{r_i-1}, \cdots, a_{r_i-n} \right|, \quad i = 0, 1, \cdots, n.$$

In its expansion α_j, the diagonal term, is the term of highest order: $\delta_j = \alpha_j +$ terms α_h preceding α_j. Taking then successively $j = s$, $s - 1, \cdots$, this relation will enable us to replace in succession, in the base $\{\alpha_j\}$, the elements $\alpha_s, \alpha_{s-1}, \cdots$ by $\delta_s, \delta_{s-1}, \cdots$. In other words $\Delta = \{\delta_j\}$ is a base for $\mathfrak{a}^{n+1}$.

Consider now the following system obtained by equating the powers of u in $ab = c$:

$$(6.2) \qquad a_i b_0 + a_{i-1}b_1 + \cdots = c_i, \quad i = 0, 1, 2, \cdots m + n.$$

We may view (6.2) as a set of linear equations in the b_i. The equations beginning with $a_{r_0}, \cdots, a_{r_n}$ have δ_j for determinant of the b's. Hence if $\delta_j \neq 0$, i.e. if δ_j does figure in the base Δ, then the subsystem of the equations just mentioned yields relations

$$\delta_j b_h = \Sigma c_{r_i}\delta_{ji}, \quad h = 0, 1, \cdots, n$$

where the δ_{ji} are minors of order n of δ_j and thus elements of $\mathfrak{a}^n$. Since $\{\delta_j b_k\}$ is a base for $\mathfrak{a}^{n+1}\mathfrak{b}$, this relation implies $\mathfrak{a}^{n+1}\mathfrak{b} \subset \mathfrak{c}\mathfrak{a}^n$. This completes the proof of the lemma.

Returning now to our main problem the proof of (5.3) for $\mathfrak{q}$ primary is immediate. Let $a, b \in K(u)[x]$ where b is not in $\mathfrak{q}^*$. If $c = ab$ then $c \in \mathfrak{q}^*$ implies $\mathfrak{c} \subset \mathfrak{q}$ and b not in $\mathfrak{q}^*$ implies that $\mathfrak{b}$ is not in $\mathfrak{q}$. By the lemma $\mathfrak{a}^{n+1}\mathfrak{b} = \mathfrak{c}\mathfrak{a}^n \subset \mathfrak{q}$. Since $\mathfrak{q}$ is primary and $\mathfrak{b}$ is not in $\mathfrak{q}$, $\mathfrak{a}^{n+1}$ is in $\mathfrak{p}$, hence $\mathfrak{a}$ is in $\mathfrak{p}$ since $\mathfrak{p}$ is prime. If $\mathfrak{p}^\sigma \subset \mathfrak{q}$, then in a^σ every coefficient of u is in $\mathfrak{p}^\sigma$ hence in $\mathfrak{q}$ and so $a^\sigma \in \mathfrak{q}^*$. Hence $\mathfrak{q}^*$ is a primary ideal and this completes the proof of (5.3).

§ 5. DIFFERENTIALS (CHARACTERISTIC ZERO)

7. We shall find it convenient to organise differentiation with differentials and not derivatives in the central position. The treatment, largely following Ernst Snapper, is confined to a field Φ of finite transcendency over a groundfield K.

Let Φ be of transcendency n over K. It is referred to as a *differential field* whenever there is: (a) an n dimensional vector space $\mathfrak{B}$ with Φ as its scalar domain; (b) an operation d: $\Phi \to \mathfrak{B}$ such that if $\alpha, \beta \in \Phi$ and $k \in K$ then:

I. $d(\alpha + \beta) = d\alpha + d\beta$; II. $d\alpha\beta = \alpha d\beta + \beta d\alpha$; III. $dk = 0$; IV. the $d\alpha, d\beta, \cdots$, are a set of generators for $\mathfrak{B}$.

The space $\mathfrak{B}$ is the *space of the differentials of* Φ *over* K, and $d\alpha$ is the *differential of* α *over* K.

Immediate consequences of I, II, III are

$$(7.1) \qquad d(k\alpha) = kd\alpha; \qquad d\alpha^n = n\alpha^{n-1}d\alpha.$$

If $\gamma = \alpha/\beta$, then $\alpha = \beta\gamma$, hence quickly from II:

$$(7.2) \qquad d\frac{\alpha}{\beta} = \frac{\beta d\alpha - \alpha d\beta}{\beta^2}.$$

If $R(\alpha_1, \cdots, \alpha_p) \in K(\alpha_1, \cdots, \alpha_p)$ denote by R_{α_i} the usual partial derivative (taken as if the α_i were indeterminates). Then:

(7.3) *If* $F(x_1, \cdots, x_p) \in K[x_1, \cdots, x_p]$ *where the* x_i *are indeterminates, then* $F_{x_i} = 0$ *is a n.a.s.c. for* F *not to contain* x_i.

(7.4) *If* $R(\alpha_1, \cdots, \alpha_p) \in K(\alpha_1, \cdots, \alpha_p)$, $\alpha_i \in \Phi$ *then* $dR = \Sigma R_{\alpha_i} d\alpha_i$. It is first proved for a polynomial then by means of (7.2) for any R.

(7.5) *If* $\mathfrak{A} = \{\alpha_1, \cdots, \alpha_n\}$ *is a transcendence base for* Φ *then* $d\mathfrak{A} = \{d\alpha_i\}$ *is a linear base for* $\mathfrak{B}$.

If $\beta \in \Phi$ there is a relation

$$(7.6) \qquad F(\alpha; \beta) = \beta^r + F_1\beta^{r-1} + \cdots + F_r = 0, \; F_i \in K(\alpha),$$

where $F(\alpha; x)$ is irreducible as an element of $K(\alpha)[x]$. Owing to this it has no common factor with

$$F_x = rx^{r-1} + (r-1)F_1x^{r-2} + \cdots$$

whose degree $< r$, and hence $F_\beta \neq 0$. Applying (7.4) we find

$$F_\beta d\beta + \Sigma F_{\alpha_i} d\alpha_i = 0$$

and hence

$$(7.7) \qquad d\beta = -\sum \frac{F_{\alpha_i}}{F_\beta} d\alpha_i.$$

Therefore $d\mathfrak{A}$ spans $\mathfrak{B}$.

(7.8) The ordinary or partial successive derivatives of various orders are defined in the obvious way. We merely recall:

(7.9) *Let $f(x) \in K[x]$, x indeterminate. N.a.s.c. in order that $c \in \bar{K}$ be an n-tuple root of $f(x)$ are:*

$$f(c) = f'(c) = \cdots = f^{(n-1)}(c) = 0, \quad f^{(n)}(c) \neq 0.$$

(7.10) *Remark.* Ordinary or partial derivatives of any order may be defined for a groundfield of any characteristic and the formal properties (7.3) and (7.9) continue to hold.

8. Construction of a system of differentials. Take for the $d\alpha_i$ independent vectors and compute $d\beta$ for any $\beta \in \Phi$ by (7.7). This defines d obeying rules I, II, III over a simple extension $\Phi_\beta = K(\alpha; \beta)$. Let us show that it is unique over Φ_β. An element γ of Φ_β may have various representations

$$\gamma = R(\alpha; \beta) = R_1(\alpha; \beta) = \cdots,$$

and we must show that

$$dR(\alpha, \beta) = dR_1(\alpha, \beta) = \cdots.$$

In the last analysis we must prove that if $S(\alpha; \beta) \in K(\alpha; \beta)$ and $S(\alpha; \beta) = 0$ then $dS(\alpha; \beta) = 0$. This follows however by rule III.

Suppose now $\beta \in \Phi_\gamma$. Since d is uniquely defined throughout Φ_γ, $d\beta$ is the same whether obtained as element of Φ_β or of Φ_γ. Hence d is unique throughout Φ.

9. We shall now show that the system $(d, \mathfrak{V})$ is essentially unique.

Let Φ, Φ' be isomorphic fields over K under an isomorphism $\tau\colon \Phi \to \Phi'$ preserving K, and let d, $\mathfrak{V}$ and d', $\mathfrak{V}'$ have their natural meaning. A *differential isomorphism of $\mathfrak{V}$ onto $\mathfrak{V}'$* is a mapping $\Delta\colon \mathfrak{V} \to \mathfrak{V}'$ such that if $V, V_1 \in \mathfrak{V}$ and $\alpha \in \Phi$ then

$$\Delta(V + V_1) = \Delta V + \Delta V_1; \quad \Delta(\alpha V) = \tau\alpha \Delta V; \quad \Delta d\alpha = d'(\tau\alpha).$$

(9.1) *$\mathfrak{V}$ and $\mathfrak{V}'$ are differentially isomorphic. Hence in a given field differentiation is unique to within a differential isomorphism.*

If we write α_i', β', R' for $\tau\alpha_i, \tau\beta, \tau R$ then under our rules $d'\beta'$ is given by (7.7) with the appropriate changes. Define now $\Delta d\alpha_j = d'\alpha_j'$, $\Delta(\gamma d\alpha_j) = \gamma' d'\alpha_j'$, and extend Δ linearly to the whole of $\mathfrak{V}$ which can be done since $\{d\alpha_j\}$ is a base for $\mathfrak{V}$. As a consequence Δ is manifestly a differential isomorphism $\mathfrak{V} \to \mathfrak{V}'$.

10. (10.1) *If $\alpha_1, \cdots, \alpha_k$ are algebraically independent elements of Φ then $d\alpha_1, \cdots, d\alpha_k$ are linearly independent elements of $\mathfrak{V}$ and conversely.*

The algebraic independence of the α_i, $i \leq k$, implies $k \leq n = \text{transc}\,\Phi$. Hence one may then augment the set by elements $\alpha_{k+1}, \cdots, \alpha_n$, to form a transcendence base $\mathfrak{A} = \{\alpha_j\}$. Since the $d\alpha_j$, $j \leq n$, are linearly independent elements of $\mathfrak{V}$ (7.5) the same holds for those with $j \leq k$.

Conversely let $d\alpha_1, \cdots, d\alpha_k$ be linearly independent elements of $\mathfrak{B}$. This implies $k \leq n = \dim \mathfrak{B}$. Suppose now $\alpha_1, \cdots \alpha_k$ algebraically dependent. Thus there is a relation $F(\alpha_1, \cdots, \alpha_k) = 0$, $F(\alpha) \in K[\alpha]$, where not every $F_{\alpha_i} = 0$. Now $F(\alpha) = 0$ implies

$$dF = \Sigma F_{\alpha_i} d\alpha_i = 0.$$

Hence the $d\alpha_i$ are linearly dependent. This contradiction shows that $\alpha_1, \cdots, \alpha_k$ are algebraically independent.

(10.2) *Noteworthy special case: If $d\alpha = 0$, $\alpha \in \Phi$, then α is algebraic over K. Hence if K is algebraically closed $\alpha \in K$. Thus if K is algebraically closed the elements of K are those and only those elements of Φ whose differentials are zero.*

11. Derivatives and Jacobians. Let again $\mathfrak{A} = \{\alpha_1, \cdots, \alpha_n\}$ be a transcendence base for Φ, and $\beta \in \Phi$. Then $d\beta$ is given by (7.7) in terms of the $d\alpha_i$. The coefficient of $d\alpha_i$ is the *partial derivative of β relative to α_i* and written $\partial\beta/\partial\alpha_i$. We have explicitly

$$\frac{\partial \beta}{\partial \alpha_i} = -\frac{F_{\alpha_i}}{F_\beta}. \tag{11.1}$$

If $\beta_1, \cdots, \beta_m$ are elements of Φ then

$$\left\| \frac{\partial \beta_i}{\partial \alpha_j} \right\| \tag{11.2}$$

is the usual *Jacobian matrix*. If $m = n$ then the determinant of (11.2) is the *Jacobian determinant* or *functional determinant* written

$$\frac{D(\beta_1, \cdots, \beta_n)}{D(\alpha_1, \cdots, \alpha_n)}.$$

From the relations

$$d\beta_i = \sum \frac{\partial \beta_i}{\partial \alpha_j} d\alpha_j \tag{11.3}$$

and the fact that $\{d\alpha_j\}$ is a linear base for the space of the differentials together with (10.1) follows:

(11.4) *A n.a.s.c. for $\beta_1, \cdots, \beta_m \in \Phi$ to be algebraically independent is that the Jacobian matrix (11.2) be of rank m, or equivalently for $m = n$ that the Jacobian determinant be $\neq 0$.*

Suppose in particular that $\{\beta_j\} = \{\beta, \alpha_1, \cdots, \alpha_{i-1}, \alpha_{i+1}, \cdots, \alpha_n\}$. Then the Jacobian determinant reduces to $\pm\, \partial\beta/\partial\alpha_i$. Hence if $\partial\beta/\partial\alpha_j = 0$, β and $\alpha_1, \cdots, \alpha_{i-1}, \alpha_{i+1}, \cdots, \alpha_n$ are algebraically dependent. Since the α_i are algebraically independent β is then algebraic over the field $K(\alpha_1, \cdots, \alpha_{i-1}, \alpha_{i+1}, \cdots, \alpha_n)$. Conversely when β has this property $d\beta$ is in the subspace of $\mathfrak{B}$ spanned by the $d\alpha_j$, $j \neq i$, hence $\partial\beta/\partial\alpha_i = 0$.

Thus:

(11.5) *A   n.a.s.c.   for $\beta \in \Phi$ to   be   algebraic   over   the   field* $K(\alpha_1, \cdots, \alpha_{i-1}, \alpha_{i+1}, \cdots, \alpha_n)$ *is that* $\partial\beta/\partial\alpha_i = 0$.

12. Subfields. Let $K \subset \Psi \subset \Phi$, Ψ a subfield of Φ. Let transc $\Psi = m \leq n$. If $\{\alpha_1, \cdots, \alpha_m\}$ is a transcendence base for Ψ one may find in $\Phi - \Psi$ elements $\alpha_{m+1}, \cdots, \alpha_n$ such that $\{\alpha_1, \cdots, \alpha_n\}$ is a transcendence base for Φ. Let $\mathfrak{V}'$ be the vector space based on $\{d\alpha_1, \cdots, d\alpha_m\}$ with Ψ as its scalar domain. It is seen at once that $\mathfrak{V}'$ is a differential field for Ψ. The space $\mathfrak{V}'$ is spanned by $d\Psi$ where d is the differential operator for Φ. Thus

(12.1) *A differentiation in* Φ *induces one in every field* Ψ *between K and* Φ.

(12.2) *Application   to   homogeneous   fields.*   A   homogeneous   field $\Psi = K_H(\alpha_0, \cdots, \alpha_n)$ is defined in terms of an ordinary field $\Phi = K(\alpha_0, \cdots, \alpha_n)$ whose elements only satisfy homogeneous equations with coefficients in K in such manner that $\Psi = K(\{\alpha_i/\alpha_j\})$, $\alpha_j \neq 0$. Thus $K \subset \Psi \subset \Phi$ and so one may apply (12.1).

One of the α_j will be $\neq 0$. Let their numbering be such that $\alpha_0 \neq 0$. Then $\Psi = K(\{\alpha_i/\alpha_0\})$. If transc $\Psi = r$, r of the α_i/α_0 will be algebraically independent and the rest will be algebraically dependent on these. Let again the numbering of the α_i be such that the α_i/α_0, $i < r$, are algebraically independent. For the rest we will have algebraic relations

$$(12.3) \qquad F_j\left(\frac{\alpha_1}{\alpha_0}, \cdots, \frac{\alpha_r}{\alpha_0}, \frac{\alpha_{r+j}}{\alpha_0}\right) = 0, \quad j = 1, 2, \cdots, n - r$$

with coefficients in K or after clearing fractions

$$(12.4) \qquad f_j(\alpha_0, \cdots, \alpha_r, \alpha_{r+j}) = 0, \quad j = 1, 2, \cdots, n - r$$

where $f_j \in K_H[\alpha_0, \cdots, \alpha_r, \alpha_{r+j}]$ and actually contains α_{r+j}. Notice also that $\alpha_0, \cdots, \alpha_r$ are algebraically independent. For under our assumptions a relation between them must be of the type

$$g(\alpha_0, \cdots, \alpha_r) = 0, \quad g \in K_H[\alpha_0, \cdots, \alpha_r].$$

Now if p is the degree of g this relation yields after division by α_0^p:

$$g\left(1, \frac{\alpha_1}{\alpha_0}, \cdots, \frac{\alpha_r}{\alpha_0}\right) = 0$$

which is ruled out since the α_i/α_0, $i \leq r$ are algebraically independent.

Since $\{\alpha_0, \cdots, \alpha_r\}$ is a transcendence base for Φ one may define a differentiation in Φ by taking for $d\alpha_0, \cdots, d\alpha_r$ independent vectors and defining $d\alpha_{r+j}$ from $df_j = 0$, explicitly from

$$\sum_i f_{j\alpha_i} \, d\alpha_i = 0.$$

Since the α_i/α_0, $i \leq r$ form a transcendence base for Ψ its space of differentials $\mathfrak{V}'$ will be spanned by the

$$d\frac{\alpha_i}{\alpha_0} = \frac{\alpha_0 d\alpha_i - \alpha_i d\alpha_0}{\alpha_0^2}$$

and its elements will all be represented by the expression homogeneous in the α_i and $d\alpha_i$ combined:

$$\Sigma\beta_i(\alpha_0, \cdots, \alpha_r)\frac{\alpha_0 d\alpha_i - \alpha_i d\alpha_0}{\alpha_0^2}, \beta_i \in \Phi.$$

It is also clear that α_0 could be replaced throughout by any fixed $\alpha_h \neq 0$.

13. Differential forms. One may develop for a differential field Φ the important calculus of differential forms introduced by E. Cartan. A few indications will suffice for our purpose.

Between the elements $\xi, \eta, \cdots$, of Φ and their differentials let there be defined a product whose commutation rules are as follows: (a) $\xi, \eta, \cdots$ commute with one another and with their differentials; (b) $d\xi d\eta = - d\eta d\xi$, i.e. the products of differentials are skew-symmetric. Allowing now only the addition of elements of the same degree in the differentials there results a homogeneous ring R_H (homogeneous relative to the differentials). A differential p-form ω_p is an element of R_H of degree p in the differentials. Thus ω_p is a finite sum

$$(13.1) \qquad \omega_p = \Sigma A_{i_1 \cdots i_p} d\xi_{i_1} \cdots d\xi_{i_p}; \quad \xi_j, A_{i_1 \cdots i_p} \in \Phi.$$

Regarding the sum two conventions are used. In order to avoid repetition of the products of differentials one assumes under the first convention $i_1 < i_2 < \cdots < i_p$ throughout. However in calculations it is often more convenient to allow for all repetitions, and this is done under the second convention.

The differential forms ω_1 are simply the elements of the vector space $\mathfrak{V}$ of the differentials. More generally the set of all the forms ω_p is a vector space $\mathfrak{V}^p$ with the scalar domain Φ and $\mathfrak{V}^1 = \mathfrak{V}$.

If $\mathfrak{A} = \{\alpha_1, \cdots, \alpha_r\}$ is a transcendence base for the field Φ we may write

$$(13.2) \qquad \omega_p = \Sigma A_{i_1 \cdots i_p} d\alpha_{i_1} \cdots d\alpha_{i_p}; \qquad \alpha_j, A_{i_1 \cdots i_p} \in \Phi.$$

This shows that there are no p-forms for $p > r$ and also that all the r-forms are of type

$$\omega_r = A d\alpha_1 \cdots d\alpha_r.$$

It is a consequence of the representation (13.2) that the space $\mathfrak{V}^p$ has the dimension $\binom{r}{p}$.

With ω_p there is associated a $(p+1)$-form $d\omega_p$, the *derived* of ω_p, defined by

$$d\omega_p = \Sigma dA_{i_1 \cdots i_p} d\alpha_{i_1} \cdots d\alpha_{i_p}. \tag{13.3}$$

If $d\omega_p = 0$ the form ω_p is said to be *closed.* Thus an ω_r is always closed.

As an illustration consider

$$\omega_1 = A_1 d\alpha_1 + \cdots + A_r d\alpha_r.$$

We have

$$d\omega_1 = \Sigma dA_i d\alpha_i = \sum_{i<j} \left(\frac{\partial A_j}{\partial \alpha_i} - \frac{\partial A_i}{\partial \alpha_j} \right) d\alpha_i d\alpha_j.$$

Hence a n.a.s.c. for ω_1 to be closed is that

$$\frac{\partial A_i}{\partial \alpha_j} - \frac{\partial A_j}{\partial \alpha_i} = 0; \qquad i, j = 1, 2, \cdots, r. \tag{13.4}$$

Thus a closed ω_1 is merely a *total* differential in the usual sense.

Similarly if

$$\omega_2 = \Sigma A_{ij} d\alpha_i d\alpha_j, \quad i < j,$$

then the condition for closure is

$$\frac{\partial A_{ij}}{\partial \alpha_k} + \frac{\partial A_{jk}}{\partial \alpha_i} + \frac{\partial A_{ki}}{\partial \alpha_j} = 0, \quad i \neq j \neq k. \tag{13.5}$$

One will recognize in (13.4) and (13.5) the expressions familiar in relation to the theorems of Green and Stokes.

In concluding these formal observations let us also mention the readily verified law of transformation

$$d\beta_1 \cdots d\beta_r = \frac{D(\beta_1, \cdots, \beta_r)}{D(\alpha_1, \cdots, \alpha_r)} d\alpha_1 \cdots d\alpha_r. \tag{13.6}$$

There is no real difficulty in extending everything that we have just said to homogeneous fields.

II. Algebraic Varieties: Fundamental Concepts

With the present chapter we initiate the treatment of algebraic geometry proper. In § 1 we shall briefly recall the fundamental concepts of affine and projective spaces and their linear subspaces so that the true topic of the chapter begins really with § 2: algebraic varieties. While our basic space is always projective an auxiliary affine space will be found highly convenient in the algebraic parts of the treatment. For this reason we shall deal simultaneously with both types. Except in connection with differentials, throughout the present chapter the groundfield K is merely assumed to be infinite.

§ 1. Affine and Projective Spaces

1. Let us follow the classical approach through the medium of so-called *number spaces*, i.e. consisting of points which are merely sets of elements of a field. Certain allowable transformations broaden the concept and free the spaces from a too narrow tie-up with a specific coordinate system.

Beginning then with the more convenient affine spaces one first defines a point of m-dimensional number space over the groundfield K as an m-tuple $X = (X_1, \cdots, X_m)$, $X_i \in K$. The totality of all such m-tuples constitutes *m-dimensional affine number space over K* (denoted by KNA^m).

By a (non-singular) *affine transformation* is meant a transformation of KNA^m into itself of the form $(X) \to (X')$ where $X_i' = \Sigma a_{ij}X_j + b_i, (a_{ij}, b_i \in K$ and the determinant $|a_{ij}| \neq 0)$. An affine transformation is obviously one-one.

Let $[P]$ be a set of objects having the cardinal number of KNA^m. Any one-one correspondence $P \longleftrightarrow (X)$ between $[P]$ and KNA^m will be called an *affine coordinate system* for $[P]$ and (X) will be called the *representation* of P in this *coordinate system*. If $(X) \to (X')$ is an affine transformation, then $P \longleftrightarrow (X')$ is also a coordinate system for $[P]$. Having chosen a particular coordinate system C for $[P]$, all other coordinate systems related to C by affine transformations in this way are called *allowable coordinate systems*. C itself is evidently an allowable coordinate system.

An object $[P, (\Sigma a_{ij}X_j + b_i)]$ consisting of P together with all its representations in all the allowable coordinate systems (one and only one representation in each coordinate system) is called a *point of affine m-space over K*. The totality of such objects is called *affine m-space over K*; in symbols KA^m. Two points of KA^m are evidently distinct if and only if their representations in a particular allowable coordinate system are distinct.

Remark: We may take the points of KNA^m themselves as the objects P and the identity correspondence $(X) \longleftrightarrow (X)$ as the chosen coordinate system.

Let $(x_0, x_1, \cdots, x_m)$, $x_i \in K$ and not all zero, be an $(m+1)$-tuple of elements of K. The set of all $(m+1)$-tuples of the form $(kx_0, \cdots, kx_m)$, where k is a non-zero element of K, (see however 2.2) is called a *point of m-dimensional projective number space over K*. The totality of such points is called *m-dimensional projective number space* over K; (in symbols, KNP^m). Any one of the proportional $(m+1)$-tuples of a point of KNP^m is called a *representative* of that point. A point is fully determined by any one of its representatives $(x_0, \cdots, x_m) = (x)$.

By a (non-singular) *projective transformation* of KNP^m onto itself is meant a transformation of the form $(x) \rightarrow (x')$ where $\rho x'_i = \Sigma a_{ij} x_j$ (ρ is a non-zero element of K; $a_{ij} \in K$ and $|a_{ij}| \neq 0$).

A projective transformation is obviously one-one.

Let $[P]$ be a set of objects having the cardinal number of KNP^m. Any one-one correspondence of $[P]$ with KNP^m is called a *projective coordinate system* for $[P]$. Let $P \longleftrightarrow (x)$ be a particular coordinate system for $[P]$. If $(x) \rightarrow (x')$ is a projective transformation, then $P \longleftrightarrow (x')$ is also a coordinate system for $[P]$. Having chosen a particular coordinate system, all coordinate systems related to it in this way by projective transformations are called *allowable coordinate systems*. Evidently the originally chosen coordinate system is itself an allowable coordinate system.

An object $[P, (\Sigma a_{ij} x_j)]$ consisting of P together with all its representatives in all the allowable coordinate systems is called a *point of projective m-space over K*. The totality of all such objects is called projective m-space over K; in symbols KP^m. Notice that here also there is one and only one representation in each coordinate system, provided of course that $(x_0, \cdots)$ and $(kx_0, \cdots)$, with k as before, are not considered as distinct.

Two points, A, B of KP^m are evidently distinct if and only if their representations in a particular allowable coordinate system are distinct.

Remark: We may take the points of KNP^m themselves as the objects $[P]$ and the identity correspondence $(x) \longleftrightarrow (x)$ as the chosen coordinate system.

The purpose of the seeming circumlocution of this section is to free our results from dependence on a particular coordinate system. We shall work in a KA^m or a KP^m, and while we may frequently operate in a particular coordinate system, our theorems will be independent of this choice. Similarly we shall be free to change coordinate systems in the course of an argument.

It will often be convenient to indicate the coordinate system by a subscript as KA^m_X, KP^m_x.

Let KA^m_X, KA^m_Y be two affine spaces. An *affine transformation* of the first space into the second is a transformation from the points of the first to those of the second defined by a system

$$(1.1) \qquad Y_i = \Sigma a_{ij} X_j + b_i; \qquad (a_{ij}, b_i \in K, |a_{ij}| \neq 0).$$

It is readily seen that:

(1.2) *Under affine transformations of coordinates in one or the other space an affine transformation goes into an affine transformation.*

(1.3) *Affine transformations are one-one.*

(1.4) *The product of two affine transformations and the inverse of an affine transformation are affine transformations of appropriate spaces into one another.*

One may of course consider an affine transformation T of KA^m_X into itself. Such a transformation will assign to a point X the point X' *in the same coordinate system* given by a system

$$(1.5) \qquad X'_i = \Sigma a_{ij} X_j + b_i; \qquad (a_{ij}, b_i \in K, |a_{ij}| \neq 0),$$

which looks formally like a change of coordinates for the space. Indeed the two distinct geometric situations: (points unchanged, change of coordinates) and (points transformed, coordinates unchanged) give rise to the same algebraic system (1.5).

We note the following property which is a consequence of (1.4).

(1.6) *The affine transformations of KA^m into itself form a group.*

Let now KP^m_x, KP^m_y be two projective spaces. A *projective transformation* of the first space into the second is a transformation from the points of the first to those of the second defined by a system

$$(1.7) \qquad \rho y_i = \Sigma a_{ij} x_j; \qquad \rho, a_{ij} \in K; \qquad \rho\, |a_{ij}| \neq 0.$$

(We shall liberalize the condition $\rho \in K$ in a moment). One will verify at once next:

(1.8) *Properties* (1.2), (1.3), (1.4), (1.6) *hold for projective transformations.*

The system (1.7) has likewise two distinct geometric interpretations whose formulation is left to the reader.

It may be remarked that *affine* geometry and *projective* geometry are respectively the study of those properties of configurations which are invariant under affine and projective transformations.

We have already observed that the properties to be discussed later relative to KA^m or KP^m are invariant under changes of coordinates. Since they will always be algebraic properties, we infer that they are likewise invariant under affine transformations of KA^m or projective transformations of KP^m.

2. Since the groundfield K is our field of constants, the points of the spaces KA^m, KP^m in the strict sense just defined will play the role of "fixed" points. They will be designated as *points strictly in KA^m or KP^m*. One will obtain the analogues of "variable" points by admitting points in ΦA^m or ΦP^m where Φ is an overfield of K. The transcendency of a point $M(\alpha_1, \cdots, \alpha_m)$ of KA^m in this more general sense is transc $\{\alpha_i\}$. A point of transcendency zero (the α_i are algebraic over K) is said to be *algebraic*. Similarly for $M(\alpha_0, \cdots, \alpha_m)$ of KP^m in the more general sense, its transcendency being that of the set $\{\alpha_i/\alpha_j\}$. In particular M is *algebraic* if every $\alpha_i/\alpha_j(\alpha_j \neq 0)$ is algebraic over K.

It is immediately seen that:

(2.1) *A transformation of coordinates of KA^m or KP^m does not affect the transcendencies of the points of KA^m or KP^m.*

(2.2) *Remark:* In connection with projective coordinates we have already seen appearing proportionality factors: $k, \rho, \cdots$; henceforth we shall allow them to be drawn from some field over K. In general this will be understood in the sequel. One may say that in projective coordinates what matters is not the field containing the coordinates but the field containing their ratios.

3. Notations. We shall repeatedly go back and forth between KA^m and KP^m and identify certain related objects. To standardize the process let the coordinates be written $X_1, \cdots, X_m$ for KA^m and $x_0, \cdots, x_m$ for KP^m. For points of KP^m not in $x_0 = 0$ one may choose $x_0 = 1$. We will then identify the point $(X_1, \cdots, X_m)$ of KA^m with the point $(1, X_1, \cdots, X_m)$ of KP^m thus identifying KA^m with the complement of $x_0 = 0$ in KP^m. The passage from one set of coordinates to the other is by means of the relations $X_i = x_i/x_0$. However, for KA^2 we will often write X, Y instead of X_1, X_2 where $X = x_1/x_0$, $Y = x_2/x_0$. The points of KP^m in $x_0 = 0$ are sometimes referred to as "points at infinity."

A similar identification is made of course at the same time between the points of ΦA^m and ΦP^m not in $x_0 = 0$ for every field Φ over K. Obviously:

(3.1) *Identified points have the same transcendency.*

It is convenient to describe the identification discussed above as a correspondence τ: $x \rightarrow X$ such that $\tau x_i = X_i$, $i > 0$, $\tau x_0 = 1$. This correspondence sends all the forms $x_0^s f(x)$ where f is of degree r fixed and not divisible by x_0, into the same polynomial of degree r: $F(X) = f(1, X_1, \cdots, X_m)$. Conversely the only forms which τ sends into a given F of degree r are represented by $x_0^s f(x)$, where f is of degree r, not divisible by x_0 and defined by the relation $f = x_0^r F(x_1/x_0, \cdots, x_m/x_0)$.

We note the important geometric property that the point $M(X_1, \cdots, X_m)$ satisfies the relation $F(X) = 0$ if and only if its associated projective image $(x_0, \cdots, x_m)$ satisfies the relation $f(x) = 0$.

4. Linear spaces. Consider a linear homogeneous system with coefficients in K:

$$\sum_{j=0}^{m} a_{ij}x_j = 0, \quad i = 1, 2, \cdots, n. \tag{4.1}$$

If the rank of the matrix $\| a_{ij} \|$ is $m - p$, then the set of points of KP^m which satisfy (4.1) is known as a *linear p-dimensional space in* KP^m, also as a *subspace* of KP^m. Similarly for KA^m referred to coordinates X_i and a system

$$\sum b_{ij}X_j = b_i. \tag{4.2}$$

For $p = 0$ the subspace is a point, for $p = 1$ it is a *line*, for $p = 2$ a *plane*, for $p = m - 1$ a *hyperplane*.

The spaces KA^m, KP^m are linear m-dimensional spaces.

A set of $p + 1$ points $M_i(\xi_{i0}, \cdots, \xi_{im})$ of KP^m is said to be *linearly independent* or to form a *p-simplex*, written σ^p, whenever the matrix $\| \xi_{ij} \|$ of their coordinates is of rank $p + 1$. Similarly in KA^m except that if $\eta_{i1}, \cdots, \eta_{im}$ are the coordinates of M_i then the matrix

$$\| 1, \eta_{i1}, \cdots, \eta_{im} \|, \quad i = 0, \cdots, p,$$

is to be of rank $p + 1$. A σ^2 is a *triangle*, a σ^1 is a *segment*, a σ^0 a point. A subsimplex of σ^p is a *face* of σ^p. The M_i are the *vertices* of σ^p.

Let δ_{ij} be the Kronecker deltas: $\delta_{ii} = 1$, $\delta_{ij} = 0$ for $i \neq j$ and let A_i be the point of KP^m whose coordinates are δ_{ij}. The simplex $A_0A_1 \cdots A_m$ is the *simplex of reference* of KP^m.

The following properties are carried over from the well-known theory of systems of linear equations. Wherever no explicit statement is made they hold for both KA^m and KP^m. In the statements the symbol S^p will stand for "linear p-dimensional space."

(4.3) *An S^p contains simplexes of dimension up to and including p but no higher.*

(4.4) *An S^p is uniquely determined by any one of the σ^p which it contains. In particular a line is uniquely determined by two distinct points and a plane by three non-collinear points.*

(4.5) *Let* $\sigma^p = M_0 \cdots M_p$ *be in* S^p *of* KP^m *and let* ξ_{ij} *be the coordinates of* M_i. *Then the coordinates of the points of* S^p *are given by relations*

$$\rho\xi_j = \Sigma\xi_{ij}\lambda_i; \qquad \rho, \lambda_i \in K \tag{4.5a}$$

where the λ_i *are not all zero and are unique up to a proportionality factor. A change of* σ^p *merely causes a projective transformation of the* λ_i. *Thus* S^p *is turned into a* KP^p *with the* λ_i *as projective coordinates.*

(4.6) *Similarly for* S^p *in* KA^m *save that if* η_{ij} *are the affine coordinates then the representation is*

$$\eta_j = \frac{\Sigma\eta_{ij}\lambda_i}{\Sigma\lambda_i}. \tag{4.6a}$$

This last representation is often normalized to

$$\eta_j = \Sigma\eta_{ij}\lambda_i, \quad \Sigma\lambda_i = 1. \tag{4.6b}$$

The λ_i *are then referred to as "barycentric coordinates for* S^p."

(4.7) *Noteworthy special case:* $p = 1$ *and* S^p *is a line. The segment of reference consists of two points and* (4.5a) *becomes*

$$\rho\xi_i = \lambda_1\xi_{1i} + \lambda_2\xi_{2i}, \quad i = 0, 1, \cdots, m, \tag{4.7a}$$

with λ_1, λ_2 *not both zero. The cartesian form is*

$$\eta_i = \frac{\lambda_1\eta_{1i} + \lambda_2\eta_{2i}}{\lambda_1 + \lambda_2}, \quad i = 1, 2, \cdots, m, \tag{4.7b}$$

which is often normalized as

$$\eta_i = \lambda\eta_{1i} + (1 - \lambda)\eta_{2i}, \quad i = 1, 2, \cdots, m. \tag{4.7c}$$

§ 2. Algebraic Varieties and Their Ideals

5. An algebraic variety V is simply the set of all the points of KP_x^m, strictly or not, which annul a finite set of forms, i.e. satisfy a system

$$f_i(x) = 0; \qquad i = 1, 2, \cdots, s; \qquad f_i \in K_H[x].$$

Now if $\mathfrak{a}_H$ is the ideal generated by the f_i, i.e. if $\mathfrak{a}_H = (f_1, \cdots, f_s)$, then every form of $\mathfrak{a}_H$ annuls all the points of V, and conversely every point annulled by all forms of $\mathfrak{a}_H$ is in V. Hence one may define the variety V as the set of all the points common to every form of $\mathfrak{a}_H$. This is the definition to which we adhere in the sequel. We refer to V as the variety of the ideal $\mathfrak{a}_H$.

(5.1) *The Hilbert zero theorem. A n.a.s.c. for a form* f *to vanish identically at all algebraic points of the variety* V *of the ideal* $\mathfrak{a}_H$ *is that some power* f^ρ *of* f *lies in* $\mathfrak{a}_H$.

Strictly speaking Hilbert's original theorem refers only to polynomial ideals and their zeros. It asserts that if a polynomial $F \in K[X]$ vanishes at all (affine) algebraic points where the polynomials of an ideal $\mathfrak{a}$ vanish then some power $F^\rho \in \mathfrak{a}$. In this form the proof is given in van der Waerden [1], II, pp. 6 and 60. The passage to the formulation (5.1) is immediate. By the Hilbert base property (I, 1.3), $\mathfrak{a}_H$ has a finite base $\{f_1, \cdots, f_s\}$. Let the forms f_i span a polynomial ideal $\mathfrak{a}$. If f vanishes at all algebraic points of V, then it fulfills the conditions of Hilbert's zero theorem relatively to $\mathfrak{a}$. Hence there is a relation

$$f^\rho = \Sigma\varphi_i f_i, \quad \varphi_i \in K[x].$$

Upon replacing throughout the coordinates x_j by tx_j and equating powers of t, there results a relation such as just written but with the $\varphi_i \in K_H[x]$ and hence $f^\rho \in \mathfrak{a}_H$. The converse is obvious.

We shall now consider some elementary properties of varieties.

(5.2) *The variety V is independent of the coordinate system.*

(5.3) *The union of a finite number and the intersection of any number of varieties are varieties.*

The proof for the infinite case follows from Hilbert's base property.

Since distinct ideals may give rise to the same variety, it will be convenient to associate with each variety a unique ideal. By the *ideal $\mathfrak{a}_H$ of a variety V* will be meant the ideal of all forms of $K_H[x]$ which vanish identically on V. This is clearly the largest ideal giving rise to V. In particular, a form vanishes on the variety V of a prime ideal $\mathfrak{p}_H$ if and only if it is in $\mathfrak{p}_H$. A variety whose ideal is prime is said to be *irreducible.*

(5.4) *The variety of a primary ideal $\mathfrak{q}_H$ is the irreducible variety of its prime ideal $\mathfrak{p}_H$.*

Let the ideal $\mathfrak{a}_H$ of a variety V admit a canonical decomposition $\mathfrak{a}_H = \mathfrak{q}_{1H} \cap \cdots \cap \mathfrak{q}_{sH}$ and let $\mathfrak{p}_{iH}$ be the prime ideal of $\mathfrak{q}_{iH}$ and V_i its variety. Among the $\mathfrak{p}_{iH}$ discard those which contain the intersection of the rest. Let the remaining set properly numbered be $\mathfrak{p}_{1H}, \cdots, \mathfrak{p}_{rH}$. This set is unique. Going back to the varieties this yields:

(5.5) *There is a unique decomposition $V = V_1 \cup \cdots \cup V_r$ where the V_i are irreducible and none is contained in the union of the rest.*

The irreducible varieties $V_1, \cdots, V_r$ are called the *components* of V. Clearly:

(5.6) *If V has a single component it is irreducible and conversely.*

The following irreducibility criterion is sometimes taken as definition of irreducibility:

(5.7) *The variety V is irreducible if and only if it is not the union of two varieties V', V'' neither of which contains the other.*

Let $V = V' \cup V''$ where V' contains a point M' which is not in V'' and V'' contains a point M'' which is not in V'. Let $V'_1, \cdots, V'_\mu$ and $V''_1, \cdots, V''_\nu$ be the components of V' and V''. Thus $V =$

$V_1' \cup \cdots \cup V_\mu' \cup V_1'' \cup \cdots \cup V_\nu''$. Upon suppressing in the union the V_i' or V_j'' contained in the union of the rest, there will still remain a V', say V_1' containing M', and a V'', say V_1'' containing M'', and we will have a decomposition $V = V_1' \cup V_1'' \cup \cdots$, into irreducible varieties none contained in the union of the rest. Thus V has at least the two components V_1', V_1'' and so it is reducible.

Conversely if V is reducible it has at least two components. Let V' be one and V'' the union of the rest. Then $V = V' \cup V''$ where neither of V', V'' contains the other.

If $\mathfrak{p}_{iH}$ is again the ideal of the component V_i of V then any form containing V contains also V_i and hence is in $\mathfrak{p}_{iH}$ and therefore in $\mathfrak{a}_H = \mathfrak{p}_{1H} \cap \cdots \cap \mathfrak{p}_{rH}$. The converse is clear and so $\mathfrak{a}_H$ is the ideal of V. Thus:

(5.8) *The ideal of a variety is the intersection of the ideals of its components.*

6. A *subvariety* V' of a variety V is a variety contained in V but distinct from V: $V' \subset V$, $V' \neq V$.

(6.1) *If V' is a subvariety of V then $V - V'$ is non-vacuous. Hence if V is a variety distinct from KP^m there are points of KP^m not contained in V.*

(6.2) *If $V' \subset V$ then each component of V' is contained in a component of V.*

It is clearly sufficient to assume that V' is irreducible and V is not. Let $V_1, \cdots, V_s$ be the components of V. Then

$$V' = (V_1 \cap V') \cup \cdots \cup (V_k \cap V').$$

By (5.7) some $(V_i \cap V')$ contains the others and therefore contains V'. But this implies (6.2).

(6.3) *If $\mathfrak{a}_H$, $\mathfrak{a}_H'$ are the ideals of V, V' then V' is a subvariety of V if and only if $\mathfrak{a}_H$ is a proper subideal of $\mathfrak{a}_H'$: $\mathfrak{a}_H \subset \mathfrak{a}_H'$, $\mathfrak{a}_H \neq \mathfrak{a}_H'$.*

This follows at once from the uniqueness of the ideal of a variety combined with the fact that the inclusions $\mathfrak{a}_H \subset \mathfrak{a}_H'$ and $V' \subset V$ are equivalent.

7. The following are noteworthy special ideals and varieties.

I. *Ideal zero.* This ideal consists of the single element zero of $K_H[x]$ and its variety, which is irreducible, is the space KP^m itself.

II. *Ideal unity.* This is $K_H[x]$ and its variety, likewise irreducible, consists (formally) of the null set.

III. *Linear ideal.* We mean thereby an ideal spanned by linear forms $l_1, \cdots, l_s$ of $K_H[x]$. If the coefficient matrix of the l_i is of rank ρ and $\rho = 0$ we are in case I and if $\rho = m + 1$ we are in case II. For $0 < \rho < m + 1$, the variety is a linear subspace $S^{m-\rho}$ of KP^m and any subspace may be obtained in this manner. These subspaces are all irreducible varieties. For the ideal $\mathfrak{a}_H = (l_i)$ may be generated by

ρ of its forms. In a suitable coordinate system we may assume that $\mathfrak{a}_H = (x_{m-\rho+1}, \cdots, x_m)$. Now a form $f \in \mathfrak{a}_H$ when and only when

$$f = \Sigma f_i x_{m-\rho+i}, \quad f_i \in K_H[x], \tag{7.1}$$

i.e. when and only when every term of f contains one of the variables $x_{m-\rho+i}$. Hence if $gh \in \mathfrak{a}_H$, g and $h \in K_H[x]$, one of the factors g, h is of the type (7.1) and hence it is in $\mathfrak{a}_H$. It follows that $\mathfrak{a}_H$ is prime and so $S^{m-\rho}$ is irreducible.

IV. Let $\mathfrak{a}_H$ be a *principal* ideal, i.e., generated by a single form f. The corresponding variety is known as an *algebraic hypersurface,* also *algebraic surface* and *algebraic curve* for $m = 3, 2$. The degree of f is referred to as the *degree* or *order* of V. We usually refer to V as the hypersurface f, or surface f, or curve f as the case may be. It consists of the points which satisfy $f = 0$, and the variety is *irreducible* when and only when the form f is irreducible.

8. Affine varieties. All the preceding considerations may be automatically transferred to the ideals $\mathfrak{a}$ of the ordinary ring $K[X]$ thus giving rise to the affine varieties V_A of KA^m. This transfer is assumed in the sequel.

Our basic varieties will be throughout the projective varieties. Geometrically they offer the well-known advantage of enabling one to dispense with special statements regarding the "points at infinity." It is true nevertheless that as regards algebraic manipulations and related concepts affine varieties are often more convenient. For this reason we shall associate a certan affine variety with every projective variety.

(8.1) The variety V is said to be *in general position* (understood relative to the coordinate system) whenever either $\mathfrak{a}_H = 1$ (V has no points) or else the hyperplane x_0 contains no component of V. Leaving aside the trivial case $\mathfrak{a}_H = 1$, a coordinate system may always be chosen for V placing it in general position. For let $V_1, \cdots, V_r$ be the components of V and take a point M_i in V_i, which is possible since V_i now contains points. Then one may always select a linear form l annulled by no M_i and hence containing no V_i. Taking now a coordinate system in which l is x_0, the desired result will be achieved. Notice that one may even select coordinates such that each of a given finite set of varieties is in general position, or as a special case (varieties consisting of a finite set of points) that a given finite point set is not in x_0.

In the sequel whenever we wish to pass to affine coordinates we shall always assume x_0 fixed once for all and that the variety V is in general position. The resulting affine variety V_A will thus depend upon the choice of x_0 and no attempt is made to unite all the affine models thus obtained into a single variety. This will, however, be immaterial since the affine models V_A will always be considered as subordinated to the basic projective model V. One may also note in passing that if one does not wish to modify V_A then the only allowable changes of coordinates in KP^m are of the form

$$\rho x_0 = x_0', \quad \rho x_i = a_i x_0' + \Sigma\, a_{ij}\, x_j',\; i, j > 0,$$

where the determinant $|a_{ij}| \neq 0$. The corresponding affine transformation is

$$X_i = \Sigma a_{ij} X_j' + a_i.$$

Returning now to the correspondence τ of (3) sending $(x_0, \cdots, x_m)$ into $(1, X_1, \cdots, X_m)$, let us examine its effect on the homogeneous ideals. Any form of the homogeneous ring $K_H[x]$ may be written $x_0^s f(x)$ where f is not divisible by x_0. Similarly for a second form and $x_0^{s'}f'$. Let $f(1, X_1, \cdots, X_m) = F(X)$, $f'(1, X_1, \cdots, X_m) = F'(X)$. Thus $\tau x_0^s f = F$, $\tau x_0^{s'} f' = F'$ whatever s, s'. Conversely given $F(X) \in K[X]$ and of degree r, and $f = x_0^r F(x_1/x_0, \cdots, x_m/x_0)$ then $\tau^{-1}F = x_0^s f$ whatever s.

Given an ideal $\mathfrak{a}_H$ of $K_H[x]$ one verifies readily that the set $\mathfrak{a}$ of all polynomials $F = \tau f$, $f \in \mathfrak{a}_H$, is an ideal. This ideal is unique and we denote it by $\tau\mathfrak{a}_H$. Conversely if $\mathfrak{a}$ is an ideal of $K[X]$ the set $\mathfrak{a}_H$ of all the forms $f \in K_H[x]$ such that $\tau f \in \mathfrak{a}$ is seen to form an ideal of $K_H[x]$. We denote this ideal for convenience by $\tau^{-1}\mathfrak{a}$. It is characterized uniquely as the largest ideal whose image under τ is $\mathfrak{a}$, or else also as the union of all the ideals with this property.

Let now $\mathfrak{p}_H$ be a prime ideal not containing x_0, or which is the same whose variety is in general position. Then $\mathfrak{p} = \tau\mathfrak{p}_H$ is likewise prime and $\neq 1$. For let FF' be in $\mathfrak{p}$ while F' is not and let $F = \tau f$, $F' = \tau f'$. Then a certain product $x_0^s ff' \in \mathfrak{p}_H$ while neither x_0 nor f' are in $\mathfrak{p}_H$. Since $\mathfrak{p}_H$ is prime $f \in \mathfrak{p}_H$, hence $F \in \mathfrak{p}$. Therefore $\mathfrak{p}$ is prime.

Conversely let $\mathfrak{p}$ be prime and $\neq 1$ and let $\mathfrak{p}_H = \tau^{-1}\mathfrak{p}$. Suppose that $ff' \in \mathfrak{p}_H$ and f' is not in $\mathfrak{p}_H$. We have $\tau f = F$, $\tau f' = F'$, $FF' \in \mathfrak{p}$, F' not in $\mathfrak{p}$. Hence $F \in \mathfrak{p}$ and therefore $f \in \mathfrak{p}_H$. Thus $\mathfrak{p}_H$ is likewise prime. It also clearly does not contain x_0. Thus we may state:

(8.2) *The correspondence* τ: $(x_0, x_1, \cdots, x_m) \to (1, X_1, \cdots, X_m)$ *sends the elements of an ideal* $\mathfrak{a}_H$ *of* $K_H[x]$ *into those of an ideal* $\mathfrak{a} = \tau\mathfrak{a}_H$ *of* $K[x]$. *Given the ideal* $\mathfrak{a}$ *of* $K[X]$ *there is a unique maximal ideal* $\mathfrak{a}_H$ *such that* $\tau\mathfrak{a}_H = \mathfrak{a}$, *and* $\mathfrak{a}_H$ *is the union of all the ideals satisfying this relation. This particular ideal is denoted by* $\tau^{-1}\mathfrak{a}$. *If* $\mathfrak{p}_H$ *is a prime ideal not containing* x_0 *then* $\mathfrak{p} = \tau\mathfrak{p}_H$ *is also prime, and* $\neq 1$, *and if* $\mathfrak{p}$ *is prime and* $\neq 1$ *then* $\mathfrak{p}_H = \tau^{-1}\mathfrak{p}$ *is prime and does not contain* x_0.

Henceforth the varieties V and V_A of $\mathfrak{a}_H$ and $\mathfrak{a}$ are to be identified. The new entity is still called an algebraic variety. It is defined as irreducible or reducible accordingly as V is one or the other, or accordingly as V_A is one or the other if V is in general position. One refers to V and V_A as a *projective model* and an *affine model of the variety.*

Extension of the groundfield. Referring to (I,5) one may state:

(8.3) *A finite pure transcendental extension preserves all the inclusion, union and intersection properties of varieties, their reducibility or irreducibility, and in particular it sends a variety and its components into a variety and its components.*

(8.4) *Absolute irreducibility.* An irreducible V^r is said to be *absolutely irreducible* whenever it remains irreducible under an arbitrary extension of the groundfield.

§ 3. GENERAL POINTS. DIMENSION. FUNCTION FIELD

9. Following van der Waerden we say that a point $M(\xi)$ of an irreducible variety V is a *general point* of V, if whenever a form f is annulled by M then it is annulled by every point of the variety. Evidently:

(9.1) *A n.a.s.c. for a form f to be in the prime ideal $\mathfrak{p}_H$ of the irreducible variety V, is that f vanish at a general point of the variety.*

We also have at once:

(9.2) *Given a point M there is a unique irreducible variety V with M as general point.*

For the prime ideal $\mathfrak{p}_H$ of V must consist of those and only those forms of $K_H[x]$ which vanish at M, and they do make up a unique prime ideal.

(9.3) *A subvariety V_1 of V cannot contain any general point of V. Hence all the general points are in $V - V_1$.*

Let the general point $M(\xi)$ of V be contained in V_1. Let $\mathfrak{a}_H$ be the ideal of V_1. Since $V_1 \neq V$, $\mathfrak{p}_H$ is a proper subset of $\mathfrak{a}_H$. Hence the latter contains a form f which is not in $\mathfrak{p}_H$. On the other hand by hypothesis $f(\xi) = 0$ hence $f \in \mathfrak{p}_H$, a contradiction from which (9.3) follows.

The following properties require no proof:

(9.4) *A point of KP^m is general for the space when and only when its transcendency is m.*

(9.5) *The property for M to be general for V is independent of the choice of coordinates.*

(9.6) *Let V be in general position (x_0 is not in $\mathfrak{p}_H$) and let KA^m be identified with the part of KP^m outside of the hyperplane x_0. Then a general point M of V is not in x_0 and so M is in the affine model V_A whose (prime) ideal $\mathfrak{p}$ corresponds to $\mathfrak{p}_H$ as in* (8.2). *Under these conditions M is a general point for V_A also. Such a point has the property that if $F \in K[X]$ is annulled by M then it is annulled by every point of V_A. Furthermore* (9.1) *holds as regards such polynomials and the prime ideal $\mathfrak{p}$.*

(9.7) *The "almost everywhere" terminology.* The concept goes back to van der Waerden. A property Π is said to hold *almost everywhere* on the irreducible variety V, or at *almost all points* of V, whenever there exists a subvariety V_1 of V such that Π holds at the points of $V - V_1$.

When V is an algebraic curve V_1 is a finite point set of the curve or else it is void. When the groundfield K is algebraically closed any finite subset of V_1 is a subvariety V_0. Hence the statement "property Π holds almost everywhere on the algebraic curve f" is then equivalent to "Π holds at all but a finite number of points of the curve."

The general intent of the "almost everywhere" locution is to indicate that one neglects the points of some subvariety whose precise nature is an indifferent matter.

(9.8) *If property* Π *holds almost everywhere on* V *then it holds for all the general points of the variety* (see 9.3).

10. A variety V is the algebraic analogue of a manifold in topology. When the groundfield is real or complex the variety may be turned in fact, at least in its "smooth" parts, into a manifold in the sense of topology. In that case the dimension concept may be borrowed directly from topology. For a general groundfield one may expect an algebraic analogue which might also lead to many fruitful results.

We shall find it expedient here, as in dimension theory, to anchor the concept "in the large" to a local property, the transcendency of the points.

We observe then that the definition of general point of an irreducible variety V implies at once:

(10.1) *All general points of* V *have the same transcendency* r: *it is at least as great as that of any other point of the variety and* $r \leq m$. *Moreover* $r = m$ *when and only when* $V = KP^m$. *Similarly for* V_A *and* KA^m.

The number r is known as the *dimension* of the irreducible variety or also of its ideal $\mathfrak{p}_H$ and its value is often indicated by writing V^r, V_A^r.

Suppose now that V is *reducible* and let the V_i be its components. Then the dimension r of V or of its ideal $\mathfrak{a}_H$ is defined as the maximum dimension of any V_i, or equivalently as the maximum transcendency of any point M of V. The affine representation is dealt with, as before, and V^r has its natural meaning.

One refers sometimes to V as a *pure* variety whenever all the components V_i have the same dimension. A pure V^2 is known as an *algebraic surface*, a pure V^1 as an *algebraic curve*. Notice that a hypersurface is a pure $(m - 1)$-dimensional variety. Hence the designations of "surface" and "curve" introduced in (7) are in agreement with those introduced above.

(10.2) *Evidently the dimension of a variety in general position is independent of the choice of projective or allowable affine coordinates.*

Let $M(\xi)$ be a general point of the irreducible variety V^r. Thus transc $M = r$. Hence one may choose $r + 1$ of the coordinates ξ_i, and with proper numbering they may be $\xi_0, \cdots, \xi_r$, such that for $h \leq r$ the ratios ξ_i/ξ_h, $i \leq r$, are algebraically independent. Moreover this ceases to hold when r is replaced by $r + 1$. Referring to (9.1) we conclude that the ideal $\mathfrak{p}_H$ of V^r contains no form in $x_0, \cdots, x_r$. On the other hand $\mathfrak{p}_H$ does contain forms in any $r + 2$ sets of coordinates, since the ratios of these coordinates must then be algebraically dependent. Thus:

(10.3) *The dimension of an irreducible variety V is the largest integer r such that there are sets of $r + 1$ coordinates with the property that no form of the ideal of V contains these coordinates alone.*

11. The fundamental notion of the field of rational functions, or more briefly the *function field* of an irreducible variety dominates everything that follows.

Historically the starting point lies in the study of what was first called integrals of algebraic functions. In actuality they were the abelian integrals, or integrals of rational functions taken along paths on the Riemann surface of a curve C. What matters clearly in such cases is merely the values along the curve. Thus if C is $Y^2 = X^3 - X$ then XY and $XY - X(Y^2 - X^3 + X)$ are to be identified. It is this principle of identification which has given rise to the function field.

The function field may also be obtained by taking the values of the rational functions at a general point. Sometimes one approach is convenient, sometimes the other. They do lead of course to the same result.

As we shall see function fields are only defined for irreducible varieties. Without this restriction one would merely obtain rings with zero divisors, i.e. not even integral domains.

(11.1) Let $M(\xi)$ be a general point of the irreducible variety and $f(x)$ a form of $K_H[x]$. The transformation $f(x) \to f(\xi)$ defines a homomorphism $\tau: K_H[x] \to K_H[\xi]$. The kernel of τ consists of the elements $f(x)$ such that $f(\xi) = 0$, and these make up the prime ideal $\mathfrak{p}_H$ of V. It follows that $K_H[\xi]$ is an integral domain and so it has a quotient field $K_H(\xi)$. For another general point $M'(\xi')$ we would have τ', $K_H[\xi']$ and $K_H(\xi')$. Since τ' has the same kernel $\mathfrak{p}_H$ as τ, $K_H[\xi']$ is isomorphic with $K_H[\xi]$ and the isomorphism is defined by the correspondence $\xi_i \to \xi'_i$. It follows that the same correspondence induces an isomorphism θ of the quotient fields $K_H(\xi)$, $K_H(\xi')$ under which K corresponds to itself. Upon identifying elements corresponding under θ, and likewise for all pairs of general points M, M' there results a unique field written K^V (also K^f when V is a hypersurface f) and called the *field of rational functions of* V, or the function field of V. The elements of K^V are the *rational functions* of the variety. The particular field $K_H(\xi)$ is merely a representation of K^V and in this particular representation any element of K^V is represented as a quotient $A(\xi)/B(\xi)$, where $A(x)$ and $B(x)$ are forms of $K_H[x]$ and of the same degree.

Since M is a general point and, since V is in general position $\xi_0 \neq 0$ hence we may choose $\xi_0 = 1$. Thus the projective coordinates of M will now be $1, \xi_1^*, \cdots, \xi_m^*$ where the ξ_i^* are its affine coordinates. As a consequence we obtain the representation $K[\xi^*]$ for the ring $K_H[\xi]$ and $K(\xi^*)$ for the function field K^V. In this representation, more particularly associated with the affine model V_A, the elements of K^V appear as quotients $A(\xi^*)/B(\xi^*)$, where $A(X)$ and $B(X) \in K[X]$, with $B(X)$ not in the ideal $\mathfrak{p}$ of V_A.

Since $K_H(\xi)$ is a representation of K^V and general points have maximum transcendency, we have:

(11.2) *The transcendency of the function field K^V is equal to the dimension of V.*

12. One may obtain a representation of the function field K^V directly from the prime ideal $\mathfrak{p}_H$ of the variety and without an appeal to general points. This is done in the following way. Since $\mathfrak{p}_H$ is prime $K_H[x]/\mathfrak{p}_H$ is an integral domain and its quotient field Φ is merely a representation of the function field K^V. The proof is quite simple. Let $\bar{x}_i$ denote the class of x_i mod $\mathfrak{p}_H$. Thus $\{\bar{x}_i\}$ is a set of generators for $K_H[x]/\mathfrak{p}_H$, and $f(\bar{x}_i)$ is the class of $f(x) \in K_H[x]$. It follows that $f(\bar{x}) = 0$ if and only if $f(x) \in \mathfrak{p}_H$. Hence $M(\bar{x})$ is a general point of V. Moreover if $R(x) = A(x)/B(x)$, A and $B \in K_H[x]$, its value $R(\bar{x}) = R(M)$ is precisely the element of Φ determined by $R(x)$. Since it is also the element of K^V determined by $R(x)$ in the representation determined by M, Φ is precisely that representation.

It is hardly necessary to observe that a transformation of coordinates merely replaces Φ by another representation Φ' of the function field K^V.

We have proved incidentally:

(12.1) *Every irreducible variety possesses a general point.*

(12.2) *Values of the rational functions.* Any element $\alpha \in K^V$ may be written $\alpha = R(\xi) = A(\xi)/B(\xi)$, where $R(x)$, $A(x)$, $B(x)$ are as before, and $M(\xi)$ is a general point. Take now any point $N(\eta)$ of the variety. The value $\alpha(N)$ of α at N is by definition the value $R(N)$ of R at N if this value exists, i.e., if $B(\eta) \neq 0$. Let this be the case and let $R_1(x) = A_1(x)/B_1(x)$ yield a second representation $\alpha = R_1(\xi)$ such that $B_1(\eta) \neq 0$. Thus $R_1(\eta)$ exists also. Since $R(\xi) = R_1(\xi)$ and the point $M(\xi)$ is general necessarily $R_1(\eta) = R(\eta)$. In other words the values of the elements of the function field at the points of the variety where these values exist, are unique.

In point of fact:

(12.3) *All the elements of a finite subset $\{\alpha_i\}$, $i = 1, 2, \cdots, s$ of the function field K^V have values at almost all points of the variety.*

For if $\alpha_i = A_i(\xi)/B_i(\xi)$ and $B = B_1 \cdots B_s$ these values will exist where $B \neq 0$, and as B is not in $\mathfrak{p}_H$, (12.3) follows.

A convenient and almost obvious property is the following:

(12.4) *If $M(\xi^*)$ is a general point of V^r and say $\xi_1^*, \cdots, \xi_r^*$ are algebraically independent then there is a general point $N(\eta^*)$ in which $\eta_1^*, \cdots, \eta_r^*$ are preassigned indeterminates. Similarly for the projective coordinates ξ_i of M save that if the ξ_i/ξ_0, $i \leq r$, are algebraically independent then one may take for the η_i, $i \leq r$, preassigned indeterminates.*

One may construct $K(\xi^*)$ from $L = K(\xi_1^*, \cdots, \xi_r^*)$ by successive adjunction of $\xi_{r+1}^*, \cdots, \xi_m^*$, each being a simple algebraic extension. Since the ξ_i^*, $i \leq r$, are algebraically independent L is a pure transcendental extension. Hence upon replacing the ξ_i^* in L by the corresponding η_i^*, then the remaining ξ_i^* by the same successive adjunctions as before, of the η_i^*, the new field $K(\eta^*)$ is isomorphic with $K(\xi^*)$, i.e. with K^V and this implies (12.4).

13. We shall now utilize the function field to prove the following important result:

(13.1) **Theorem.** *A n.a.s.c. for a point $N(\eta)$ of the irreducible variety V^r to be general for V^r is that transc $N = r$.*

As necessity is implicit in (10.1) we only need to prove sufficiency. Let then $N(\eta)$ be a point of transcendency r of the variety V^r and $M(\xi)$ a general point of V^r. Let the coordinates be chosen in accordance with (8.1) and so that N is not in x_0. Since M is then likewise not in x_0 we can pass to affine coordinates and the two points will both be in the affine space. In keeping with our notations their affine coordinates are written ξ_i^*, η_i^*.

Since transc $N = r$, r of the η_i^* which we may again take to be $\eta_1^*, \cdots, \eta_r^*$ are algebraically independent. Since M is general $\xi_1^*, \cdots, \xi_r^*$ are likewise algebraically independent. Let $\Phi = K(\xi_1^*, \cdots, \xi_r^*)$.

If N is not a general point of V there exists a non-zero element α of $K(\xi^*)$ with a value $\alpha(N) = \alpha(\eta^*) = 0$. That is to say if we represent α in the form $\alpha = A(\xi^*)/B(\xi^*)$, where $A(X)$, $B(X) \in K[X]$, then $A(\xi^*) \neq 0$, $A(\eta^*) = 0$. In other words we may assume that $\alpha = A(\xi^*)$.

Since α is algebraic over Φ it satisfies a relation

$$F(\xi_1^*, \cdots, \xi_r^*, \alpha) = F_0\alpha^s + \cdots + F_s = 0,$$

$$F_i \in K[\xi_1^*, \cdots, \xi_r^*], \quad F_s \neq 0.$$

Thus $G(X) = F(X_1, \cdots, X_r; A(X)) \in K[X]$ is such that $G(\xi^*) = 0$. Since M is general, we also have $G(\eta^*) = 0$. Since $\alpha(\eta^*) = 0$, it follows that $F_s(\eta_1^*, \cdots, \eta_r^*) = 0$. Since $F_s(X) \neq 0$, $\eta_1^*, \cdots, \eta_r^*$ are not algebraically independent, and hence transc $N < r$. This contradiction completes the proof of theorem (13.1).

Let us discuss certain corollaries of the theorem.

(13.2) *There is one and only one irreducible r dimensional variety V^r containing a given point M of transcendency r and M is a general point for V^r.* (See 9.2.)

(13.3) *A subvariety V_1 of an irreducible variety V^r is of dimension $< r$.*

For V_1 contains no general point of V^r (9.3) and hence its points have transcendencies $< r$.

(13.4) *If V^r, V^s are such that no component of one of them contains a component of the other, then* $\dim (V^r \cap V^s) < \min (r, s)$.

One may clearly suppose V^r and V^s irreducible, and such that neither of the two varieties contains the other. Then $W = V^r \cap V^s$ is a subvariety of each and so (13.4) follows from (13.3).

Property (13.2) underscores very heavily the extent to which the points of maximum transcendency characterize an irreducible variety. The next two show on the other hand how "thin" subvarieties are within a given variety.

Reducible varieties. Let V be reducible and let $\mathfrak{a}_H$ be its ideal and $V_1, \cdots, V_s$ its components with $\dim V_i = r_i$. If M_i is a general point of V_i then the set $\{M_i\}$ will be referred to as a *canonical set* for V. The following properties are immediate consequences of the Hilbert zero theorem coupled with property (9.1) or else obvious directly:

(13.5) *A n.a.s.c. for a form f to contain V or equivalently to have a power f^ρ in the ideal $\mathfrak{a}_H$ of V is that f contain the points of a canonical set.*

(13.6) *A n.a.s.c for V to be pure is that the points of a canonical set have the same transcendency r and then* $\dim V = r$.

(13.7) *A n.a.s.c. for $\mathfrak{a}_H$ to be a primary ideal is that a canonical set consist of a single point.*

14. Let V^* be the variety resulting from V^r through a finite extension of K. Both varieties have the same points and the extension cannot raise the transcendency of any point. Hence $\dim V^* \leq r = \dim V$. On the other hand let $M(\xi)$ be a general point of V^r so chosen that in a suitable coordinate system ξ_i/ξ_0, $i = 1, 2, \cdots, r$ are indeterminates distinct from those of the finite extension (12.4). Thus N still has transcendency r relative to the new groundfield and therefore $\dim V^* \geq r$. Hence $\dim V^* = r$ and M is likewise a general point for V^*. Thus:

(14.1) *A finite extension does not affect the dimension of the variety V^r. Moreover there exists a general point of V^r which remains general for the new variety resulting from the extension.*

There is of course no reason to expect every general point to remain general. Thus with M as before if one chooses as new groundfield $K_H(\xi)$ the new transcendency of M will be zero and M will cease to be a general point.

15. General elements. The concept of "general element" is as useful for many entities of algebraic geometry as it is for points. The general rule might be formulated something like this: Whenever there may be set up a one-one correspondence between the elements of a collection $A = \{\alpha\}$ and the points of an irreducible V^r then an element α which corresponds to a general point of V^r is said to be a general element of A. The following examples will serve to illustrate our meaning and will, at the same time, cover most of the instances of the term occurring later.

Example 1. Let $\{f_i\}$, $i = 0, 1, \cdots, \mu$ be a collection of linearly independent forms of $K_H[x]$ of the same degree d. Consider all the forms

$$f = \Sigma u_i f_i$$

and let KP^μ be a space referred to the coordinates u_i. Then there is a one-one correspondence between the points of KP^μ and the hypersurfaces f. A particular f is general whenever its representative point u in KP^μ is general, i.e., has the transcendency μ.

Noteworthy special cases: $\{f\}$ consists of all the forms of degree d in $K_H[x]$. Then one may take as the f_i all the monomials of degree d in the x_j and so here $\mu = \binom{m+d}{d} - 1$. In particular for the set of all the hyperplanes

$$\Sigma u_i x_i = 0$$

we have $\mu = m$ and a general hyperplane is one for which

$$\text{transc } \{u_i/u_j\} = m.$$

Example 2. The set $\{u_{ij}\}$ of all $p \times q$ matrices may be represented in one-one manner by the points of an affine space KA_u^{pq} referred to the coordinates u_{ij}. A given matrix is general if its set of elements has transcendency pq. "Almost" every matrix will naturally mean all the matrices which, in the space of the u_{ij} are not represented by the points of a certain variety of the space.

Example 3. A transformation of coordinates, or a projective transformation of KP^m is said to be general whenever the matrix of the transformation is general. Similarly for KA^m.

16. A noteworthy property of general hyperplanes is the following:

(16.1) *The intersection W of an irreducible variety V^r with a general hyperplane*

$$l = \Sigma u_i x_i$$

is an irreducible variety of dimension $r - 1$ in LP^m, $L = K_H(u)$.

By repetition we obtain:

(16.2) *The intersection W of V^r with s general hyperplanes*

$$l_j = \Sigma u_i^j x_i$$

is an irreducible $r - s$ dimensional variety of LP^m, $L = K_H^s(u^1; \cdots; u^s)$. In particular when $s = r$, W consists of d points conjugate relative to L.

The number d is known as the *degree* of V^r. When $r = m - 1$, i.e. when V^r is a hypersurface f then d is evidently the degree of the form f, i.e. the degree of the hypersurface as previously defined.

Notice that when dim $W = 0$, the fact that it is irreducible over L simply means that its d component points are conjugate with respect to L.

We proceed with the proof of (16.1). Let $L = K_H^{m-1}(u)$ and $v = u_0/u_m$. Observe that $L(v) = K_H(u)$. By (8.3) V^r is still irreducible in LP^m. Let coordinates be so chosen that l becomes $u_0x_0 + u_mx_m = 0$, or passing to affine coordinates $X_m + v = 0$. Let $\mathfrak{p}$ be the prime ideal of V^r in $L[X]$ and let $\mathfrak{p}^*$ be the ideal of the intersection W of V^r by l as a variety of $L(v)P^{m-1}$ referred to the coordinates X_i, $i < m$. In view of the criterium (5.7) to prove the irreducibility of W as variety of $L(v)P^m$ it is sufficient to show that it is irreducible as the variety of $\mathfrak{p}^*$ or in the last analysis to show that $\mathfrak{p}^*$ is prime.

If $G(X) \in L(X)$ let $G^* = G(X_1, \cdots, X_{m-1}, v)$. If $\{F_i\}$ is a base for $\mathfrak{p}$ then $\{F_i^*\}$ is a base for $\mathfrak{p}^*$. Suppose that $G^*, H^* \in (L(v))^{m-1}[X]$ are such that $G^*H^* \in \mathfrak{p}^*$. We may as well assume that $G^*, H^* \in L[X_1, \cdots, X_{m-1}, v]$. There will then take place a relation:

$$\psi(v)G^*H^* = \Sigma\psi_i^*F_i^*, \quad \psi \in L[v], \quad \psi_i^* \in L[X_1, \cdots, X_{m-1}, v].$$

From this follows $$\psi(X_m)GH = \Sigma\psi_iF_i \in \mathfrak{p}.$$

Now under our choice of coordinates V^r is not contained in any hyperplane $X_m = \alpha$, $\alpha \in L$, and hence $\psi(X_m)$ is not in $\mathfrak{p}$. It follows that one of G, H say G is in the ideal. Then $G^* \in \mathfrak{p}^*$. Hence $\mathfrak{p}^*$ is prime and W is irreducible.

There remains to show that dim $W = r - 1$. Since $X_m = -v$ is general it does not contain V^r. Hence X_m is transcendental on V^r. Hence V^r contains a general point $M(\xi^*)$, relative to K, with ξ_m^* transcendental and hence such a point with $\xi_m^* = -v$. Then $M \in W$ and transc$_L$ $M = r - 1$. Hence dim$_L$ $W \geq r - 1$. On the other hand since V^r is not in $X_m + v$, W is a subvariety of V^r. Hence dim $W < r$ and so dim $W = r - 1$. This completes the proof of (16.1).

§ 4. Projections

17. The two classical operations on algebraic varieties are projections and intersections. We deal here and there with intersections and shall now consider projections.

Take a fixed point O strictly in KP^m and let S be a hyperplane not containing O. If M is any point of KP^m other than O the line OM cuts

S in a unique point M'. The operation Pr on KP^m such that Pr $M = M'$ is called a *projection* of KP^m onto S, and O is the *center* of the projection. This is projection in the classical sense. The same operation may be defined in KA^m. As a special case the center is at infinity and the projecting lines MM' are parallel to a fixed direction. These operations are so well known that it is not necessary to dwell at length upon them.

A natural generalization is as follows: Take in KP^m two fixed subspaces S^{m-k-1} and S^k which do not intersect. Given any point M not in S^{m-k-1}, S^{m-k-1} and M span a subspace S^{m-k} which intersects S^k in M' (see below) and the projection is now $M \to M'$. The space S^{m-k-1} is again called the *center* of the projection.

Since S^k and S^{m-k-1} do not intersect one may select a k-simplex $A_0 \cdots A_k$ in S^k and an $(m-k-1)$-simplex $A_{k+1} \cdots A_m$ in S^{m-k-1} such that $A_0 \cdots A_m$ is an m-simplex. It is to be chosen as the simplex of reference. The points of S^k are now defined by

$$x_{k+1} = \cdots = x_m = 0 \tag{17.1}$$

and those of S^{m-k-1} by

$$x_0 = x_1 = \cdots = x_k = 0.$$

The assertion made regarding M not in S^{m-k-1} and $M' =$ Pr M is equivalent to the following: If M is in S^k take $M' = M$; otherwise there is a unique point M' of S^k such that $M'M$ meets S^{m-k-1}. Alternatively: For M not in S^k nor in S^{m-k-1}, there is a unique pair of points M' in S^k and M'' in S^{m-k-1} such that the line $M'M''$ contains M. In fact if ξ_i, ξ'_i, ξ''_i are the coordinates of M, M', M'', we must have relations

$$\rho\xi_i = \lambda\xi'_i + \mu\xi''_i,$$

where λ and μ are not both zero. Since $\xi'_{k+j} = 0$ and $\xi''_h = 0$ for $h \leq k$, necessarily

$$\xi'_i = \sigma\xi_i, \quad i \leq k; \qquad \xi''_j = \tau\xi_j, \quad j > k$$

and our assertion follows. Notice that M' is merely the point of S^k whose first $k + 1$ coordinates are the same as those of M. This is a simple rule of operation for obtaining the projection.

The extension to a KA^m is automatic and may be left to the reader.

18. Projection of a variety. The forms of $\mathfrak{a}_H$ contained in $K^k_H[x]$, i.e., the forms of $\mathfrak{a}_H$ lacking the x_{k+i} make up an ideal $\mathfrak{a}^k_H$ of $K^k_H[x]$. They define a variety V_k of the space $x_{k+1} = \cdots = x_m = 0$, called the *projection* of V onto S^k from the *center* S^{m-k-1}: $x_0 = \cdots = x_k = 0$. We verify at once:

(18.1) *The points of V not in S^{m-k-1} are projected into points of V_k.*

(18.2) *If $\mathfrak{a}_H$ is prime so is $\mathfrak{a}^k_H$. Hence if V is irreducible so is its projection V_k.*

The elements of $\mathfrak{a}_H^k$ generate an ideal of $K_H[x]$ itself which we denote by $\mathfrak{a}_H^*$. The latter defines a variety W_k of KP^m known as the *projecting cone* of V or in relation to V_k the *cone based on* V_k. The cone contains all the spaces S^{m-k} each spanned by S^{m-k-1} and a point of V_k. These spaces S^{m-k} are known as the *generators* of the cone.

(18.3) *If* V_k *is irreducible so is the cone* W_k *based on* V_k. *Furthermore* $\dim W_k = m - k + \dim V_k$.

Let $\mathfrak{p}_H^k$ be the prime ideal of V_k and $\mathfrak{p}_H^*$ the induced ideal of $K_H[x]$. Let also $\dim V_k = r$ and take a general point $M'(\xi_0, \cdots, \xi_k)$ of V_k. Then $M(\xi_0, \cdots, \xi_k, u_1, \cdots, u_{m-k})$, where the u_i are indeterminates algebraically independent of the ξ_i is a point of W_k. Suppose that $f(x) \in K_H[x]$ contains M. Thus $f(\xi; u) = 0$. Since the u_j are algebraically independent of the ξ's, their coefficients in $f(\xi; u)$ are all zero. If $\varphi(\xi)$ is any one of these coefficients then $\varphi(x) \in \mathfrak{p}_H^k$ and hence $f(x) \in \mathfrak{p}_H^*$.

Conversely let $f(x) \in \mathfrak{p}_H^*$. If $\{f_i(x_0, \cdots, x_k)\}$, $i = 1, 2, \cdots, s$ is a base for $\mathfrak{p}_H^k$ then identically

$$f(x) = \Sigma g_i(x_0, \cdots, x_m) f_i(x_0, \cdots, x_k),$$

and hence $f(\xi; u) = 0$, i.e. f contains M. Thus $\mathfrak{p}_H^*$ consists of all the forms annulled by M. Its variety W_k is therefore irreducible (9.2) and it has M as general point. As a consequence

$$\dim W_k = \text{transc } M' + m - k = r + m - k,$$

and (18.3) is proved.

§ 5. Differentials. Singular Points. Tangent Spaces. (Groundfield of Characteristic Zero)

19. Let as before V^r be irreducible and in general position, with $M(\xi)$ a general point and $\mathfrak{p}_H$ the prime ideal of the variety. The differentials of the function field K^V may be based on its representation $K_H(\xi)$. Let $\{\xi_i/\xi_0\}$, $i = 1, 2, \cdots, r$ be a transcendence base for $K_H(\xi)$. Proceeding as in (I, 12.2) take $r + 1$ independent vectors $d\xi_0, \cdots, d\xi_r$ as a base for the auxiliary space $\mathfrak{W}(\xi)$ of the projective differentials of the field $K(\xi)$. Then the space $\mathfrak{V}(\xi)$ of the differentials of $K_H(\xi)$ is spanned by the $d(\xi_i/\xi_j)$ and has $K_H(\xi)$ for scalar domain. Or equivalently $\mathfrak{V}(\xi)$ is spanned by the $d\xi_i^*$, $i = 1, 2, \cdots, r$, where $\xi_i^* = \xi_i/\xi_0$ are the affine coordinates of M. If $M'(\xi')$ is another general point then $\mathfrak{V}(\xi)$ and $\mathfrak{V}(\xi')$ are merely differentially isomorphic so that, as we know, $\mathfrak{V}(\xi)$ is essentially unique. This is the space of primary interest in the sequel.

We recall that $\dim \mathfrak{V}(\xi) = r$, $\dim \mathfrak{W}(\xi) = r + 1$.

We emphasize once more the purely auxiliary role of the space $\mathfrak{W}(\xi)$.

Actually the only elements of $\mathfrak{W}(\xi)$ that we shall consider are of course those of $\mathfrak{V}(\xi)$ and besides them elements of the form

(19.1) $\Sigma R_i(\xi)d\xi_i$

where the $R_i(\xi)$ are homogeneous and of the same degree. In particular if $f(\xi) \in K_H[\xi]$ then

(19.2) $df = \Sigma f_{\xi_i} d\xi_i$

is of the type (19.1). Notice also that (19.1) may be written

(19.3) $$\frac{\Sigma g_i(\xi)d\xi_i}{g(\xi)}$$

where g, g_i are forms and the $g_i(\xi)$ are of the same degree.

20. Since M is a general point the properties $f(\xi) = 0$ and $f(x) \in \mathfrak{p}_H$ are equivalent. Hence $f(x) \in \mathfrak{p}_H$ implies

(20.1) $df(\xi) = \Sigma f_{\xi_i} d\xi_i = 0,$

and these are the only relations that are imposed upon the vectors $d\xi_i$.

Let $\{f_1(x), \cdots, f_s(x)\}$ be a base for the ideal $\mathfrak{p}_H$. Thus

(20.2) $f(x) = \Sigma\varphi_j(x)f_j(x), \quad \varphi_j(x) \in K_H[x].$

From this follows, since $f_j(\xi) = 0$,

(20.3) $df(\xi) = \Sigma f_{\xi_i} d\xi_i = \Sigma\varphi_j(\xi)df_j(\xi) = 0.$

Hence to impose (20.1) for each $f \in \mathfrak{p}_H$ is equivalent to imposing the finite system

(20.4) $\Sigma f_{j\xi_i} d\xi_i = 0, \quad j = 1, 2, \cdots, s.$

Since among the vectors $d\xi_i$ exactly $r + 1$ are linearly independent the functional matrix

(20.5) $\|f_{j\xi_i}\|$

is of rank $m - r$. Suppose that the minor $\Delta_{j_1 \cdots j_{m-r}}^{i_1 \cdots i_{m-r}} \neq 0$, where the i_h, j_k are respectively the indices of the rows and columns from which the minor is taken. Let $k_0, \cdots, k_r$ be such that together with $j_1 \cdots$ they form the set $0, 1, \cdots, m$. We will prove

(20.6) *The ratios of the coordinates $\xi_{k_0}, \cdots \xi_{k_r}$ to one of them $(\neq 0)$ are algebraically independent and $\{d\xi_{k_i}\}$ is a base for the space of projective differentials* $\mathfrak{W}(\xi)$.

For convenience let us write ξ_i' for ξ_{k_i}. Under our assumptions all the $d\xi$ depend linearly upon the $d\xi'$. Since the number of the latter is $r + 1 = \dim \mathfrak{W}(\xi)$, $\{d\xi_i'\}$ is a base for $\mathfrak{W}$. Assume now a non-trivial relation $\Psi(\xi') = 0$, $\Psi(\xi') \in K_H[\xi']$. Some of the $\Psi_{\xi_i'}$ will certainly be $\neq 0$.

Hence the differentiation of Ψ provides a linear relation between the $d\xi'$:

$$d\Psi(\xi') = \Sigma \Psi_{\xi'_i} d\xi'_i = 0$$

which is non-trivial. This means that $\{d\xi'_i\}$ is not a base for the space $\mathfrak{W}$ and this contradiction proves (20.6).

Property (20.6) implies essentially that in constructing our system of differentials one may replace the set $\{\xi_0, \cdots, \xi_r\}$ by any set of $r + 1$ coordinates of the general point $M(\xi)$ whose ratios to one of them are algebraically independent.

21. The useful and intuitive notion of the values of the differentials of V^r at a point $N(\eta)$ of the variety may be introduced formally as follows: Let $d\eta_0, \cdots, d\eta_m$ be elements of a vector space with scalar domain $K_H(\eta)$ and solely subjected to the following relations entirely analogous to (20.1): if $f(x) \in \mathfrak{p}_H$ then

$$\Sigma f_{\eta_i} d\eta_i = 0. \tag{21.1}$$

If say (19.3) is an element of $\mathfrak{W}(\xi)$ and $g(\eta) \neq 0$ then its value at N is by definition

$$\sum \frac{g_i(\eta) d\eta_i}{g(\eta)}$$

Similarly for a form $f(\xi)$, the value of $df(\xi)$ at N, written $df(\eta)$ is by definition

$$df(\eta) = \Sigma f_{\eta_i} d\eta_i.$$

In particular (21.1) may now be written merely $df(\eta) = 0$.

We may now show as before that the system (21.1) is equivalent to the finite system

$$\Sigma f_{j\eta_i} \, d\eta_i = 0, \quad j = 1, 2, \cdots, s. \tag{21.2}$$

Thus all the relations imposed upon the $d\eta_i$ are consequences of the system (21.2).

Consider now the Jacobian matrix

$$D(x) = \| f_{jx_i} \|.$$

Any minor of $D(x)$ is a form $\Delta(x) \in K_H[x]$. Since M is a general point of V^r, $\Delta(\xi) = 0$ implies $\Delta(\eta) = 0$. Hence the rank $m - \rho$ of $D(x)$ assumes its largest value at the general points. We have seen that this rank is $m - r$. Thus $\rho \geq r$.

Now the systems

$$l(x) = \Sigma x_i f_{\eta_i} = 0, \quad f(x) \in \mathfrak{p}_H; \tag{21.3}$$

$$l_j(x) = \Sigma x_i f_{j\eta_i} = 0, \quad j = 1, 2, \cdots, s \tag{21.3a}$$

differ only formally from (21.1), (21.2). They are then equivalent and one or the other represents a space S^ρ of $K_H(\eta)P^m$. This space is the *tangent space* to V^r at the point N. The points N where the dimension of the tangent space assumes its least value r are the *ordinary* points, the others are the *singular* points of the variety. All the general points are ordinary points.

At the singular points certain forms $\Delta(x)$ vanish which do not vanish at the general points. Hence the singular points are the points of a subvariety S of V^r, the *singular variety* of V^r.

Since dim $S < r$, we have dim $S \leq 0$ for a curve. Hence:

(21.4) *An algebraic curve has at most a finite number of singular points.*

Evidently:

(21.5) *A n.a.s.c. for a point N of V^r to be an ordinary [a singular] point of the variety is that the tangent space to V^r at N be of dimension $r[> r]$.*

Upon applying a non-singular transformation of coordinates whose matrix is E, $D(\eta)$ is multiplied to the right by E. Hence the rank ρ is fixed. Moreover the $l_j(x)$ remain formally unchanged. Hence:

(21.6) *A transformation of coordinates does not affect the ordinary points, nor the singular points nor their tangent spaces.*

In point of fact the tangent spaces at the singular points have but minor significance. This is clearly brought out by the following two examples: (a) If a plane curve C has a multiple point N then the tangent space at N is the plane of the curve; (b) at a vertex N of a cone in KP^3 the tangent space is KP^3. Intuitively speaking one expects the tangent space at a point of V^r to be the linear space of the "directions of approach" to the point on the variety. Under our more general definition it is generally the smallest linear space which these directions span. The space thus defined behaves correctly at the ordinary points but may behave abnormally at the singular points, for instance in the two examples given above.

If we denote for a moment by $\mathfrak{V}(V^r)$ the space of differentials $\mathfrak{V}(\xi)$ of V^r we see at once that

(21.7) *The elements of $\mathfrak{V}(S^r)$ are merely the values of those of $\mathfrak{V}(V^r)$ at the point $N(\eta)$.*

This corresponds to the intuitive idea that "in the first approximation" at the point N one may replace the variety V^r by the tangent space S^r.

22. If V^r is a hypersurface f then the matrix $D(x)$ is the one-rowed matrix of the f_{x_i}. Hence the equation of the tangent hyperplane at an ordinary point is (21.3). The singular variety S is the intersection with f of the varieties

$$f_{x_i} = 0, \quad i = 0, 1, \cdots, m. \tag{22.1}$$

They belong to the family of the first polars to be more fully discussed in connection with intersections in the next section. At a singular point of f the tangent space is KP^m itself.

From Euler's relation

$$\mu f = \Sigma x_i f_{x_i}$$

where μ is the degree of f, follows that the singular variety S of f is in fact the variety defined by the system (22.1).

In view of Euler's relation we have for $N(\eta) \in V^r$:

$$\Sigma \eta_i f_{j\eta_i} = 0, \quad j = 1, 2, \cdots, s.$$

Hence if N is not in the hyperplane x_0 one may replace the matrix $D(\eta)$ by

$$\| f_{i,\eta_1}, \cdots, f_{i,\eta_m} \|.$$

Passing then to affine coordinates we see that if the ideal $\mathfrak{p}$ of V^r has the base $\{F_i(X)\}$ then the singular points are those where the rank of the Jacobian matrix

$$\| F_{iX_j} \|$$

is $< m - r$ and the ordinary points those where its rank is actually $m - r$. For a hypersurface $F(X)$ the singular variety is the intersection with F of the variety defined by

(22.2) $$F_{X_i} = 0, \quad i = 1, 2, \cdots, m.$$

If $N(\eta)$ is in the affine space we may take $\eta_0 = 1$, and the other η_i become the affine coordinates η_i^* of N. We have then the affine differentials $d\eta_i^*$ with the relations

(22.3) $$\Sigma F_{\eta_i^*} d\eta_i^* = 0$$

where $F \in \mathfrak{p}$, the affine prime ideal of V^r. The space $\mathfrak{B}(\eta^*)$ of these differentials is the same as for the S^r which is the intersection of the hyperplanes

(22.4) $$L(X) = \Sigma(X_i - \eta_i^*) F_{\eta_i^*} = 0,$$

for all $F \in \mathfrak{p}$. This S^r is then the tangent space to V^r at N. For a single hypersurface F for which N is an ordinary point the tangent hyperplane at N is given by (22.4).

Returning to projective coordinates it is convenient to define tangent hyperplanes for reducible hypersurfaces. If $f = f_1 \cdots f_q$ where the factors are irreducible but may be repeated then an ordinary point of f is a point N which belongs to one and only one factor say f_i and is an ordinary point of f_i. The other points are singular points. Thus if f_i is repeated it contributes no ordinary points. It is seen at once that the singular points are determined as before by the intersections of all the f_{x_j}. At an ordinary point $N(\eta)$ of both f_i and f the tangent hyperplane to f at N is by definition the tangent hyperplane to f_i at the same point. This leads immediately for an irreducible V^r to the following property:

(22.5) *The tangent space S^r to V^r at an ordinary point N is the intersection of all the tangent hyperplanes to the hypersurfaces f containing V^r and for which N is an ordinary point.*

Let now V^p, $p < r$, be an irreducible subvariety of V^r and suppose that N is an ordinary point for both. Since the hypersurfaces mentioned in (22.4) relative to V^p include those of V^r we have:

(22.6) *If V^p is an irreducible subvariety of V^r and N is an ordinary point for both then the tangent space S^p to V^p at N is a subspace of the tangent space S^r to V^r at the same point.*

From this we infer readily the following result which may also be proved directly:

(22.7) *The spaces of differentials $\mathfrak{V}(\eta)$, $\mathfrak{W}(\eta)$ for V^p at N are subspaces of the corresponding spaces for V^r at the same point.*

§ 6. Some Intersection Properties

23. Let $f(x)$ be a form of degree d and $M(\xi)$ any point. For convenience introduce the polar operator ξD_x defined by

$$\xi D_x f = \Sigma \xi_i f_{x_i}.$$

The successive forms $\xi D_x f$, $(\xi D_x)^2 f$, $\cdots$ (symbolic powers) of degree one, two, $\cdots$, in the ξ_i, are the *first*, the *second*, $\cdots$, *polars* of f *with respect to the point M*. The last, the dth, is $d! f(\xi)$. Note the following elementary and readily verifiable properties

I. $$\frac{(\xi D_x)^k}{k!} = \frac{(x D_\xi)^{d-k}}{(d-k)!}, \quad (0! = 1).$$

II. *The coefficients of the form $(x D_\xi)^k$ are merely (to within integral factors) all the partials of degree k of $f(\xi)$.*

III. *Under a projective transformation of determinant Δ all the polars of f are merely multiplied by Δ^d.*

Referring to (21) when the characteristic of K is zero and M is an ordinary point of the hypersurface f then $x D_\xi f$ is the tangent hyperplane to f at M.

24. Consider now the intersections of the hypersurface f with the line l joining two distinct points $A(a)$ and $B(b)$. The coordinates of any point of l are given by expressions

(24.1) $$\rho x_i = \lambda a_i + \mu b_i, \quad i = 0, 1, \cdots, m.$$

If the point is to be on f then

(24.2) $$f(\lambda a + \mu b) = \lambda^d f(a) + \lambda^{d-1} \mu \frac{b D_a f}{1!}$$
$$+ \frac{\lambda^{d-2} \mu^2}{2!} (b D_a)^2 f + \cdots = \Phi(\lambda, \mu) = 0,$$

where $\Phi \in K_H[\lambda, \mu]$. If $\Phi = 0$ (as ring element) then $l \subset f$ and conversely. Assuming from now on that l is not in the hypersurface f, there will be a factorization of Φ in linear factors in $\bar{K}$:

$$\Phi(\lambda, \mu) = \gamma \Pi(\lambda\beta_j - \mu\alpha_j)^{\sigma_j}, \quad \sigma_j > 0, \quad \Sigma\sigma_j = d,$$

where $\gamma, \alpha_j, \beta_j \in \bar{K}$. The λ, μ of the intersection points are given by $\Phi = 0$. The points in question are then the points M_j, where M_j has the coordinates $\alpha_j a_i + \beta_j b_i$. We assign to M_j the *intersection multiplicity* σ_j. This multiplicity is at once seen to be independent of the coordinate system and of the choice of the points A and B on l. This gives geometric content to the multiplicities. Counting each intersection with its multiplicity their total number is the degree d of f.

Take in particular for A one of the points of the line on the hypersurface f itself. If k denotes the multiplicity of A and since for A: $\lambda = 1$, $\mu = 0$ we will have

$$\Phi(\lambda, \mu) = \gamma\mu^k \Pi(\lambda\beta_j - \mu\alpha_j)^{\sigma_j}. \tag{24.3}$$

This time the count of the points of intersection other than A gives $d - k$ as their number. This is sometimes expressed as: the point A *absorbs* k intersections of l with f.

Upon comparing with (24.2) we see that first $f(a) = 0$, as expected, and then that at the point B

$$xD_a f = 0, \cdots, \quad (xD_a)^{k-1} f = 0, \quad (xD_a)^k f \neq 0.$$

That is to say the $(d - k)$th polar hypersurface of f with respect to A is the first which does not contain the point A.

We are particularly interested in the *least* value of k for *all* lines through A. This value will be k itself, when and only when all the $(xD_a)^h f = 0$, for $h < k$, but $(xD_a)^k f \neq 0$. Referring to (23.11) this is equivalent to the property that all the partials of f of order $< k$ vanish at A, but that some of order k do not.

It is seen at once that $k = 1$ when and only when A is an ordinary point. If $k > 1$ the point A is singular and conversely. Such a point is also known as a point of *multiplicity* k or a k-*tuple* point of f (*double*, *triple*, $\cdots$, point for $k = 2, 3, \cdots$).

If A is a k-tuple point the hypersurface

$$g(x) = (xD_a)^k f = 0$$

is of particular interest. It has the property that if B is in g then the point A absorbs at least k intersections of the line AB with f. Hence if $B \in g$ every point of AB is also in g. Therefore g is a cone of vertex A. It is known as the *tangent cone* to f at the point A. In fact when $k = 1$, i.e. when A is an ordinary point the tangent cone becomes

$$xD_a f = \Sigma x_i f_{a_i} = 0$$

which is the tangent hyperplane at the point A as defined for K of characteristic zero. This justifies the term "tangent cone" applied to $g(x)$ in the general case.

The generators of the cone g are known as the *tangents* to the hypersurface f at the point A. Thus:

(24.4) *The tangents at a k-tuple point A of f are the lines through A for which A absorbs at least $k + 1$ intersections with f. In particular at an ordinary point A the tangents are the lines through A in the tangent hyperplane at A and for each such line A absorbs at least two intersections.*

(24.5) *If f is not a cone then the multiplicity of a point of f does not exceed $d - 1$, where d is the degree of f.*

For if $k = d$, the hypersurface f reduces to its own tangent cone at the multiple point. As an application:

(24.6) *An irreducible plane curve of degree $d > 1$ has no point of multiplicity $> d - 1$.*

For if $d > 1$ at a d-tuple point the "tangent cone" consists of d lines.

A property of some interest, likewise a direct consequence of the definitions is:

(24.7) *At a k-tuple point of f the polars of order $h < k$ have multiplicity at least $k - h$ and some have exactly that multiplicity.*

Since the polars are projectively invariant we may state:

(24.8) *Projective transformations do not affect the multiplicities of the points of a hypersurface.*

In the applications it is convenient to have direct information regarding the behavior in affine coordinates. We find at once that a n.a.s.c. for the point $(1, 0, \cdots, 0)$ to be a k-tuple point of f is that

$$f = x_0^{d-k} f_k(x_1, \cdots, x_m) + x_0^{d-k-1} f_{k+1}(x_1, \cdots, x_m) + \cdots.$$

Hence in affine coordinates with $F(X) = f(1, X_1, \cdots, X_m)$ the origin is a k-tuple point when and only when

$$F = F_k(X) + F_{k+1}(X) + \cdots + F_d(X)$$

where F_h is a form of degree h. One verifies also directly that $F_k(X)$ (the set of terms of lowest degree in F) is the tangent cone at the origin (tangent hyperplane for $k = 1$). Thus for the curve in the X, Y plane:

$$F_k(X, Y) + F_{k+1}(X, Y) + \cdots = 0$$

the equation of the tangents at the origin is $F_k(X, Y) = 0$. In particular for the curve

$$aX + bY + F_2(X, Y) + \cdots = 0$$

where a and b are not both zero, the origin is an ordinary point and $aX + bY = 0$ is the tangent at the origin.

At a point $A(a_1, \cdots, a_m)$ in the affine space KA^m the situation is the same as above save that the X_i must be replaced by $X_i - a_i$ throughout.

25. Let us discuss now intersections of m hypersurfaces in KP^m. The central property is:

(25.1) **Theorem of Bezout.** *Let $f_1, \cdots, f_m$ be hypersurfaces of KP^m which only intersect in a finite set $\{M_j\}$ of points, and let d_i be the degree of f_i. There may then be assigned multiplicities σ_j to the M_j independent of the coordinate system, such that counted with these multiplicities the number of intersections is $d = d_1 \cdots d_m$.*

Introduce a hyperplane

$$l(u; x) = \Sigma u_i x_i$$

with indeterminate coefficients u_i. Referring to (1, 3.7) the resultant $R_H(f_1, \cdots, f_m, l) = R_H(u)$ is a form of degree d of $K_H[u]$. This form admits the factorization in $\bar{K}(u)$ (see van der Waerden [1], II, p. 17)

$$(25.2) \qquad R_H(u) = \Pi l^{\sigma_j}(u; M_j), \quad \Sigma\sigma_j = d.$$

By (I, 3.10) the f_i intersect if and only if one of the factors $l(u; M_j) = 0$, i.e. as one might have expected if and only if $l(u; x)$ contains an M_j. The multiplicity of M_j is by definition the exponent σ_j at the right. Since their sum is d, and they evidently do not depend upon the coordinate system the theorem follows.

Under the assumptions of the theorem let the coordinate system be such that none of the points M_j is on the simplex of reference. Hence if $M(\xi)$ is any one of them none of the ξ_i is zero. Take now $l = u_0x_0 + u_1x_1$ and such that $l(M) = 0$. Thus we may assume that $l = \xi_1x_0 - \xi_0x_1$. Since $l(M) = 0$ we have then the non-trivial relation

$$R_H(\xi_1, -\xi_0, 0, \cdots, 0) = 0.$$

Thus ξ_1/ξ_0 and similarly all the other coordinate ratios are in K. Or:

(25.3) *If the hypersurfaces f_i intersect in a finite number of points, these points are strictly in KP^m. (If K is not algebraically closed one must replace it by its closure).*

(25.4) *Application. If the hypersurface f has only a finite number of singularities these are strictly in KP^m (in $\bar{K}P^m$ if K is not algebraically closed).*

For the singularities are the intersections of all the first polars. Hence one may choose m intersecting only in the singular points and (25.4) follows then at once.

As a complement to Bezout's theorem we may prove:

(25.5) *For almost all sets of hypersurfaces in Bezout's theorem, and hence for a general set there are actually d distinct intersections.*

Assuming again as in (I, 3) that the coefficients of the f_i are indeterminates, let L be the closure of the field which they generate. Then $R_H(u)$ represents a hypersurface in LP^m_u, which is in fact a collection of hyperplanes. Now a n.a.s.c. in order that some of the $\sigma_i > 1$ is that the discriminants of the binary forms $R_H(0, \cdots, 0, x_i, 0, \cdots, 0, x_j, 0, \cdots, 0)$ i.e. the resultants of their first partial derivatives vanish. These discriminants are multiforms in the coefficients of the f_i with integral coefficients, and if they vanish identically they will do so for all special choices of the f_i. However upon taking for f_i (and every i) a binary form in x_0, x_i without multiple factors and without factor in x_0 alone, one verifies at once that there are d distinct intersections. Hence our discriminants are not all identically zero and in particular they are not so when the f_i are general. Thus for general f_i there will actually be d distinct intersections.

26. It so happens that for the intersections of a line and a hypersurface f, and for those of two plane curves there are actually alternate methods to obtain the intersections and their multiplicities. We shall therefore examine each of these two special cases and show that the two available methods yield the same result.

Consider first the intersection of a line λ and a hypersurface f, where λ is not in f. The two methods of (24) and (25) are independent of the coordinate system. Let us apply the (u)-method by considering λ as the intersection of $m - 1$ hyperplanes. We choose coordinates such that these hyperplanes are $x_2, \cdots, x_m$. Thus λ becomes the line A_0A_1 of the simplex of reference, i.e. joining $A_0(1, 0, \cdots, 0)$ to $A_1(0, 1, 0, \cdots, 0)$. These two points are also chosen not on f. By the first method the intersections correspond to the binary factors of $f(x_0, x_1, 0, \cdots, 0)$. That is to say by that method if in $\bar{K}$

$$f(x_0, x_1, 0, \cdots, 0) = \gamma\Pi(x_0\alpha_{j1} - x_1\alpha_{j0})^{\zeta_j} \tag{26.1}$$

then the intersections are the points $M_j(\alpha_{j0}, \alpha_{j1}, 0, \cdots, 0)$ and the ζ_j are their multiplicities. We have $\Sigma\zeta_j = d$, as prescribed by Bezout's theorem.

According to the (u)-method we take $R_H(f, x_2, \cdots, x_m, l(u))$ and we have the identity

$$\begin{aligned} A_{i0}l(u) + A_{i1}f + A_{i2}x_2 + \cdots + A_{im}x_m &= x_i^{s_i}R_H \\ &= x_i^{s_i}\Pi l(u; M_j)^{\sigma_j}, \quad i = 0, 1, \cdots, m \end{aligned} \tag{26.2}$$

where if d is the degree of f then $\Sigma\sigma_j = d$. Thus σ_j is the multiplicity of M_j according to the (u)-method and we must show that $\zeta_j = \sigma_j$.

Let $M(x_0, x_1, 0, \cdots, 0)$ be any point of the line λ and let $l(u)$ contain M. Thus $u_0x_0 + u_1x_1 = 0$ and we may take $u_0 = -x_1$, $u_1 = +x_0$. Then

$$l(u; M_j) = x_0\alpha_{j1} - x_1\alpha_{j0}.$$

Hence (26.2) for $i = 0$ yields a relation

$$B(x_0, x_1)f(x_0, x_1, 0, \cdots, 0) = x_0^{s_0}\Pi(x_0\alpha_{j1} - x_1\alpha_{j0})^{\sigma_j}.$$

Since the product at the right is of the same degree d as $f(x_0, x_1, 0, \cdots, 0)$ and the latter is not divisible by x_0, we have $B(x_0, x_1) = \delta x_0^{s_0}$, $\delta \in \bar{K}$. Hence from (26.1) at once $\zeta_j = \sigma_j$. This establishes the concordance of the two methods for the intersection multiplicities of a line and a hypersurface. Since the first method is independent of the choice of the $m - 1$ hyperplanes which intersect in λ, this holds also for the second method.

27. Consider now the intersections of two plane curves $f(x)$ and $g(x)$ of degrees m and n. We choose coordinates such that f and g are regular in x_2 and take the resultant $R_H(f, g; x_2)$ (see I, 3). It is a binary form $\varphi(x_0, x_1)$ of degree mn. If $\varphi = 0$, f and g have a common factor, the number of intersections is infinite and conversely. We suppose then that $\varphi \neq 0$ so that there is only a finite number of intersections. Choose now a triangle of reference such that f, g are regular in the x_i, that no M_j is on the triangle, and that no two are collinear with the vertex (0, 0, 1). We may then choose for M_j coordinates $\alpha_j, 1, \beta_j$. Since $\varphi(x_0, x_1) = 0$ is a n.a.s.c. for f, g to intersect we have in $\bar{K}$

$$(27.1) \qquad \begin{cases} \varphi(x_0, x_1) = \gamma \Pi (x_0 - \alpha_j x_1)^{\zeta_j}, \\ \Sigma \zeta_j = mn, \quad \zeta_j > 0, \gamma \in \bar{K}. \end{cases}$$

Suppose that explicitly

$$f = a x_2^m + \cdots, \quad g = \cdots + b x_0^n + \cdots.$$

Then according to (I, 3.1) φ must contain a term $a^n b^m x_0^{mn}$. Hence $\gamma = a^n b^m$ and

$$(27.2) \qquad \varphi(x_0, x_1) = a^n b^m \Pi (x_0 - \alpha_j x_1)^{\zeta_j}.$$

Under our assumptions the factors are all distinct and the jth corresponds to M_j. We therefore assign naturally the intersection multiplicity ζ_j to M_j and these multiplicities do conform with Bezout's theorem.

On the other hand the u-resultant

$$R_H(f, g, l(u)) = \delta \Pi (u_0 \alpha_j + u_1 + u_2 \beta_j)^{\sigma_j},$$

and it yields the multiplicities σ_j. Referring to (I, 3.11) this resultant contains the term $a^n b^m u_1^{mn}$. Hence $\delta = a^n b^m$ and so

$$\psi(u) = R_H(f, g, u) = a^n b^m \Pi (u_0 \alpha_j + u_1 + u_2 \beta_j)^{\sigma_j}.$$

Let us consider more particularly the lines $l(u)$ through the vertex (0, 0, 1), i.e. with $u_2 = 0$. The coordinates x_0, x_1 of points on such lines satisfy $u_0 x_0 + u_1 x_1 = 0$. Hence they correspond to the binary factors of

$$(27.3) \qquad \psi(-x_1, x_0) = a^n b^m \Pi (x_0 - \alpha_j x_1)^{\sigma_j}.$$

Now both $\varphi(x_0, x_1)$ and $\psi(-x_1, x_0)$ are triply homogeneous forms in the coefficients of f, g and the pair x_0, x_1. Take then for f, g forms with indeterminate coefficients. There are now mn distinct points M_j and since $\Sigma\sigma_j = \Sigma\zeta_j = mn$, and $\sigma_j, \zeta_j > 0$, necessarily $\sigma_j = \zeta_j = 1$. Therefore in that case

$$\psi(-x_1, x_0) = \varphi(x_0, x_1). \tag{27.4}$$

This relation holds identically in the coefficients of f and g and in x_0, x_1. Hence it holds also where the coefficients of f and g are specialized and as a consequence $\sigma_j = \xi_j$. Thus here again the two methods for assigning multiplicities to the intersections of two curves are concordant.

III. *Transformations of Algebraic Varieties*

After the basic concepts have been laid down and clarified the first general question to attack is that of algebraic transformations of varieties into one another. This is the basic problem discussed in the present chapter. The rational and birational transformations are first taken up. This enables us to give a formal definition of birational geometry. Related questions of parametric representation are then considered. The general theory of algebraic correspondence is then attacked by an appeal to product varieties, a procedure which has become classical in all questions of transformations.

Notations. The notations and general assumptions of the preceding chapter are essentially retained throughout the present chapter. In addition we shall constantly consider two irreducible varieties V^r in KP_x^m and W^s in KP_y^n. The previous designations will continue to be used for V^r and analogous designations with y, Y, η, $\mathfrak{q}$ in place of x, X, ξ, $\mathfrak{p}$, for W^s.

§ 1. Rational Transformations

1. A rational transformation T of the variety V^r *into* the variety W^s is a set of relations

$$\rho y_i = a_i(x); \quad i = 0, \cdots, n; \quad a_i(x) \in K_H[x] \tag{1.1}$$

such that if $M(x)$ is a point of V^r then the point $N(y)$ given by these relations is a point of W^s or the null-set. We often write $T : V^r \to W^s$, $TM = N$, etc.

Unless some restrictions are placed upon the $a_i(x)$ the transformation T may have but scant interest. Thus if the a_i are all in the ideal $\mathfrak{p}_H$ of V^r then TM is merely the null-set, i.e. TM does not exist. A first restriction is then:

(*a*) *The* $a_i(x)$ *are not all in* $\mathfrak{p}_H$.

It follows that the a_i together with the forms of $\mathfrak{p}_H$ generate an ideal $\mathfrak{a}_H \supset \mathfrak{p}_H$. The variety V_0 of $\mathfrak{a}_H$ is a subvariety of V^r known as the *fundamental variety* of the transformation T. The points of V_0 are those and only those whose transform is the null-set. The fundamental variety plays an important role in all questions related to rational transformations.

Let us suppose that $N = TM$ exists, i.e., is a true point of W^s (not the null-set). If $b(x)$ is a common factor of all the a_i then $b(M) \neq 0$ and so one may suppress $b(x)$ without affecting the points M which already possess transforms. However, for a general point $M(\xi)$ in view of (a): $b(\xi) \neq 0$, hence TM exists. Thus the suppression of $b(x)$ will not affect the transforms of the general points but it does of course make the fundamental variety as small as possible. We may as well assume then that:

(b) *The $a_i(x)$ are relatively prime.*

Let $N(\eta) = TM(\xi)$ and let W' be the irreducible variety with N as general point. If $\mathfrak{q}'_H$ is the prime ideal (in $K_H[y]$) of W' and $g(y) \in \mathfrak{q}'_H$ then $g(\eta) = g(a_0(\xi), \cdots, a_n(\xi)) = 0$. Hence if $M'(\xi')$ is any point of $V^r - V_0$ and $N'(\eta') = TM'$ then $g(\eta') = g(a_0(\xi'), \cdots, a_n(\xi')) = 0$. Hence N' is in W'. Thus all the transforms of points of V^r are in W'. Since the general point N of W' is in W^s, necessarily $\mathfrak{q}'_H \supset \mathfrak{q}_H$ and hence $W' \subset W^s$. Thus W' is either W^s or else a subvariety of W^s and the latter will occur when and only when TM is *not* general for W^s. By analogy with the point-set situation we shall say: T is a transformation of V^r *into* W^s when W' is a subvariety of W^s and T is a transformation of V^r *onto* W^s when $W' = W^s$. Unless otherwise stated we shall assume:

(c) *T is a transformation of V^r onto W^s.*

An equivalent property is:

(c′) *T sends the general points of V^r into general points of W^s.*

(1.2) *The affine formulation.* Assuming properties (a), (b), (c) and both V^r and W^s in general position, T will operate on V^r_A to W^s_A. Since $a_0(x)$ is then not in $\mathfrak{p}_H$, if we set

$$R_i(X) = \frac{a_i(1, X_1, \cdots, X_m)}{a_0(1, X_1, \cdots, X_m)} \tag{1.3}$$

the relations

$$Y_i = R_i(X), \quad i = 1, 2, \cdots, n \tag{1.4}$$

will define T as a rational transformation $V^r_A \to W^s_A$. In any case given (1.4) such that it sends points of V^r_A into points of W^s_A then (1.3) will yield a set of a_i's in the obvious way satisfying conditions (a) and (b). Moreover (c), or (c′) will hold as stated if they hold for V^r_A and W^s_A.

2. Some examples. *First example.* T is the projective transformation

$$y_i = \Sigma a_{ij} x_j; \quad i = 0, 1, \cdots, n; \quad a_{ij} \in K.$$

If the rank $s + 1$ of the matrix of the coefficients is $< n + 1$, T is a projective transformation of KP^m_x onto an s-subspace of KP^n_y and there is a fundamental variety which is a subspace S of KP^m_x of dimension $m - s - 1$. If $s = m = n$ we have a non-singular projective transformation of one space onto the other.

Second example. Let Q be an irreducible quadric of KP^3, which is not a cone, A a point of Q, P a plane of $KP^3 - A$. The projection of Q from A onto P is a rational transformation with A as fundamental variety.

3. We assume now definitely that the rational transformation T: $V^r \to W^s$ satisfies conditions (1abc) and discuss some of its properties.

(3.1) *A n.a.s.c. for the existence of a rational transformation T of V^r onto W^s is that the function field K^W be isomorphic with a subfield L of the function field K^V in an isomorphism τ which preserves the elements of the groundfield K.*

If T exists as above the relations $\rho\eta_i = a_i(\xi)$ deduced from (1.1) give rise to an isomorphic imbedding $K_H(\eta) = K_H(\{a_i(\xi)\}) \subset K_H(\xi)$ which is a suitable τ. Conversely let such a τ exist and identify the elements of $K_H(\eta)$ with their images under τ. Assuming the varieties in general position we will have $\xi_0\eta_0 \neq 0$. We may then write $\tau(\eta_i/\eta_0) = a_i(\xi)/a_0(\xi)$, where the $a_h(x)$ have properties (1abc). Since T given by (1.1) transforms V^r into an irreducible variety with the same general point N as W^s, W^s is TV^r and (3.1) follows.

(3.2) *A rational transformation T of V^r does not increase the transcendency of the general points and hence* dim $TV^r \leq r$.

(3.3) *Rational transformation of V^r onto W^r. The degree.* When dim $TV^r = r$, $K_H(\eta)$ has the same transcendency r as $K_H(\xi)$, and so $K_H(\xi)$ is merely a finite algebraic extension of $K_H(\eta)$. The degree $\mu = K_H(\xi){:}K_H(\eta)$ of this extension depends solely upon T and is known also as the *degree* of T. It is in fact the degree $K^V{:}K^W$ and does not depend upon the representations of the two function fields through general points.

§ 2. Birational Transformations

4. Let V^t be an irreducible variety in KP^q_z and T' a rational transformation $W^s \to V^t$ given by

$$\sigma z_h = b_h(y), \quad h = 0, 1, \cdots, q. \tag{4.1}$$

Then the relations

$$\sigma z_h = b_h(a_0(x), \cdots, a_n(x)) \tag{4.2}$$

define a rational transformation: $V^r \to V^t$, written $T'T$ and called the *product* of T and T'. This product is associative.

Suppose in particular that $r = s$ and that T' is a transformation of W^r onto V^r. Then $T'T$ is also a rational transformation $V^r \to V^r$. Let us assume that $T'T$ transforms one general point $M(\xi)$ of V^r into itself: $T'TM = M$. Then $T'T$, operating on M assumes the form $\tau\xi_i = \xi_i$, and hence its general form is $\tau x_i = x_i$, i.e. it is the identity transformation on V^r. If $TM = N$, so that N is a general point of W^r, then from

$TT'TM = TM$ there follows $TT'N = N$. Hence TT' is the identity transformation on W^r. Under the circumstances T' is known as the *inverse* of T, written T^{-1}, and the operation T is described as a *birational* transformation. A simple example of a birational transformation is a non-singular projective transformation of a space onto another of equal dimension. Another is the transformation of a KP_x^m referred to coordinates x_i to KP_y^m given by

$$\rho y_i = (\Pi x_j)/x_i, \quad i = 0, 1, \cdots, m$$

whose inverse reads the same way with x and y interchanged. The fundamental varieties are the spaces of the faces of dimension less than $m - 1$ of the simplexes of reference in the two spaces.

The simplest case is the quadratic transformation from plane to plane

$$\rho y_0 = x_1 x_2, \quad \rho y_1 = x_2 x_0, \quad \rho y_2 = x_0 x_1$$

From the properties of rational transformations we deduce at once the following properties:

(4.3) *A n.a.s.c. for the existence of a birational transformation T: $V^r \to W^r$ is that their function fields be isomorphic in an isomorphism preserving K.*

If rational transformations T, T' induce isomorphisms θ, θ' with the appropriate subfields of the function fields then $T'T$ induces $\theta'\theta$, and if T is the identity so is θ. Hence if $T' = T^{-1}$, $\theta'\theta$ and $\theta\theta'$ are both the identity. Hence a birational transformation T induces a θ which is an isomorphism. Conversely if θ is an isomorphism the identification of corresponding elements of $K_H(\xi)$ and $K_H(\eta)$, where $M(\xi)$ and $N(\eta)$ are as before, induces a T which has an inverse. Hence T is a birational transformation and (4.3) follows.

(4.4) *If there is a birational transformation T: $V \to W$, the two varieties have the same dimension* (see 3.2).

(4.5) *A n.a.s.c. for a rational transformation T: $V^r \to W^r$ to be birational is that the degree of T be unity.*

For this is also the n.a.s.c. that $K_H(\xi)$ coincide with $K_H(\eta)$.

(4.6) *Birational equivalence.* Two irreducible varieties V, W are said to be *birationally equivalent* whenever there exists between their function fields K^V, K^W an isomorphism τ which preserves the groundfield K. Each variety is also called a *birational image* or *birational model* of the other. It is clear that birational equivalence is a true relation of equivalence in the customary sense. Furthermore, since dim V = transc K^V, and likewise for W, we have:

(4.7) *Birationally equivalent varieties have the same dimension.*

We may rephrase (4.3) as:

(4.8) *A n.a.s.c. for the birational equivalence of V and W is that there exist a birational transformation of one onto the other.*

(4.9) If T is a birational transformation $V^r \to W^r$ then there is a fundamental subvariety V_0 for T in V^r and a fundamental subvariety W_0 for T^{-1} in W^r. The transformation T operates on $V^r - V_0$ and T^{-1} on $W^r - W_0$. Moreover T and hence T^{-1} is one-one between the sets of general points of the two varieties.

5. Birational geometry. By the birational geometry of an irreducible variety is meant the study of those properties of the variety which are preserved under birational transformations. In essence they are then the properties which depend solely upon the function field K^V. The simplest are the transcendencies of the points and the dimension but there are others to be discussed in later chapters.

It is a familiar fact that projective equivalence of figures has the advantage over affine equivalence of bringing under one category apparently dissimilar geometric objects, for instance ellipses and hyperbolas. A similar advantage is possessed by birational over projective equivalence. Thus it may be shown that a non-ruled surface of order three in KP^3 is birationally equivalent to a projective plane. Therein lies one of the basic reasons for the importance of birational geometry within the whole domain of geometry.

Examples of birational equivalence. We have already observed that non-singular projective transformations between two spaces KP^m are birational transformations. Let us examine some more sophisticated examples.

Example I. Let V^r of KP^m have the following property: the secants of V^r, or lines of KP^m which meet the variety in two or more points, lie in a variety V^s, $s < m$. It may be shown that this holds in fact when $m \geq 2r + 1$, and will be proved explicitly later for algebraic curves. Let then O be a point of KP^m not in V^s and S a hyperplane not passing through O. If M is a general point of the variety the line OM will meet S in a single point N and $M \to N$ defines a birational transformation T of V^r into a variety V'^r contained in S. As is well known T is merely a central projection of center O.

Notice that without information about the locus of the secants one could merely affirm that T is rational. Take for instance a cone V^{m-1} of vertex O and its intersection V^{m-2} with a hypersurface f of degree $\mu > 1$ not passing through the vertex. Assuming V^{m-2} and the base V'^{m-2} of the cone in S both irreducible, the projection is now merely a rational transformation of V^{m-2} onto V'^{m-2}. On the other hand if f is a quadric through O the projection is again birational.

Example II. Rational varieties. If the function field K^V of V^r is a pure transcendental extension of transcendency r over K then V^r is birationally equivalent to a projective r dimensional space and is said to be *rational*. The field K^V is then in fact isomorphic with the field $K_H(y)$

of the space KP^r_y. Under the general theory, there is a birational transformation T of V^r onto the space and T and its inverse are represented by relations:

$$\rho y_i = a_i(x), \qquad i = 0, 1, \cdots, r,$$

$$\sigma x_j = b_j(y), \qquad j = 0, 1, \cdots, m.$$

The variety being assumed in general position there results the associated affine relations

$$Y_i = \frac{a_i(1, X_1, \cdots, X_m)}{a_0(1, X_1, \cdots, X_m)} = R_i(X), \quad i = 1, 2, \cdots, r,$$

$$X_j = \frac{b_j(1, Y_1, \cdots, Y_r)}{b_0(1, Y_1, \cdots, Y_r)} = S_j(Y), \quad j = 1, 2, \cdots, m,$$

$$R_i \in K(X), \quad S_j \in K(Y).$$

Example III. Planar duality. Dual curves. To give differentials free play the groundfield is assumed of characteristic zero.

Consider first a line in the plane KP^2_x:

$$l(u) = \Sigma u_i x_i = 0.$$

Let the u_i be considered as coordinates of a point (u) of KP^2_u. The correspondence $(u) \longleftrightarrow l(u)$ between the points of KP^2_u and the lines of KP^2_x is one-one and lies at the root of the classical duality of plane projective geometry. Owing to this correspondence the u_i are also referred to as *line-coordinates* for KP^2_x. We merely recall that the lines $l(u)$ through a given point $M(\xi)$ of KP^2_x are imaged into the points of a given line $L(\xi)$ of KP^2_u and conversely with the two planes interchanged. One must also bear in mind that the relationship between the two planes is symmetrical. Thus the x_i are line-coordinates for KP^2_u.

Consider now an irreducible curve f of KP^2_x. With any non-multiple point A of f associate the point B of KP^2_u which represents the tangent to f at A. Let T denote this operation on the curve f. If $M(\xi)$ is a general point of f then $N(\eta) = TM$ is given by

$$\rho \eta_i = f_{\xi_i}.$$

Hence T is the rational transformation represented by

$$\rho u_i = f_{x_i}. \tag{5.1}$$

If m is the degree of f then Euler's relation yields

$$\Sigma \xi_i f_{\xi i} = mf(\xi) = 0.$$

Hence

$$\Sigma \xi_i \eta_i = 0. \tag{5.2}$$

By differentiation and since

$$\Sigma f_{\xi_i} d\xi_i = 0$$

we find

$$(5.3) \qquad \Sigma \xi_i d\eta_i = 0, \quad \Sigma \eta_i d\xi_i = 0.$$

Now the f_{ξ_i} cannot all be zero since M would then be a multiple point of f and hence transc $M = 0$. It follows that N is not the null-set. Suppose that transc $N = 0$, i.e. the ratios $\eta_i/\eta_j \in \bar{K}$. Then (5.2) yields, with the $\alpha_i \in \bar{K}$ and not all zero:

$$\Sigma \alpha_i \xi_i = 0.$$

As a consequence $l(\alpha) = \Sigma \alpha_i x_i$ must be divisible by f, hence $m = 1$ and f is a line. Conversely when f is a line the point N is fixed.

Let us suppose then that f is not a line. Thus Tf is an irreducible curve g of KP_u^2 and we will have $g(\eta) = 0$. Upon treating now g like f and taking its transform in KP_x^2, the image of N will be a point $M'(\xi')$. Here again M' is not the null-set. Then (5.3) with M', N in place of M, N yields

$$(5.4) \qquad \Sigma_i' \xi d\eta_i = 0.$$

Since transc $N = 1$, the $d\eta_i$ can only satisfy essentially one linear relation. Comparing (5.4) with (5.3) we see that the ξ_i and the ξ_i' are proportional and hence $M' = M$. Thus the relationship between f and g is symmetrical and T is one-one, hence birational The curves f and g are then birationally equivalent and each is known as the *dual* of the other.

From the definition of g we deduce at once the following results:

(5.5) *There is an almost one-one correspondence between the points of g and the tangents of f. In this correspondence the tangents to f through a point of KP_x^2 are imaged into the intersections of g with a line of KP_u^2 and conversely. Similarly with f and g interchanged.*

The order n of g, or number of tangents to f through a general point of KP_x^2 is known as the *class* of f. The order m of f is the class of g.

(5.6) *Remark.* The extension to space duality and hypersurfaces is quite automatic and may be left to the reader.

§ 3. Normal Systems

6. Let us drop for a moment the assumption that V^r is irreducible, so that its ideal $\mathfrak{a}_H$ is for the present arbitrary. If $\{\varphi_1, \cdots, \varphi_q\}$ is a base for $\mathfrak{a}_H$ then the points of V^r consist of all the solutions of the system

$$\varphi_i(x) = 0, \quad i = 1, 2, \cdots, q.$$

This is then a system of equations for V^r in the commonly accepted sense. Often, however, there exist more restricted systems but with convenient properties. Certain noteworthy systems of restricted type will now be discussed.

Let again V^r, $r < m$, $\mathfrak{p}_H$, $M(\xi)$ be an irreducible variety, its prime ideal and a general point of the variety. As in (II, 18) set $\mathfrak{p}_H^i =$ the prime ideal $\mathfrak{p}_H \cap K_H^i[x]$, $V_i =$ the projection of V^r into the space

$$S_i\colon x_{i+1} = \cdots = x_m = 0,$$

or space of the vertices $A_0, \cdots, A_i$ of the simplex of reference. We shall describe a certain choice of coordinates in terms of a choice of simplex of reference.

Since $r < m$ necessarily $\mathfrak{p}_H \neq 0$. Hence there are forms $f(x) \neq 0$ in the ideal. Let us select one f_m of least degree s. Then f_m must be irreducible; for a factorization $f_m = gh$ implies that one of the factors say $g \in \mathfrak{p}_H$, a contradiction since the degree of g is less than s. Choose now A_m not in f_m hence not in V^r. Thus f_m will be regular in x_m.

If $r = m - 1$ we stop here. If $r < m - 1$, then $V_{r-1} \neq x_m$ and $\mathfrak{p}_H^{m-1} \neq 0$. The process is repeated and by taking A_{m-1} not in V_{m-1} it yields an irreducible $f_{m-1}(x_0, \cdots, x_{m-1}) \in \mathfrak{p}_H^{m-1}$, regular in x_{m-1} and $\neq 0$. One may proceed until V_{r+1} is reached and forms $f_m, f_{m-1}, \cdots, f_{r+1}$ are obtained, where $f_{r+i} \in \mathfrak{p}_H^{r+i}$ and is irreducible and regular in x_{r+i}. We now choose $A_0, \cdots, A_r$ not in Πf_{r+i}. Thus every f_{r+i} will be regular in $x_0, \cdots, x_r$ and in particular f_{r+1} will be regular in all its variables. Since every $f_{r+i} \in \mathfrak{p}_H$, every point of V_r satisfies the system

$$(6.1) \qquad f_{r+i}(x_0, \cdots, x_{r+i}) = 0, \quad i = 1, \cdots, m - r.$$

This is the first system which we had in view. We refer to it as the *first normal system* for V^r.

Since $f_{r+i}(\xi_0, \cdots, \xi_{r+i}) = 0$, and $f_{r+i}(\xi)$ is regular in ξ_{r+i}, ξ_{r+i} is algebraic over $K_H^{r+i-1}(\xi)$. Hence $K_H(\xi)$ is algebraic over $K_H^r(\xi)$. Since dim $V^r = r$, there exists no homogeneous relation among the $\xi_0, \cdots, \xi_r$ and $\mathfrak{p}_H^r = 0$. In particular $\xi_0 \neq 0$ since otherwise $x_0 \in \mathfrak{p}_H^r \neq 0$. As a consequence the affine coordinates ξ_i^*, $i \leq r$, of M form a transcendence base for the function field. Notice also that since $f_{r+i} \in \mathfrak{p}_H^{r+i}$, we have $\mathfrak{p}_H^{r+i} \neq 0$ for $i > 0$.

A useful observation is the following: Since f_{r+i} is regular in x_{r+i}, $\xi_i^* = \xi_i/\xi_0$ is *integral algebraic* over the ring $K^{i-1}[\xi^*]$. Hence all the ξ_i^* are integral algebraic over $K^r[\xi^*]$. The principal value of the representation (6.1) lies in this property.

7. A second normal system which we shall now derive will be found to go much more deeply into the properties of the variety and of its ideal. One may observe that the derivation of the new normal system will require no change of the coordinate system utilized for the first normal system. In particular we will still have $\xi_0 \neq 0$ and $\{\xi_i/\xi_0\}$, $i \leq r$, will continue to be a transcendence base for the function field $K_H(\xi)$.

Our new normal system rests upon the selection of certain forms $g_{r+1}, \cdots, g_m$, where $g_{r+i} \in \mathfrak{p}_H^{r+i}$. We choose $g_{r+1} = f_{r+1}(x_0, \cdots, x_{r+1})$ so that g_{r+1} is certainly regular in x_{r+1} and irreducible.

Since f_{r+i} is in $\mathfrak{p}_H^{r+i}$ and regular in x_{r+i}, it is not spanned by the elements of $\mathfrak{p}_H^{r+i-1}$. Assuming $i > 1$, let g_{r+i} be an element of $\mathfrak{p}_H^{r+i}$ of lowest positive degree in x_{r+i} and not spanned by the forms of $\mathfrak{p}_H^{r+i-1}$. It follows that the leading coefficient $c_{r+i}(x)$ of x_{r+i} in g_{r+i} is not in $\mathfrak{p}_H^{r+i-1}$. As a consequence

$$g_{r+i}(\xi_0, \cdots, \xi_{r+i}) = 0$$

and the degree of $g_{r+i}(\xi)$ in ξ_{r+i} is the least possible. Consequently $\varphi_{r+i}(x_{r+i}) = g_{r+i}(\xi_0, \cdots, \xi_{r+i-1}, x_{r+i})$ is irreducible as a polynominal of $K_H^{r+i-1}(\xi)[x_{r+i}]$. Conversely if $\varphi_{r+i}(x_{r+i})$ has the irreducibility property just stated $g_{r+i}(x)$ behaves in the desired way.

Let δ be the degree of the form $g_{r+i}(x)$ and let us write

$$\xi_0^{-\delta}\varphi(x_{r+i}) = g_{r+i}\left(1, \frac{\xi_1}{\xi_0}, \cdots, \frac{x_{r+i}}{\xi_0}\right).$$

The leading coefficient $c_{r+i}(\xi/\xi_0)$ of (x_{r+i}/ξ_0) at the right is integral algebraic over $K^r[\xi/\xi_0]$. Hence the product $\gamma(\xi/\xi_0)$ of the conjugates of $c_{r+i}(\xi/\xi_0)$ is in $K^{r+i-1}[\xi/\xi_0]$. Hence upon multiplying $\varphi_{r+i}(x_{r+i})$ by $\gamma(\xi/\xi_0)$ the situation will be the same as before save that the new $c_{r+i}(\xi/\xi_0) \in K^r[\xi/\xi_0]$. In substance this means that $g_{r+i}(x)$ may be so chosen that the leading coefficient $c_{r+i}(x)$ of x_{r+i} in it is in $K_H^r[x]$. It may mean that the coefficients of x_{r+i} in $g_{r+i}(x)$ have a common factor, necessarily in $K^r[x]$, but this does not really matter.

Of course the preceding considerations are only necessary for $i > 1$. The form $g_{r+1}(x) \in K^{r+1}[x]$ remains irreducible and regular in x_{r+1} and unchanged.

For later purposes let us summarize the results just obtained:

(7.1) *There can be found in the prime ideal* $\mathfrak{p}_H$ *of* V^r, *forms* $g_{r+i}(x_0, \cdots, x_{r+i})$, $i = 1, 2, \cdots, m - r$ *with the following properties:*

(a) $g_{r+i}(x) \in \mathfrak{p}_H^{r+i}$, *but* $c_{r+i}(x)$, *the leading coefficient of* x_{r+i} *in* $g_{r+i}(x)$, *is in* $K_H^r[x]$.

(b) *Irreducibility property: The degree of* $g_{r+i}(x)$ *in* x_{r+i} *is the least possible compatible with property* (a).

(c) $g_{r+1}(x)$ *is irreducible and regular in* x_{r+1}.

Let d_{r+i} be the degree of g_{r+i} in x_{r+i}. Take any form $g(x) \in K_H[x]$ and divide it by $g_m(x)$ as to x_m. The result is a relation

$$c_m^{\alpha_m}(x)g(x) = \gamma_m g_m + \Sigma\psi_j x_m^j, \quad \psi_j \in K_H^{m-1}[x]; \qquad 0 \leq j < d_m.$$

Upon repeating with ψ_j and division by g_{m-1} as to x_{m-1}, then substituting back, continuing down to division by g_{r+1} as to x_{r+1} and setting

$$c(x) = \Pi c_{r+i}(x) \in K_H^r[x]$$

we shall obtain a relation

$$(7.2)\qquad \begin{cases} c^\alpha(x)g(x) = \Sigma\gamma_{r+i}(x)g_{r+i}(x) + \rho(x), \\ \gamma_{r+i}(x), \quad \rho(x) \in K_H[x], \\ \rho(x) \text{ of degree } < d_{r+j} \text{ in } x_{r+j}. \end{cases}$$

This leads at once to the following noteworthy result:

(7.3) *Theorem. A n.a.s.c. for a form* $g(x) \in K_H[x]$ *to belong to the prime ideal* $\mathfrak{p}_H$ *is that it satisfy a relation:*

$$(7.3a)\qquad c^\alpha(x)g(x) = \Sigma\gamma_{r+i}(x)g_{r+i}(x), \quad \gamma_{r+i} \in K_H[x].$$

Since the sum is in $\mathfrak{p}_H$ but $c(x)$ is not (7.3a) implies that $c(x)g(x) \in \mathfrak{p}_H$, hence that $g(x) \in \mathfrak{p}_H$.

Let now $g(x) \in \mathfrak{p}_H$. From (7.2) follows then that $\rho(x) \in \mathfrak{p}_H$. Since $\rho(x)$ is of degree $< d_m$ in x_m, the coefficients of x_m in it must be in $\mathfrak{p}_H^{m-1}$. Treating the coefficients in the same way, etc., we will find in the last analysis that the coefficients of all monomials $x_{r+1}^{j_1} \cdots x_m^{j_{m-r}}$ in $\rho(x)$ are in $\mathfrak{p}_H^r = 0$. Hence $\rho(x) = 0$, (7.2) reduces to (7.3a) and (7.3) is proved.

Consider now the system

$$(7.4)\qquad g_{r+i}(x_0, \cdots, x_{r+i}) = 0, \quad i = 1, 2, \cdots, m - r.$$

Since $g_{r+i} \in \mathfrak{p}_H$ every point of V^r satisfies the system. On the other hand in view of (7.3a), if $N(\eta)$ satisfies (7.4) and it is not in $c(x)$, then $g(\eta) = 0$ whatever $g \in \mathfrak{p}_H$ and hence $N \in V^r$. Since $c(x) \in K_H^r[x]$ and is not in $\mathfrak{p}_H$ it represents a cone Γ which intersects V^r in a subvariety V'. Hence:

(7.5) *The points of* V^r *all satisfy the system* (7.4). *The points which satisfy* (7.4) *are in* $\Gamma \cup V^r$.

We refer to (7.4) as our *second normal* system for V^r. If $M(\xi)$ is such that the polynomials $\varphi_{r+i}(x_{r+i})$ formed as previously have the same irreducibility property as before then $M(\xi)$ is referred to as a *normal solution* of the normal system.

(7.6) *A normal system* (7.4) *which has a normal solution* $M(\xi)$ *of transcendency r is the normal system of the irreducible* V^r *which has* M *as general point.*

From (7.4) itself follows that transc $\{\xi_i/\xi_j\}$ $i, j \leq r$, is r, and this is the transcendency of M. Hence the variety which has M as general point is an irreducible V^r. The construction of a normal system for V^r by means of M leads then back to (7.4)

8. Monoidal system. This is a special case of the second normal system, characterized by the fact that for $i > 1$, g_{r+i} is linear in x_{r+i}. It is obtained as follows. Since K is infinite and perfect one may choose a coordinate system such that $K_H(\xi) = K_H^{r+1}(\xi)$ and $\xi_0 \neq 0$. For the proof see the Appendix (23.1). The coordinates being chosen in the special way just indicated, let $g(\xi_0, \cdots, \xi_{r+1}) = 0$ be the irreducible relation satisfied by the ξ_j, $j \leq r+1$. If $g(x)$ is not regular in x_{r+1} we may make it so by a linear transformation in the variables x_i, $i \leq r+1$, alone. Since $\xi_{r+1+i}/\xi_0 \in K_H^{r+1}(\xi)$, the second normal form in our new coordinate system becomes

$$(8.1) \quad \begin{cases} g(x_0, \cdots, x_{r+1}) = 0 \\ \lambda_k(x) = a(x_0, \cdots, x_r)x_{r+1+k} - a_k(x_0, \cdots, x_{r+1}) = 0 \\ k = 1, 2, \cdots, m-r-1 \end{cases}$$

where g, a and the a_k are in $K_H[x]$, and g is irreducible and regular in x_{r+1}. The system (8.1) is known as *monoidal*. This designation arises from the term "monoid" applied to surfaces of KP^3 represented by a relation

$$x_3a(x_0, x_1) - b(x_0, x_1, x_2) = 0.$$

In affine coordinates the monoidal system assumes the form

$$(8.2) \quad \begin{cases} G(X_1, \cdots, X_{r+1}) = 0 \\ X_{r+1+k} = R_k(X_1, \cdots, X_{r+1});\ k = 1, 2, \cdots, m-r-1, \end{cases}$$

where $G \in K[X]$ and is irreducible and regular in X_{r+1} and $R_k \in K(X)$.

(8.3) *Application. Let the variety V^r be given by a system*

$$(8.3a) \qquad x_0^{m_i-1}x_{r+i} = f_i(x_0, \cdots, x_r), \quad i = 1, 2, \cdots, m-r$$

where $f_i \in K_H[x]$ and is of degree m_i. Then V^r is rational.

For (8.3a) is merely a monoidal system with g linear in x_{r+1} and hence $K^V = K_H^r(x)$.

For later purposes we shall now discuss in a general way the nature of the variety represented by the system (8.1). We first have:

(8.4) *A n.a.s.c. in order that the system* (8.1) *be a monoidal system for an irreducible V^r is that $a(x) \neq 0$ and that the form $g(x)$ be irreducible.*

Suppose that (8.1) is a monoidal system for V^r. Then there is a general point $M(\xi)$ of V^r, with $\xi_0 \neq 0$, the ξ_j/ξ_0, $j \leq r$, algebraically independent and such that $g(\xi_0, \cdots, \xi_r, x_{r+1})$ is irreducible in $K_H^r(\xi)[x_{r+1}]$ and also that $a(\xi) \neq 0$. This implies that $a(x) \neq 0$, and that $g(x)$ is irreducible. Thus the conditions are necessary.

Conversely suppose that they hold. Take $\xi_0 = 1$ and for $\xi_1, \cdots, \xi_r$ indeterminates. Then one may solve in succession the equations of (8.1) where $x_i = \xi_i$, $i \leq r$, for $x_{r+1}, \cdots, x_m$. If ξ_{r+i} are the solutions, then since λ_k is linear in x_{r+k+1}, and $g(\xi_0, \cdots, \xi_r, x_{r+1})$ irreducible in $K_H^r(\xi)$ the proper irreducibility conditions will be fulfilled to have (8.1) be a normal system with a normal solution $M(\xi)$. Hence (8.1) will represent an irreducible V^r, and the proof of (8.4) is completed.

As regards (8.1) as a normal system and since $g(x)$ is regular in x_{r+1}, the analogue of $c(x)$ of (7) is a power of $a(x)$. Hence (7.3) as applied to (8.1) yields:

(8.5) *A n.a.s.c. in order that* $h(x) \in K[x]$ *be in* $\mathfrak{p}_H$ *is that it satisfy a relation*

$$(8.5a) \qquad \begin{cases} a^{\alpha}(x)h(x) = b(x)g(x) + \Sigma b_k \lambda_k, \\ b, b_k \in K_H[x]. \end{cases}$$

(8.6) *An irreducible* V^r *has a birational model which is a hypersurface in* KP^{r+1}. *One may in fact obtain such a model by a birational projection into an* $(r + 1)$*-subspace of the space of* V^r.

Referring to (8.1) the hypersurface $g(x_0, \cdots, x_{r+1}) = 0$ of the space of the coordinates $x_0, \cdots x_{r+1}$ is a transform of V^r obtained by a projection T of degree unity. Thus T is birational and g is a birational model of V^r which is obtained by means of a birational projection.

9. Parametric representations. According to (8.6) there exists a birational model of V^r which is a hypersurface $g(y)$ in KP_y^{r+1}. There exists then a birational transformation T of $g(y)$ onto V^r, represented by a system of relations

$$(9.1) \qquad \rho x_i = a_i(y) \in K_H[y], \quad i = 0, 1, \cdots, m,$$

where the forms a_i have the same degree. There will be similar relations for T^{-1}:

$$(9.2) \qquad \sigma y_j = b_j(x), \quad j = 0, 1, \cdots, r + 1,$$

with the b_i of the same degree. It is known that T establishes a one-one relation between the general points $M(\xi)$ and $N(\eta)$ of V^r and g such that $M = TN$, $N = T^{-1}M$. Moreover for almost all points (y) of g the point (x) given by (9.1) is in V^r and similarly for T^{-1} and (9.2). The system

$$(9.3) \qquad \begin{cases} \rho x_i = a_i(y), \quad i = 0, 1, \cdots, m \\ f(y) = 0 \end{cases}$$

is a *parametric representation* for V^r and the y_j are *parameters* of the representation.

Notice that (9.3) as it stands, even with g birationally equivalent to V^r, is not necessarily a parametric representation. For even if (9.3) represents a rational transformation T of g *onto* V^r, T may well be of degree > 1 and hence T will not be birational and (9.3) will not be a parametric representation. As an example let $V = KP_x^1$ and let g be the conic $y_0^2 + y_1^2 - y_2^2 = 0$. It is an elementary exercise to show that they are birationally equivalent. Nevertheless T: $g \to KP^1$ given by $\rho x_0 = y_0$, $\rho x_1 = y_1$, is not birational since its degree is two.

The affine parametric representation corresponding to (9.3) is obvious and need not detain us here.

10. Generalization of monoidal systems. The generalization consists in allowing the basic form g in (8.1) to be *reducible*. We continue to expect it to be regular in x_{r+1}. This situation will be found to be amply adequate for later applications.

Whether $g(x)$ is reducible or not, the forms $h(x) \in K_H[x]$ which satisfy a relation (8.5a) clearly make up an ideal $\mathfrak{a}_H$. We shall analyze this ideal in a moment. However let us state at once our central geometric result. It refers to the variety V of the ideal $\mathfrak{a}_H$. Namely

(10.1) *The variety V is pure r-dimensional.*

Consider first a certain "star" operation on a form $f(x) \in K_H[x]$ to a form $f^*(x) \in K_H^{r+1}[x]$ defined in the following way. Divide $f(x)$ by $\lambda_1(x)$ as to x_{r+2}; the remainder $f_1(x)$ will not contain x_{r+2} and is to be divided by $\lambda_2(x)$ as to x_{r+3}, etc. The last remainder is of the form $f^*(x_0, \cdots, x_{r+1})/a^{\alpha}$, where f^* is the announced form. We will thus have a relation

$$(10.2) \qquad \begin{cases} a^{\beta}(x)f(x) = f^*(x) + \Sigma c_k(x)\lambda_k(x), \\ c_k(x) \in K_H[x]. \end{cases}$$

In particular if $h(x)$ satisfies (8.5a) then we will have a relation of the form

$$a^{\gamma}(x)h^*(x) = b(x)g(x) + \Sigma b_k(x)\lambda_k(x).$$

Since we may replace $b(x)$ by $b^*(x)$ without changing the form of this relation, we may assume that $b(x) \in K_H^{r+1}[x]$. Making then $x_{r+k+1} = a_k(x)/a$, the sum disappears and we have

$$a^{\gamma}(x)h^*(x) = b(x)g(x).$$

Since $g(x)$ is regular in x_{r+1}, and $a(x)$ does not contain x_{r+1}, $a(x)$ and $g(x)$ are relatively prime. Hence $g(x)$ divides $h^*(x)$. Conversely if g divides h^*, then (10.2) with h replacing f, yields (8.5a). Thus:

(10.3) *A n.a.s.c. in order that $h \in \mathfrak{a}_H$ is that g divides h^*.*

Let us suppose now that $g(x)$ is irreducible so that $\mathfrak{a}_H$ is a prime ideal $\mathfrak{p}_H$. Side by side with (8.5a) consider the associated system with g replaced by g^{ν}:

$$(10.4) \qquad a^{\alpha}(x)h(x) = b(x)g^{\nu}(x) + \Sigma b_k(x)\lambda_k(x),$$

and let $\mathfrak{q}_H$ be its ideal. For $\nu = 1$ clearly $\mathfrak{q}_H = \mathfrak{p}_H$. In general however:

(10.5) *$\mathfrak{q}_H$ is a primary ideal and its associated prime ideal is $\mathfrak{p}_H$.*

We have to prove:

(10.5a) $\mathfrak{q}_H \subset \mathfrak{p}_H$; (10.5b) *if $h \in \mathfrak{p}_H$ then some power $h^{\rho} \in \mathfrak{q}_H$;*
(10.5c) *if $hh' \in \mathfrak{q}_H$ and h' is not in $\mathfrak{q}_H$ then $h \in \mathfrak{p}_H$.*

The first two properties are immediate. Regarding the third we have at once $(hh')^* = h^*h'^*$. Under our assumptions and in view of (10.3), $h^*h'^*$ is divisible by g^{ν} and h'^* is not. Since g is irreducible it must divide h^*. Hence by (10.3) $h \in \mathfrak{p}_H$ and (10.5) follows.

Returning to the general case let the factorization of $g(x)$ into powers of distinct irreducible forms be

$$g(x) = g_1^{\nu_1} \cdots g_s^{\nu_s}, \; (g_i \in K_H^{r+1}[x] \text{ and regular in } x_{r+1}).$$

Consider now the two associated systems

$$(10.6)_i \qquad a^\alpha h(x) = b_i(x) g_i(x) + \Sigma b_{ik} \lambda_k(x),$$

$$(10.7)_i \qquad a^\alpha h(x) = b_i'(x) g_i^{\nu_i}(x) + \Sigma b_{ik}' \lambda_k(x).$$

By (10.5) the $h(x)$ make up respectively a prime ideal $\mathfrak{p}_H^i$, and a primary ideal $\mathfrak{q}_H^i$ associated with $\mathfrak{p}_H^i$. We propose to prove:

(10.8) *The ideal* $\mathfrak{a}_H$ *has the canonical decomposition*

$$\mathfrak{a}_H = \mathfrak{q}_H^1 \cap \cdots \cap \mathfrak{q}_H^s.$$

To the ideal $\mathfrak{p}_H^i$ there corresponds an irreducible variety V_i^r with the normal system

$$(10.9) \qquad g_i(x) = 0; \quad \lambda_k(x) = 0, \quad k = 1, 2, \cdots, m - r - 1.$$

As a consequence of (10.8) we will then have the important property:

(10.10) *The variety* V *of the ideal* $\mathfrak{a}_H$ *has the* V_i^r *as its components. This implies* (10.1).

We first show that if the relation of (10.8) holds it is a canonical decomposition. This merely requires to show that $V_i^r \neq V_j^r$ for $i \neq j$. For then neither of $\mathfrak{p}_H^i$, $\mathfrak{p}_H^j$ will contain the other.

Let $M_i(\xi^i)$ be a general point of V_i^r obtained as in the proof of (8.4) from the same first coordinates $\xi_0, \cdots, \xi_r$. Thus ξ_{r+1}^i is a solution of $g_i(\xi_0, \cdots, \xi_r, x_{r+1}) = 0$, but not of $g_j(\xi_0, \cdots, \xi_r, x_{r+1}) = 0$ for $j \neq i$. That is to say $g_i(M_i) = 0$, $g_j(M_i) \neq 0$. Hence if the decomposition indicated in (10.8) is correct, it will actually be canonical. Thus if $\mathfrak{b}_H = \mathfrak{q}_H^1 \cap \cdots \cap \mathfrak{q}_H^s$, and we succeed in showing that $\mathfrak{a}_H \subset \mathfrak{b}_H$ and also $\mathfrak{b}_H \subset \mathfrak{a}_H$, then (10.8) will follow.

Let $h(x) \in \mathfrak{a}_H$ so that (10.3) holds. Then $h^*(x)$ is divisible by $g(x)$, hence by $g_i^{\nu_i}(x)$ and therefore $h(x) \in \mathfrak{q}_H^i$. Hence $h(x) \in \mathfrak{b}_H$ and so $\mathfrak{a}_H \subset \mathfrak{b}_H$.

Let now $h(x) \in \mathfrak{b}_H$. Thus $h(x) \in \mathfrak{q}_H^i$. Hence $h^*(x)$ is divisible by $g_i^{\nu_i}$. Since the g_i are relatively prime h^* is divisible by $g(x)$. Hence $h \in \mathfrak{a}_H$, $\mathfrak{b}_H \subset \mathfrak{a}_H$ and (10.8) is proved, together with its consequence.

(10.11) *Remark.* The only properties of the ring $K_H^r[x_0]$ which have been used is that it is an integral domain and that $a(x)$ is a non-zero element of the ring. In affine coordinates X_i the assumptions would be that $K^r[X]$ is an integral domain and that $a(X)$ is a non-zero element of this ring. Under these assumptions the results just proved hold. This remark will play a basic role in an important application later.

11. There is a noteworthy criterium for the dimension r of an irreducible variety V^r which goes back to Emmy Noether [2]. See also Krull [1]. The significant element is that in formulation it dispenses completely with coordinates.

Let $V_1 \supset V_2 \supset \cdots \supset V_s$ where the V_i are irreducible and distinct. The collection $\{V_i\}$ is referred to temporarily as a *chain* and the V_i as the *links* of the chain: V_1 is the *initial* link and V_s is the *terminal* link. The number s is the *length* of the chain. And now we have:

(11.1) **Theorem of E. Noether.** *The dimension of an irreducible V^r is the number r such that $r + 1$ is the length of any one of the longest chains beginning with V^r.*

Let $V_1 = V^r, V_2, \cdots, V_s$ be a chain beginning with V^r. Since the dimension drops by at least one unit from any link to the next and since $s \geq 0$ we have $s \leq r + 1$. Thus all that is necessary is to show that there is a chain of length $r + 1$. Since $(11.1)_0$ is trivial we assume $(11.1)_{r-1}$, $r > 0$, and prove $(11.1)_r$. To that end let V^r be taken in the monoidal representation (8.1) and let the coordinates $x_0, \cdots, x_r$, undergo if need be a transformation such that x_0 is not a factor of $a(x_0, \cdots, x_r)$. The section of V^r by the hyperplane $x_0 = 0$ is represented by the system

$$g(x_1, \cdots, x_{r+1}) = 0, \quad x_0 = 0,$$
$$a(x_1, \cdots, x_r)x_{r+1+k} - a_k(x_1, \cdots, x_{r+1}) = 0,$$
$$k = 1,2, \cdots, m - r - 1.$$

More precisely the ideal $\mathfrak{a}_H$ of the section referred to the same coordinates consists of all the forms $h(x_0, \cdots, x_m) \in K_H[x]$ such that

$$a^{\alpha}(x_1, \cdots, x_r)h(x_0, \cdots, x_m) = b(x_0, \cdots, x_m)g(x_1, \cdots, x_m)$$
$$+ b(x_0, \cdots, x_m)\, x_0 + \Sigma b_k(x_0, \cdots, x_m)\lambda_k(x_1, \cdots, x_m),$$
$$b, b_0, b_k \in K_H[x].$$

Now according to (10.1) the variety of $\mathfrak{a}_H$ is pure $(r - 1)$-dimensional. Let V^{r-1} be a component of this subvariety of V^r. By $(11.1)_{r-1}$ there is a chain $V^{r-1}, \cdots, V^0$ beginning with V^{r-1}. Hence $V^r, V^{r-1}, \cdots, V^0$ is a chain of length $r + 1$ beginning with V^r and (11.1) follows.

It should be observed that Emmy Noether phrased her criterium in terms of an ascending chain of ideals. The passage from her phrasing to (11.1) is obvious.

§ 4. Product Spaces

12. The role of product spaces in the theory of sets as a framework for correspondences and transformations is classical. They are introduced here for a similar purpose—as a framework for algebraic correspondences and transformations.

Let KP_x^m and KP_y^n be our earlier spaces. Let $M(x)$ be a point of the first and $N(y)$ one of the second. It is natural to associate with the pair (M, N) the numbers x_i, y_j provided that one agrees to identify the set $\{x_i; y_j\}$ with $\{\rho x_i; \sigma y_j\}$ where ρ and σ are in some field over K and $\neq 0$. Under the circumstances the sets in question will be placed in one-one correspondence with the pairs (M, N), i.e. with the points of the cartesian product $KP^m \times KP^n$. The sets $\{x_i; y_j\}$ are to be considered as coordinates for the product space. The allowable transformations are separate and simultaneous projective transformations on the x_i and the y_j. The transcendency of (M, N) is by definition transc $\{x_i/x_j; y_h/y_k\}$, $x_j y_k \neq 0$.

The role of the forms is taken over by the elements of the doubly homogeneous ring $K_H^2[x; y]$. Varieties are defined as previously. The extension of the notions of function field, general point and all the rest goes through likewise. The passage to multi-projective spaces is quite automatic, and so are the notions of rational or birational equivalence or transformation. Thus V^r in KP^m and W^r in $KP^n \times KP^\nu$ are birationally equivalent if their function fields are isomorphic.

Side by side with $KP^m \times KP^n$ one may consider the doubly affine space $KA^m \times KA^n$, the $(m + n)$-dimensional affine space referred to the coordinates X_i, Y_j, and the varieties in $KA^m \times KA^n$. The allowable coordinate transformations are simultaneous affine transformations on KA^m and KA^n. One may then identify the point $(x_i; y_j)$ of $KP^m \times KP^n$ for which $x_0 y_0 \neq 0$ with the point of $KA^m \times KA^n$ whose coordinates are x_i/x_0, y_j/y_0. The appropriate ideals for $KA^m \times KA^n$ are merely those of $K[X; Y]$.

As regards the relation between the varieties of $KP^m \times KP^n$ and those of $KA^m \times KA^n$, a variety of $KP^m \times KP^n$ is in general position whenever no component of the variety is in the space $x_0 = 0$ or the space $y_0 = 0$, (considered as subspaces of $KP^m \times KP^n$).

Let V^r, W^s be two varieties of KP^m, KP^n with the respective ideals $\mathfrak{a}_H$, $\mathfrak{b}_H$. The elements $f(x)$, $g(y)$ of $\mathfrak{a}_H$, $\mathfrak{b}_H$ are also elements of $K_H^2[x; y]$. In that last ring they generate an ideal known as the *product* of $\mathfrak{a}_H$, $\mathfrak{b}_H$ and written $\mathfrak{a}_H \times \mathfrak{b}_H$. The corresponding variety of $KP^m \times KP^n$ is known as the *product* of V^r, W^s and written $V^r \times W^s$.

We note the following immediate properties:

(12.1) *The points of the product variety are the pairs of points of the factor varieties.*

(12.2) $$\dim V \times W = \dim V + \dim W.$$

13. We shall require in a moment the following property:

(13.1) *An irreducible variety over an algebraically closed groundfield K is absolutely irreducible.*

Let V be irreducible in KP_x^m. Let K be extended to K' and as a consequence V to V' and the (prime) ideal $\mathfrak{p}_H$ of V in $K_H[x]$ to $\mathfrak{p}'_H$ in $K'_H[x]$.

It is to be shown that $\mathfrak{p}'_H$ is prime. Let $f', g' \in K'_H[x]$ and $f'g' \in \mathfrak{p}'_H$. We must show that one of f', g' is in $\mathfrak{p}'_H$.

Suppose that neither f' nor g' is in $\mathfrak{p}'_H$. Upon reducing if need be f' mod $\mathfrak{p}_H$ we may write

$$f' = \Sigma a'_i f_i$$

where $f_i \in K_H[x]$, the f_i are linearly independent mod $\mathfrak{p}_H$ over K, and where the $a'_i \in K'$ and are linearly independent over K. In particular we may assume $f_1 \neq 0$. Similarly

$$g' = \Sigma b'_j g_j, \quad g_1 \neq 0.$$

Since f_1 and g_1 are not in $\mathfrak{p}_H$ neither is $f_1 g_1$.

Since $\mathfrak{p}_H$ is prime and does not contain $f_1 g_1$ and K is algebraically closed, by the Hilbert zero theorem there is a point $A(\alpha) \in V$ strictly in K and such that $f_1(\alpha)g_1(\alpha) \neq 0$. Since $A \in V'$, we have $f'(\alpha)g'(\alpha) = 0$, hence say $f'(\alpha) = 0$, or

$$\Sigma a'_i f_i(\alpha) = 0.$$

Since $f_1(\alpha) \neq 0$ this is a relation of linear dependence between the a'_i over K. Since no such relation can exist (13.1) follows.

14. (14.1) **Theorem.** *A product of irreducible varieties over an algebraically closed groundfield is irreducible.*

Let $V_0 \times \cdots \times V_n$ be the product in question. Suppose that $V_0 \subset KP^m_x$, $V_i \subset KP^{m_i}_{y_i}$, $i > 0$, and let W denote $V_1 \times \cdots \times V_n$, and KP_y the product of the spaces $KP^{m_i}_{y_i}$. Accordingly a multiform in the coordinates x_h and y^i_h is written $\varphi\,(x; y)$, etc.

Since the theorem holds trivially for $n = 0$, we assume it for n and prove it for $n + 1$.

By hypothesis W is irreducible and hence it has a general point $N(\eta)$. The variety V_0 is irreducible and remains so (13.1) when the groundfield K is enlarged to $K^n_H(\eta)$. Let V^* be the irreducible variety of $KP_x \times KP_y$ which has for general point (M, N). To prove our theorem it is sufficient to prove

$$V_0 \times W = V^*. \tag{14.2}$$

Since (14.2) is trivial for $n = 0$ we assume it for n and prove it for $n + 1$. Thus if $N_i(\eta^i)$ is general for V_i then W is by hypothesis the variety whose general point is $N = (N_1, \cdots, N_n)$ and we must show that $V_0 \times W$ is the variety whose general point is $(M, N) = (M, N_1, \cdots, N_n)$.

Let $\mathfrak{p}_H, \mathfrak{Q}_H, \mathfrak{P}_H$ be the ideals of V_0, W and $V_0 \times W$. The first two are prime and the third is the ideal which they span together in $K^{n+1}_H[x; y]$. Let also $\mathfrak{P}^*_H$ be the (prime) ideal of V^*. The relation (14.2) is equivalent to

$$\mathfrak{P}_H = \mathfrak{P}^*_H \tag{14.3}$$

and this is the relation which we shall now derive.

At all events $(M,N) \in V_0 \times W$, hence $\mathfrak{P}_H \subset \mathfrak{P}_H^*$. Therefore we merely need to show that

$$\mathfrak{P}_H^* \subset \mathfrak{P}_H, \tag{14.4}$$

or finally that if $\varphi(x;\, y) \in K_H^{n+1}[x;\, y]$ and $\varphi(\xi;\, \eta) = 0$ then $\varphi \in \mathfrak{P}_H$.

Let d be the degree of φ in the variables x_j and let $X_1, \cdots, X_\nu$ be the distinct monomials $x_i^\alpha \cdots x_j^\beta$ of degree d. Thus

$$\varphi = \Sigma X_h(x) Y_h(y), \qquad Y_h \in K_H[y].$$

Among the X_i there is a maximum set of elements linearly independent mod $\mathfrak{p}_H$ over K, and we may assume that the set is $X_1, \cdots, X_\mu$. Under the circumstances we have relations

$$X_{\mu+j} = a_{j1}X_1 + \cdots + a_{j\mu}X_\mu \bmod \mathfrak{p}_H,\ a_{jq} \in K.$$

Hence one may now write

$$\varphi(x;\, y) = X_1(x)Y_1(y) + \cdots + X_\mu(x)Y_\mu(y), \bmod \mathfrak{P}_H,\ Y_h \in K_H^n[y].$$

By hypothesis

$$\varphi(\xi;\, \eta) = X_1(\xi)Y_1(\eta) + \cdots + X_\mu(\xi)Y_\mu(\eta) = 0. \tag{14.5}$$

Let $\bar{\mathfrak{p}}_H$ denote the extension of $\mathfrak{p}_H$ due to the extension of the groundfield from K to $K_H(\eta)$. Since $\mathfrak{p}_H$ is the ideal of the irreducible variety deduced from V_0 under the extension of the groundfield it is prime. The relation (14.5) means that

$$X_1(x)Y_1(\eta) + \cdots + X_\mu(x)Y_\mu(\eta) \in \bar{\mathfrak{p}}_H.$$

Since the $X_i(x)$, $i \leq \mu$, remain linearly independent mod $\bar{\mathfrak{p}}_H$ in the enlarged groundfield we have $Y_i(\eta) = 0$ for $i = 1, 2, \cdots, \mu$. Since $N(\eta)$ is a general point of W, the irreducible variety of $\mathfrak{Q}_H$, every $Y_i(y) \in \mathfrak{Q}_H$. Hence $\varphi(x; y) \in \mathfrak{P}_H$. This proves (14.4) and therefore the theorem.

§ 5. ALGEBRAIC CORRESPONDENCES

15. Let V^r, W^s be the same irreducible algebraic varieties of KP_x^m, KP_y^n as before with their associated prime ideals $\mathfrak{p}_H$ and $\mathfrak{q}_H$. By an *algebraic correspondence* $\mathfrak{C}$ between V^r and W^s is meant a system of relations

$$h_i(x;\, y) = 0, \qquad h_i \in K_H^2[x;\, y], \qquad i = 1, 2, \cdots, p \tag{15.1}$$

satisfied by some points $(M,\, N)$ of $V^r \times W^s$. The forms of $\mathfrak{p}_H$, $\mathfrak{q}_H$ together with the $h_i(x;\, y)$ generate an ideal $\mathfrak{A}_H$ of $K_H^2[x;\, y]$ and hence they determine an algebraic variety $\mathfrak{B}^t \subset V^r \times W^s$, referred to as the *graph* of the correspondence $\mathfrak{C}$. The allusion is here to the special case where the varieties are the x and y axis and $\mathfrak{C}$ a graph in the xy plane. If $\mathfrak{B}^t$ is irreducible or equivalently if $\mathfrak{A}_H$ is prime, we say that the correspondence $\mathfrak{C}$ is *irreducible*.

The various designations applied to varieties are extended in obvious manner from $\mathfrak{B}^t$ to the correspondence $\mathfrak{C}$. It is at once apparent that $\mathfrak{C}$ is fully determined by the ideal $\mathfrak{A}_H$ or equivalently by the graph $\mathfrak{B}^t$. Thus to specify $\mathfrak{C}$ or its graph is the same thing.

Let $M(\xi) \in V^r$ and $f(x; y) \in \mathfrak{A}_H$. If d is the degree of f in the x_i choose any $\varphi(x) \in K_H[x]$, of degree d and such that $\varphi(\xi) \neq 0$. Then $f(\xi; y)/\varphi(\xi) \in (K_H(\xi))_H[y]$ and in this ring all such elements make up a homogeneous ideal $\mathfrak{A}_H(M)$ with its variety $W(M)$. The assignment of $W(M)$ to M for all M defines an *algebraic transformation* T of V^r into W^s. By operating in similar manner from W^s to V^r there is obtained an algebraic transformation T' of W^s into V^r. It is convenient to designate T' as the *inverse* of T and T as the inverse of T', writing T^{-1} for T' and T'^{-1} for T. One should not attach too much importance to the term "inverse" as used here and it will not be utilized very much in the sequel.

After the manner of point-set theory one may define the operation Π_W: $M \times N \to N$ as a projection of the product $V^r \times W^s$ into the factor W^s, and there is an analogous projection Π_V into the factor V^r. Then $W(M)$ may be defined as the projection under Π_W of the intersection of $\mathfrak{B}^t$ with the variety $M \times W^s$, and similarly for $V(N)$. We omit the details which may be readily supplied by the reader, and merely observe that both projections are rational transformations.

It is clear that as regards all the dimensions involved one may replace the graph $\mathfrak{B}^t$ by one of its components $\mathfrak{B}^\tau$ and accordingly $\mathfrak{C}$ by the related irreducible correspondence $\mathfrak{C}_\tau$.

Let $\mathfrak{P}_H$ be the prime ideal of $\mathfrak{B}^\tau$. The elements of $\mathfrak{P}_H \cap K_H[x]$, or forms of $\mathfrak{P}_H$ containing the x_i alone make up an ideal $\mathfrak{p}_H$ of $K_H[x]$, which is at once seen to be prime since $\mathfrak{P}_H$ is prime. Hence $\mathfrak{p}_H$ defines an irreducible variety V^ρ of KP^m and there are similar $\mathfrak{q}_H$ and W^σ in the space KP^n. The two varieties V^ρ, W^σ may also be defined as follows: If $(M(\xi), N(\eta))$ is a general point of $\mathfrak{B}^\tau$ then V^ρ is the variety of KP^m with M as general point and W^σ the same for KP^n and N. In fact n.a.s.c. for $f(x) \in K_H[x]$ to be in $\mathfrak{p}_H$ is $f(\xi) = 0$, and this is the same as the condition for M to be generic for V^ρ. Similarly for W^σ and N.

Let now $(M'(\xi'), N'(\eta'))$ be any point of $\mathfrak{B}^\tau$. Since (M, N) is a general point of $\mathfrak{B}^\tau$, the relations (of the obvious type) which it satisfies are also satisfied by (M', N'). Hence if $f(x) \in \mathfrak{p}_H$ then $f(M') = 0$ or $M' \in V^\rho$ and likewise $N' \in W^\sigma$. Thus, the irreducible correspondence $\mathfrak{C}_\tau$ associates only points of V^ρ and W^σ.

One may in fact make the following general remark: Given *a priori* an irreducible variety $\mathfrak{B}^\tau$ in $KP^m \times KP^n$, any general point (M, N) of $\mathfrak{B}^\tau$ will be such that M is general for an irreducible V^ρ of KP^m and N for an irreducible W^σ of KP^n and $\mathfrak{B}^\tau$ will be in $V^\rho \times W^\sigma$ and will be the image of an irreducible correspondence $\mathfrak{C}_\tau$ between V^ρ and W^σ. Evidently V^ρ and W^σ are uniquely determined by $\mathfrak{B}^\tau$. Thus:

(15.2) *With every irreducible variety $\mathfrak{B}^\tau$ of $KP^m \times KP^n$ there is associated a unique pair of varieties V^ρ of KP^m and W^σ of KP^n between which there is an irreducible correspondence $\mathfrak{C}_\tau$ whose graph is $\mathfrak{B}^\tau$.*

16. As the treatment henceforth will be almost exclusively concerned with the triple V, W, $\mathfrak{B}$, of (15) we shall find it more convenient to return to our earlier notations. We consider then an irreducible $\mathfrak{B}^t$ of $KP^m \times KP^n$ which is the image of a correspondence $\mathfrak{C}$ between irreducible varieties V^r of KP^m and W^s of KP^n. These varieties are the two uniquely determined by $\mathfrak{B}^t$, in the sense of (15.2). We suppose $r, s > 0$, thus excluding certain trivial cases.

We shall now utilize the general point $(M(\xi), N(\eta))$ of the graph $\mathfrak{B}^t$ to set up in suitable coordinate systems x, y a normal system of the second type for $\mathfrak{B}^t$. The system will not be unique and will be especially adapted to discuss the transformation $T\colon\ V^r \to W^s$. An analogue may of course be set up for T^{-1}, but it will not be needed, since all relevant information will be obtainable by obvious symmetry.

We first choose the coordinates os that ξ_0, η_0 are both $\neq 0$. Then we have as part of our normal system for $\mathfrak{B}^t$ the normal system (7.4) for V^r or:

(16.1) $$g_{r+i}(x_0, \cdots, x_{r+i}) = 0, \qquad i = 1, 2, \cdots, m - r,$$

where the g_{r+i} have the properties of (7.1). Among the coordinate ratios ξ_i/ξ_0, η_j/η_0 of (M, N) the ξ_i/ξ_0, $i \leq r$, are algebraically independent. Then $t - r$ of the η_j/η_0, say the first $t - r$, are algebraically independent of the ξ_i/ξ_0 and the rest depend upon the ξ_i/ξ_0 and the η^j/η_0, $j \leq t - r$. That is to say the point $N(\eta)$ is of transcendency $t - r$ relative to the groundfield $K_H(\xi)$ with $\{\eta_j/\eta_0\}$, $j \leq t - r$ as independent coordinates. Applying then the results of (7) to the variety of $K_H(\xi)P^n_y$ whose general point is N, (it will turn out to be $W(M)$), we have a normal system of the second type for this variety:

(16.2) $$h_{t-r+k}(\xi;\, y_0, \cdots, y_{t-r+k}) = 0, \qquad k = 1, 2, \cdots, n - t + r.$$

The coefficients of the y_j are supposed to be elements of $K_H(\xi)$ but by clearing fractions we may take them to be in $K_H[\xi]$. Thus

$$h_{t-r+k}(\xi;\, y) \in K^2_H[\xi;\, y].$$

The leading coefficient $d_k(\xi; y)$ of y_{t-r+k} in $h_{t-r+k}(\xi; y)$ is in $(K_H(\xi))_H[y_0, \cdots, y_{t-r}]$ but as in (7) we may multiply h_k by a suitable factor in $K_H(\xi)$ such that the new $d_k(\xi; y) \in K^2_H[\xi_0, \cdots, \xi_r; y_0, \cdots, y_{t-r}]$.

One will now verify that the system consisting of the relations (16.1) and of the relations

(16.3) $$h_{t-r+k}(x;\, y_0, \cdots, y_{t-r+k}) = 0, \qquad k = 1, 2, \cdots, n - t + r,$$

forms a normal system of the second type for $\mathfrak{B}^t$ with the normal solution

$(\xi;\eta)$. As to the h_{t-r+k} they have properties entirely analogous to those of (7.1), namely:

(16.4) (a) *$h_{t-r+k}(x;y)\in\mathfrak{P}_H$, but the leading coefficient $d_k(x;y)$ of y_{t-r+k} in h_{t-r+k} is in $K_H^2[x_0,\cdots,x_r;y_0,\cdots,y_{t-r}]$ and hence not in $\mathfrak{P}_H$;* (b) *the degree of $h_{t-r+k}(x;y_0,\cdots,y_{t-r+k})$ in y_{t-r+k} is the least possible compatible with property* (a); *$h_{t-r+1}(\xi;y_0,\cdots,y_{t-r+1})$ is irreducible in $(K_H(\xi))_H[y]$;* (c) *$h_{t-r+1}(x;y_0,\cdots,y_{t-r+1})$ is regular in y_{t-r+1}, the leading coefficient in that variable being in $K_H^r[x]$.*

We may now derive the analogues of (7.2), (7.3), (7.5). It will be sufficient for our purpose to state the following results:

(16.5) *A n.a.s.c. for a form $g(x;y)\in K_H^2[x;y]$ to belong to the prime ideal $\mathfrak{P}_H$ of the graph $\mathfrak{V}^t$ is that it satisfies a relation*

$$\text{(16.5a)}\quad\begin{cases} d^\alpha(x;y)g(x;y)=\Sigma\gamma_i(x;y)g_i(x)+\Sigma\delta_k(x;y)h_{t-r+k}(x;y),\\ \qquad\gamma_i,\ \delta_i\in K_H^2[x;y]\\ \qquad d(x;y)=c(x)\Pi d_k(x;y)\in K_H^2[x_0,\cdots,x_r;y_0,\cdots,y_{t-r}],\end{cases}$$

where $c(x)$ is the same as in (7).

(16.6) *If $M'(\xi')\in V^r$ and $N'(\eta')\in W^s$ are associated by the correspondence $\mathfrak{C}$ then ξ_i', η_j' satisfy the system S consisting of the relations* (16.1) *and* (16.3). *On the other hand if ξ_i', η_j' satisfy the system S then either M', N' are associated by $\mathfrak{C}$ or else the point (M',N') is in the "cone" Δ represented by $d(x;y)=0$ and which intersects $\mathfrak{V}^t$ in a subvariety $\mathfrak{V}'$.*

Let us return to (16.2) as a normal form relative to a certain variety of $K_H(\xi)P_y^n$. Referring to (24) we may pass to the monoidal form: (a) when K is of characteristic zero by a linear transformation of the coordinates y_i with coefficients in K; (b) when K is of characteristic $p\neq 0$ at the cost of a certain transformation T which has the various properties indicated in (24) and in particular does not affect the dimensional and reducibility properties of the varieties involved. The monoidal form replacing (16.2) is

$$\text{(16.7)}\quad\begin{cases} h(\xi;y_0,\cdots,y_{t-r+1})=0,\\ \lambda_k(\xi;y)=h_0(\xi_0,\cdots,\xi_r;y_0,\cdots,y_{t-r})y_{t-r+k+1}\\ \qquad -h_k(\xi;y_0,\cdots,y_{t-r+1})=0,\\ k=1,2,\cdots,n-(t-r+1).\end{cases}$$

We notice explicitly that $h(\xi;y)$ is regular in y_{t-r+1} and irreducible as a form in $(K_H(\xi))_H[y]$. The analogue of (16.3) is here

$$\text{(16.8)}\quad\begin{cases} h(x;y_0,\cdots,y_{t-r+1})=0,\\ \lambda_k(x;y)=h_0(x_0,\cdots,x_r;y_0,\cdots,y_{t-r})y_{t-r+k+1}\\ \qquad -h_k(x;y_0,\cdots,y_{t-r+1})=0,\\ k=1,2,\cdots,n-(t-r+1),\end{cases}$$

where all the functions are in $K_H^2[x; y]$. Moreover $h(x; y)$ is regular in y_{t-r+1} with the leading coefficient $d_0(x)$ in that variable, an element of $K_H^r(x)$ and $d_0(\xi) \neq 0$. Hence the product

$$c(x)d_0(x)h_0(x; y) = d(x_0, \cdots, x_r; y_0, \cdots, y_{t-r}).$$

In this product $c(x)$ is the same as in (7). Clearly also $d(\xi; y) \neq 0$. Our correspondence will be represented by the system Σ of the relations (16.1) and (16.8). We will then say that $\mathfrak{C}$ is *monoidal* (understood from V^r to W^s).

We may now state:

(16.9) *For a monoidal correspondence, and in particular when K is of characteristic zero for any correspondence whatever, (16.5) and (16.6) are applicable save that (16.5a) is to be replaced by*

$$(16.9a) \quad \begin{cases} d^\alpha(x; y)g(x; y) = \Sigma\gamma_i(x; y)g_{r+i}(x; y) \\ \quad + \delta(x; y)h(x; y) + \Sigma\delta_k(x; y)\lambda_k(x; y), \\ \quad\quad \gamma_i, \delta, \delta_k \in K_H^2[x; y]. \end{cases}$$

17. We shall now discuss the images of the points of V^r. For evident reasons the corresponding results for W^s will follow by symmetry.

Let first $M(\xi)$ be a general point of V^r. The image $W(M)$ is the variety of $K_H(\xi)P_y^n$ of the ideal $\mathfrak{a}_H$ of the forms $g(\xi; y) \in (K_H(\xi))_H[y]$ which satisfy (16.5a) with x replaced by ξ. One may say that $\mathfrak{a}_H$ consists of the forms $g(y) \in (K_H(\xi))_H[y]$ which satisfy

$$(17.1) \quad \begin{cases} d^\alpha(\xi; y)g(y) = \Sigma\delta_k(y)h_k(\xi; y), \\ \quad\quad \delta_k \in (K_H(\xi))_H[y]. \end{cases}$$

In view of (16.4) the ideal $\mathfrak{a}_H$ is prime and $W(M)$ is an irreducible variety of $K_H(\xi)P_y^n$ whose dimension is $t - r$. In particular it contains a point $N(\eta)$ of transcendency $t - r$ as to $K_H(\xi)$. Hence $\text{transc}_K(M, N) = t$, i.e. (M, N) is a general point of $\mathfrak{V}^t$. Consequently N is a general point of W^s. Thus we may state:

(17.2) **Theorem.** *Under the irreducible correspondence $\mathfrak{C}$ with graph $\mathfrak{V}^t$, the image $W(M)$ of a general point $M(\xi)$ of V^r is an irreducible variety of $K_H(\xi)P_y^n$ which contains a general point $N(\eta)$ of W^s and similarly with the appropriate changes for $V(N)$. The following dimensional relations take place:*

(17.2a) $\mu = \dim W(M) = t - r, \quad \nu = \dim V(N) = t - s;$

(17.2b) $\mu + r = \nu + s.$

If $t = r$, so that $\mathfrak{V}^t$ is to be written $\mathfrak{V}^r$, $TM = W(M)$ consists of a finite set of points $N_1, \cdots, N_\sigma$ each counted with the same multiplicity k and $\nu = k\sigma$ is the *index* of T. Each of these points corresponds to one of the conjugate solutions of (16.7). They have then all the same transcendency, and since one of them is general for W^s they are all general for W^s. If K is of characteristic zero $k = 1$ and there are ν distinct points.

If $t = r = s$, there is an index μ for T^{-1} and one refers to $\mathfrak{C}$ as a (μ, ν) *correspondence.*

We may thus state:

(17.3) *If $t = r$ the ν points of TM are general and they are distinct when K is of characteristic zero. Similarly for a (μ, ν) correspondence the μ points of $T^{-1}N$ and the ν points of TM.*

18. Let us consider now the image $W(M')$ of a point $M'(\xi')$ of V^r which need not be a general point of the variety. Suppose first that the correspondence is monoidal, which is certainly the case if K is of characteristic zero. Once more $W(M')$ is the variety of KP^m whose ideal $\mathfrak{a}'_H$ in the ring $(K_H(\xi'))_H[y]$ consists of the forms $g(\xi'; y)$ such that $g(x; y) \in \mathfrak{P}_H$, i.e. such that (16.9a) holds. This means that $\mathfrak{a}'_H$ is generated by the forms $g(y)$ of the above ring which satisfy a relation

$$(18.1) \qquad \begin{cases} d^\alpha(\xi'; y)g(y) = \delta(y)h(\xi'; y) + \Sigma\delta_k(y)\lambda_k(\xi'; y), \\ \qquad\qquad \delta, \delta_k \in K_H(\xi')[y]. \end{cases}$$

Our main task consists in finding what restrictions are to be imposed upon M' to make it possible to apply the results of (10) regarding generalized monoidal systems and also certain earlier "dimensional" properties of more special nature.

Now the system (18.1) will fall in the category studied in (10), relative to the groundfield $K_H(\xi')$, provided that $d(\xi'; y) \neq 0$ as a form in $y_0, \cdots, y_{t-r}$ alone. Let $\{\varphi_i(x)\}$ be the set of the coefficients of the y_j in $d(x; y)$. Since $d(\xi; y) \neq 0$ the $\varphi_i(M) = \varphi_i(\xi)$ are not all zero. Hence the variety V' of the ideal spanned by the $\varphi_i(x)$ in $K_H[x]$ does not contain V^r. Hence V' intersects V^r in a subvariety V_1. We will choose $M' \in V^r - V_1$. As a consequence $d(\xi'; y) \neq 0$ and one may then freely apply all the results of (10) to $W(M')$.

Let then

$$h(\xi'; y) = \Pi h_i^{\nu_i}(y)$$

be the decomposition of h into prime factors in $(K_H(\xi'))_H[y]$. Let $\mathfrak{p}^i_H$ and $\mathfrak{q}^i_H$ be the prime and primary ideals, ($\mathfrak{p}^i_H$ associated with $\mathfrak{q}^i_H$), defined by the systems of forms $g(y) \in (K_H(\xi'))_H[y]$ such that respectively:

$$d^\alpha(\xi'; y)g(y) = \delta(y)h_i(\xi'; y) + \Sigma\delta_k(y)\lambda_k(\xi'; y),$$

$$d^\alpha(\xi'; y)g(y) = \delta(y)h_i^{\nu_i}(\xi'; y) + \Sigma\delta_k(y)\lambda_k(\xi'; y).$$

Referring to (10) we have then for a monoidal correspondence:

(18.2) *The ideal $\mathfrak{a}_H$ admits the canonical decomposition*

$$\mathfrak{a}_H = \mathfrak{q}^1_H \cap \cdots \cap \mathfrak{q}^s_H.$$

(18.3) *The variety of* $\mathfrak{p}_H^i$ *is a*$(t-r)$*-dimensional variety* W_i^r *of* $K_H(\xi')P^n$ *and the* W_i *are the components of the image variety* $W(M')$. *Thus* $W(M')$ *is a pure* $(t-r)$*-dimensional variety.*

When the correspondence is not monoidal we merely need to apply the transformation τ of (24) and the preceding results will hold for the resulting new correspondence. Thus $\tau W(M')$ will be pure and of dimension $t-r$. By (24.8) then the same will hold for $W(M')$. Thus we may state:

(18.4) *For almost all points* $M' \in V^r$ *the image* $W(M')$ *is pure* $(t-r)$*-dimensional.*

Suppose now that $t = r$ and that the groundfield K is of characteristic zero. Then $K_H(\xi)$ is likewise of characteristic zero. Since $h(\xi;\, y_0, y_1)$ is irreducible in $K_H(\xi)$ it has no multiple linear factors. If $\Delta(x)$ is the discriminant of $h(x;\, y)$ as to y_0, y_1 then $\Delta(\xi) \neq 0$. Hence $\Delta(x)$ intersects V^r in a subvariety V_2. If $V_3 = V_1 \cup V_2$, then for $M' \in V^r - V_3$, $W(M')$ consists of ν distinct points, where ν is the degree of $h(x;\, y)$ in the variables y_i and also the index of T. The points in question are obtained as the full set of solutions of the normal system

$$(18.5) \qquad h(\xi';\, y_0, y_1) = 0, \quad \lambda_k(\xi';\, y) = 0, \quad k = 1, 2, \cdots, n-1.$$

This last statement holds even when K is not of characteristic zero and $M' \in V^r - V_1$, but in that case the ν points of TM' may not be distinct. Thus we may state:

(18.6) *If* $t = r$ *and the groundfield is of characteristic zero, then for almost all points* M' *of* V^r *(all* $M' \in V^r - V_3$*),* TM' *consists of* ν *distinct points, where* ν *is the index of* T. *The* ν *points are obtained as the full set of solutions of the system* (18.5). *When* $t = r = s$ *and* $\mathfrak{C}$ *is a* (μ, ν) *correspondence a similar statement holds for* T^{-1} *and* μ.

A noteworthy complement to the preceding results is the following property given explicitly by van den Waerden ([2], p. 107) whose proof we also follow.

(18.7) *Whatever the point* $M' \in V^r$ *the set* $W(M') = TM'$ *is non-empty. In other words every point* M' *of* V^r *is paired-off with some point* N' *of* W^s *under the correspondence* $\mathfrak{C}$ *and similarly the other way around.*

Let $\{f_i(x;\, y)\}$, $i = 1, 2, \cdots, s$ be a base for the ideal $\mathfrak{P}_H$ of $\mathfrak{B}^t$ and consider the system

$$(18.8) \qquad f_i(x;\, y) = 0.$$

Let $\{R_h(x)\}$, $h = 1, 2, \cdots, \sigma$ be the resultant system of the f_i as to the variables y_j. Since (M, N) is a general point of $\mathfrak{B}^t$ every $f_i(M;\, N) = 0$ and hence every $R_k(M) = 0$. Since M is a general point of V^r necessarily $R_k(M') = 0$. Hence if one replaces in (18.8) the x_i by the coordinates ξ_i' of M' there is a solution η_j' in the variables y, i.e. there is an $N'(\eta')$ such that $(M', N') \in \mathfrak{B}^t$. Similarly with M', N' interchanged.

(18.9) *Remark.* All the properties of correspondences hold even between varieties in product spaces. The modifications in the proofs are insignificant and need not detain us here.

19. Application to rational transformations. Returning to an earlier situation let T be a rational transformation $V^r \to W^s$ where the two varieties are again irreducible. Let the equations of T be

$$\rho y_k = a_k(x), \qquad k = 0, 1, \cdots, n \tag{19.1}$$

where the $a_k(x)$ have properties (1, *abc*). In particular one may then choose the coordinates y_k so that $a_0(x) \neq 0$.

Consider now the system Σ:

$$g_{r+i}(x_0, \cdots, x_{r+i}) = 0, \qquad i = 1, 2, \cdots, m - r \tag{19.2}$$

$$h_k(x; y) = y_k a_0(x) - y_0 a_k(x) = 0, \qquad k = 1, 2, \cdots, n, \tag{19.3}$$

where (19.2) is a normal system for V^r.

We recall that if $M(\xi)$ is general for V^r then $N(\eta)$, where the η_j are obtained from (19.1) for $x = \xi$ and $\eta_0 \neq 0$, is a general point for W^s. Now (19.2) and (19.3) form together a normal system, in the ring $K_H^2[x; y]$. Let us show that $(\xi; \eta)$ is a normal solution. The irreducibility conditions are already fulfilled as to the ξ's since (19.2) is normal with the normal solution ξ relative to $K_H[x]$. Since $\eta_0 \neq 0$ let us take $\eta_0 = 1$. Then $y_k - y_0(a_k(\xi)/a_0(\xi))$ is irreducible in $(K_H(\xi'))_H[y]$ since it is linear. Hence $(\xi; \eta)$ has the asserted normal solution property. It follows that (M, N) is a general point of an irreducible $\mathfrak{V}^t$ with (19.2), (19.3) as its normal system. Since M and N are general points for V^r and W^s, $\mathfrak{V}^t$ represents an irreducible monoidal correspondence $\mathfrak{C}$ between V^r and W^s and T is the associated transformation $V^r \to W^s$. Since the ratios $\eta_j/\eta_0 \in K_H(\xi)$, the function field of $\mathfrak{V}^t$ is the same $K_H(\xi)$ as that of V^r. Hence $t = r$ and $\mathfrak{V}^r$ is birationally equivalent to V^r.

We now extend the operation T: If (M', N') is a point of the graph $\mathfrak{V}^r$ then we agree that N' is a point of TM'. Under the circumstances it may well be that even fundamental points of V^r have an image under T but that image need not consist of a single point. Thus under the quadratic plane transformation

$$\rho x'_i = x_j x_k, \qquad i \neq j \neq k$$

the vertex A_i of the triangle of reference in the plane of the x_i, which is a fundamental point, has for image the line x'_i in the plane of x'_i.

Remembering particularly (18.7) it will be seen that our general results yield here:

(19.4) *Under a rational transformation* T: $V^r \to W^s$: (a) *every point of* W^s *has at least one inverse*; (b) *the inverse image* $T^{-1}N$ *of almost every* *point $N(\eta)$ of W^s is a pure subvariety V^{r-s} in the space $K_H(\eta)P^n$;* (c) *if N is a general point of W^s then $T^{-1}N$ contains a general point of V^r.*

Consider now the particular case where the two varieties have the same dimension r. Thus again $r = s = t$. We recognize that the correspondence associated with the transformation T is now a $(\mu, 1)$ correspondence, where μ is the degree of T (3.3). Hence (18.6) yields here:

(19.5) *If T is a rational transformation of V^r onto W^r and μ is its degree, then for almost all points N of W^r the set $T^{-1}N$ consists of points $M_1, \cdots, M_s$ where if each is counted with its proper multiplicity their total number is μ. If K is of characteristic zero then for almost all points N the M_j are distinct. In particular if N is a general point of W^r then the μ points M_j are general points of V^r, and they are distinct when K is of characteristic zero.*

§ 6. Complements on Intersections

20. One would be tempted to deal with the intersection of a hyperplane

$$l(u) = -u_0x_0 + \Sigma u_i x_i$$

with an irreducible V^r of KP^m_x in the following manner: The relation $l(u) = 0$ establishes a correspondence between the space KP^m_u of the hyperplanes $l(u)$ and V^r and the intersection is the image of the point (u). However our previous results do not provide adequate information regarding the "absolute" irreducibility or exceptions to it so that this type of problem must be attacked directly.

Let us normalize the u_i by taking $u_m = 1$. We propose to prove:

(20.1) **Theorem**· *Almost every section by $l(u)$ of an irreducible V^r, $r > 1$, of KP^m, K algebraically closed, is absolutely irreducible over $K(u)$.*

We first prove after Bertini ([1], p. 192):

(20.2) *A section of V^r by a general $l(u)$ is absolutely irreducible over $K(u)$.*

We may suppose at all events that V^r is not in any hyperplane S. For with suitable coordinates one could select S as x_m and so replace m by $m - 1$. We set then $K^* = K(u_1, \cdots, u_{m-1})$ and notice that V^r remains irreducible as variety of K^*P^m.

Let us pass now to affine coordinates X_i. Referring to (22) it will be seen that one may introduce new coordinates Y_i such that

$$Y_i = \Sigma\alpha_{ij}X_j + \alpha_i;\ \ i \neq r;\ \ i \leq r + 1;\ \ \alpha_i, \alpha_{ij} \in K,$$

$$Y_r = \Sigma u_j X_j,\ \ Y_{r+k+1} = X_{r+k+1},$$

with the following properties: If ξ^*_i, η^*_i are the old and new coordinates of a general point then $K^*(\xi^*) = K^*(\eta^*_1, \cdots, \eta^*_{r+1})$ and η^*_1 is separable in $K^*(\eta_2^*, \cdots, \eta_{r+1}^*)$. As a consequence V^r will be monoidal over $K^*[Y]$ and will have a representation

$$(20.3)\quad \begin{cases} G(Y_1, \cdots, Y_{r+1}) = 0, \\ \Lambda_k = A(Y_1, \cdots, Y_r)Y_{r+k+1} - A_k(Y_1, \cdots, Y_{r+1}) = 0, \\ k = 1, 2, \cdots, m - r - 1;\ A, A_k \in K^*[Y]. \end{cases}$$

Here G is irreducible in $K^*[Y_1, \cdots, Y_{r+1}]$ and may be taken regular and of maximum degree in all variables. Furthermore the exponents of Y_1 are not all divisible by the characteristic p of K if $p > 0$.

The prime ideal $\mathfrak{p}$ of V^r in $K^*[Y]$ consists of all the polynomials $F(Y) \in K^*[Y]$ such that

$$A^\alpha F = BG + \Sigma B_k \Lambda_k;\ B, B_k \in K^*[Y].$$

Let $A^*, B^*, \cdots$, denote what polynomials $A, B, \cdots, \in K^*[X]$ become when Y_r is replaced by u_0. The ideal $\mathfrak{p}^*$ of the section $H = l(u) \cap V^r$ as a variety of $K^*(u_0)A^{m-1}$ referred to the coordinates Y_i other than Y_r consists of all the polynomials

$$F^* \in K^*(u_0)[Y_1, \cdots, Y_{r-1}, Y_{r+1}, \cdots, Y_m]$$

such that

$$A^{*\alpha}F^* = B^*G^* + \Sigma B_k^* \Lambda_k^*;\ B^*, B_k^* \in K^*(u_0)[Y_1, \cdots, Y_{r-1}, Y_{r+1}, \cdots, Y_m].$$

Let $\alpha_1(u_0) \in K^*[u_0]$ be the product of the coefficients of the Y's in A^*. Referring to (II, 8.3) and (III, 10.10) H will be irreducible in LA^m, L a field over $K^*(u_0)$, when and only when $G(Y_1, \cdots, Y_{r-1}, u_0, Y_{r+1})$ is the power of an irreducible element of $L[Y_1, \cdots, Y_{r-1}, Y_{r+1}]$.

Notice that since the exponents of Y_1 are not all divisible by the characteristic p, and certainly if $p = 0$, $G_{Y_1}(Y_1, \cdots, Y_{r-1}, u_0, Y_{r+1}) \neq 0$ and therefore $G(Y_1, \cdots, Y_{r-1}, u_0, Y_{r+1})$ has no multiple factors in $L[Y_1, \cdots, Y_{r-1}, Y_{r+1}]$. Thus H will be irreducible in LA^m when and only when $G(Y_1, \cdots, Y_{r-1}, u_0, Y_{r+1})$ is irreducible in $L[Y_1, \cdots, Y_{r-1}, Y_{r+1}]$.

The preceding considerations hold whatever u_0 provided that $\alpha_1(u_0) \neq 0$. Suppose now that u_0 is indeterminate and let H be reducible in some field L over $K^*(u_0)$. It has then a component H_1 and there is a residual $(r - 1)$-dimensional variety H_2. Now the hyperplane at infinity (the hyperplane x_0) may be taken arbitrary and in particular so that it intersects H_1 and H_2 in distinct $r - 2$ dimensional varieties J_1 and J_2. Since these are in the hyperplane at infinity of $l(u)$, they are independent of u_0. Hence the subvariety of H going through J_1 has an equation of the form

$$G_1(Y_1, \cdots, Y_{r-1}, u_0, Y_{r+1}) = 0$$

where one may assume that $G_1 \in K^*[Y_1, \cdots, Y_{r-1}, u_0, Y_{r+1}]$, that it is irreducible and is a proper factor of $G[Y_1, \cdots, Y_{r-1}, u_0, Y_{r+1}]$ containing the Y_i. Since u_0 is an indeterminate this means that $G_1[Y_1, \cdots, Y_{r+1}]$ is a proper factor of $G[Y_1, \cdots, Y_{r+1}]$, which contradicts the irreducibility of the latter, and proves (20.2).

21. We pass now to the proof of (20.1) proper. The coefficients of Y_1 in $G(Y_1, \cdots, Y_{r-1}, u_0, Y_{r+1})$ are polynomials in $Y_2, \cdots, Y_{r-1}, Y_{r+1}$. The product of the coefficients of these polynomials is an $\alpha_2(u_0) \in K^*[u_0]$. The leading coefficient $\alpha_3(u)$ of Y_{r+1} in $G(Y_1, \cdots, Y_{r-1}, u_0, Y_{r+1})$ is likewise in $K^*[u_0]$. Let $\alpha(u) = \alpha_1(u)\alpha_2(u)\alpha_3(u) \in K^*[u_0]$ and let u_0 be so selected that $\alpha(u_0) \neq 0$. The ideal $\mathfrak{p}^*$ behaves then as before relative to $K^*(u_0)$, although this time the u_i are not necessarily indeterminates It will then represent an irreducible V^{r-1} of $K(u_0)A^{m-1}$ if and only if $G(Y_1, \cdots, Y_{r-1}, u_0, Y_{r+1})$ is irreducible.

Now according to Emmy Noether [1] a n.a.s.c. for a polynomial to be reducible in some field containing its coefficients, or else to have its degree lowered, is that its coefficients satisfy a certain number of algebraic relations. She only considered characteristic zero and so the coefficients of the relations were rational. However the same argument is valid for characteristic $p > 0$ provided that the coefficients of the algebraic relations are taken in the field of residues mod p.

Let $E(u_0)$ be what Emmy Noether's system becomes for $G(X_1, \cdots, X_{r-1}, u_0, X_{r+1})$. If $\alpha(u_0) \neq 0$ then $E(u_0)$ must hold in order that $G(X_1, \cdots, X_{r-1}, u_0, X_{r+1})$ be reducible in any overfield L of $K^*(u_0)$. Since for a general $l(u)$ we have $\alpha(u_0) \neq 0$ and the polynomial is irreducible in any L over $K^*(u_0) = K(u)$ (20.2), $E(u_0)$ is not satisfied by $l(u)$. Hence the system $E(u_0)$ determines a subvariety W_1 of the space KA^m_u. Similarly $\alpha(u_0)$ determines a hypersurface W_2 in the same space. If $W = W_1 \cup W_2$ and the representative point (u) of $l(u)$ is in $KA^m_u - W$ then $l(u) \cap V^r$ is absolutely irreducible over $K(u)$. This completes the proof of theorem (20.1).

§ 7. APPENDIX: GROUNDFIELD OF CHARACTERISTIC $p \neq 0$

22. We have relegated to this Appendix a number of difficulties particular to this case. For the main lemma (22.1) we are indebted to I. Barsotti. See notably his paper [1] p. 435. Regarding the utilization of partial derivatives in the proof of the lemma, see (I, 7.10).

Let then the groundfield K be perfect, infinite and of characteristic $p \neq 0$. Let $K(\alpha_1, \cdots, \alpha_m) = K(\alpha)$ be an extension of K of transcendency r. Then:

(22.1) **Lemma.** *If L is any infinite subfield of K there can be found in $K(\alpha)$ elements $\beta_1, \cdots, \beta_{r+1}$ given by relations*

$$\beta_i = \Sigma\mu_{ij}\alpha_j, \ \mu_{ij} \in L, \tag{22.1a}$$

such that the β_i, $i \leq r$, are algebraically independent and that $K(\beta) = K(\alpha)$.

Let first K be of characteristic zero and let the α_j be ranged in such order that the α_i, $i \leq r$, are algebraically independent. Take $\beta_i = \alpha_i$ for $i \leq r$, so that $K(\alpha)$ is a finite algebraic extension of $K^r(\alpha)$. Let d be the degree of this extension. Since L is infinite one may choose

$$\beta_{r+1} = \mu_{r+1}\alpha_{r+1} + \cdots + \mu_m\alpha_m, \ \mu_i \in L,$$

such that the d conjugate values of β_{r+1} are all distinct. As a consequence $K(\alpha) = K(\beta)$. Since the β_i, $i \leq r$ are algebraically independent (22.1) holds in this case.

We will assume then that K is infinite, perfect and of positive characteristic p. Let t_{ij} be indeterminates and let the γ_i, $i = 1, 2, \cdots, r+1$ be defined by

(22.2) $$\gamma_i = \Sigma t_{ij}\alpha_j.$$

If $K^* = K(t)$ we see at once that $\text{transc}_{K^*}\{\alpha_i\} = \text{transc}_K\{\alpha_i\} = r$. Hence the γ_i satisfy an irreducible relation

$$F(t; \gamma) = 0, \quad F \in K[t; \gamma].$$

Upon substituting for the γ_i, their expressions in terms of the α_j there results a relation

$$F(t; \gamma) = G(t; \alpha) = 0.$$

By differentiation as to t_{ij} we find then

$$\frac{\partial F}{\partial t_{ij}} + \alpha_j \frac{\partial F}{\partial \gamma_i} = 0.$$

We assert now that at least one $\partial F/\partial \gamma_i \neq 0$. For in the contrary case $\dfrac{\partial F}{\partial \gamma_i} = \dfrac{\partial F}{\partial t_{ij}} = 0$, hence every γ_i and t_{ij} appears in F with an exponent which is a positive multiple of p. Let e be the greatest power of p such that $F(t; \gamma) \in K[t^e; \gamma^e]$. Since K is perfect there is an $F_1(t; \gamma) \in K[t; \gamma]$ such that $F = F_1^e$ contrary to the assumption that $F(t; \gamma)$ is irreducible.

Thus some $\partial F/\partial \gamma_i \neq 0$. As a consequence

$$\alpha_j = -\frac{\partial F}{\partial t_{ij}} \Big/ \frac{\partial F}{\partial \gamma_i} \in K^*(\gamma),$$

and so $K^*(\alpha) = K^*(\gamma)$.

We have then

$$\alpha_i = \frac{P_i(t; \gamma)}{P_0(t; \gamma)}, \ P_i \in K[t; \gamma].$$

Upon substituting the γ_k from (22.2) we find

(22.3) $$P_i(t; \gamma) = Q_i(t; \alpha) \in K[t; \alpha].$$

Since L is an infinite subfield of K one may choose for the t_{ij} elements

$\mu_{ij} \in L$ such that $Q_0(\mu; \alpha) \neq 0$. Hence the β_i given by (22.1a) are such that

$$\alpha_i = \frac{P_i(\mu; \beta)}{P_0(\mu; \beta)} \in K(\mu; \beta) = K(\beta),$$

which proves the lemma.

23. The application to an irreducible V^r is immediate. Let $M(\xi)$ be a general point with coordinates so chosen that $\xi_0 \neq 0$. Take then affine coordinates $\xi_i^* = \xi_i/\xi_0$. Applying the lemma to $K(\xi^*)$ we obtain the property that if L is an infinite subfield of K one may choose the $\mu_{ij} \in L$ such that if

$$\xi_i'^* = \Sigma \mu_{ij} \xi_j^*, \quad i = 1, 2, \cdots, r+1$$

then $K_H(\xi) = K(\xi^*) = K(\xi'^*)$. Upon going back to projective coordinates this proves the following result:

(23.1) *If L is an infinite subfield of the groundfield K then there is a transformation of coordinates*

$$\rho x_i' = \Sigma \lambda_{ij} x_j, \; \lambda_{ij} \in L,$$

such that if ξ_i' are the new coordinates of the general point M of V^r then $K_H^{h+1}(\xi') = K_H(\xi')$ and $\xi_0' \neq 0$.

This is the property utilized in the monoidal reduction of (8).

24. Let us consider now the reduction of a system (16.2) to the monoidal form. If the characteristic of K is zero one may apply a transformation of coordinates in KP_y^n (with coefficients in K) so as to replace (16.2) by a monoidal system (16.7), and consequently (16.3) by (16.8). On the other hand if the characteristic $p \neq 0$, one may be stopped by the fact that $K_H(\xi)$ is not perfect. If that is the case to obtain a perfect field from $K_H(\xi)$ it is sufficient to adjoin to it all the p^e-th roots of all the ξ_i/ξ_0, for $e = 1, 2, 3, \cdots$. Let $\Lambda(\xi)$ be the resulting field. Since it is perfect and contains the infinite field K as a subfield we may choose the coordinates y_i so as to replace (16.2) by a monoidal system relative to $\Lambda(\xi)$:

$$(24.1) \quad \begin{cases} h(y_0, \cdots, y_{t-r+1}) = 0, \\ \mu_k(y) = h_0(y_0, \cdots, y_{t-r}) y_{t-r+k+1} - h_k(y_0, \cdots, y_{t-r+1}) = 0, \\ k = 1, 2, \cdots, n-(t-r+1), \end{cases}$$

where all the functions are in $\Lambda(\xi)[y]$. Since the coefficients of the y_i in (24.1) are in finite number there is a largest e such that they are all in $K(\{(\xi_i/\xi_0)^{1/p^e}\})$. It follows that upon applying the transformation

$$(24.2) \qquad \tau\colon\; x_i = (\bar{x}_i)^{p^e},$$

to KP_x^m and denoting by $\bar{\xi}_i$ the coordinates of $\bar{M} = \tau M$ the system assumes the form (16.7) with the x_i replaced by the $\bar{x}_i$, save that as yet $d_0(\bar{\xi})$ and $h_0(\bar{\xi}; y)$ are not in $K_H^r(\bar{\xi})$ and $(K_H^r(\bar{\xi}))_H[y]$ as they are in (16.7) (with ξ in place of $\bar{\xi}$). However by a reduction such as in (7) in the derivation of (7.1) one will arrive at the analogues of (16.7) and (16.8). Let $\bar{h}, \cdots$, denote the analogues of $h, \cdots$, thus obtained and let also $\bar{M} = TM$ for any point $M \in KP_x^m$.

(24.3) *τ is one-one and it preserves the transcendencies of the points.* (Obvious.)

(24.4) *The points of a variety V are sent by τ into those of a variety $\bar{V}$ and those of $\bar{V}$ are sent by τ^{-1} into those of V. Upon defining $\bar{V} = \tau V$, $V = \tau^{-1}\bar{V}$ and $V \longleftrightarrow \bar{V}$, there is established a one-one correspondence between the varieties of KP_x^m and $KP_{\bar{x}}^m$.*

Given any $f \in K_H[x]$ set $f^{1/p^e}(\cdots, \bar{x}_i^{p^e}, \cdots) = \bar{f}(\bar{x})$. If $\{f_1, \cdots, f_s\}$ is a base for the ideal of V, the points of V consist of all the solutions M of the system

$$S\colon\ f_1 = \cdots = f_s = 0.$$

Now the points $\bar{M}$ consist of all the solutions of

$$\bar{S}\colon\ \bar{f}_1 = \cdots = \bar{f}_s = 0$$

and so they make up an algebraic variety $\bar{V}$ and it is clear that V, $\bar{V}$ are related in the asserted way.

Conversely given a variety $\bar{V}$ of $KP_{\bar{x}}^m$ whose ideal has the base $\{g_1(\bar{x}), \cdots, g_s(\bar{x})\}$, the points of $\bar{V}$ consist of all the solutions of the system

$$\bar{S}_1\colon\ g_1 = \cdots = g_s = 0.$$

There exists, on the other hand, an $f_i \in K_H[x]$ such that $f_i(x) = g_i^{p^e}(\bar{x})$. Hence one sees at once that the variety V of the associated system S is such that $\tau V = \bar{V}$.

We now have evidently:

(24.5) *τ preserves the inclusions between the varieties.*

That is to say the relations $V \subset V'$ and $\tau V \subset \tau V'$ are equivalent.

Coupling (24.5) with (II, 5.7) and (24.3) we have then:

(24.6) *If V is irreducible so is τV and conversely. More generally under τ the components of V go into those of τV.*

(24.7) $$\dim \tau V = \dim V.$$

We will now extend τ to a transformation $KP_x^m \times KP_y^n \to KP_{\bar{x}}^m \times KP_y^n$ in the obvious way: $\tau(M, N) = (\bar{M}, N)$. Then at once:

(24.8) *Properties* (24.3), $\cdots$, (24.7) *hold for τ as extended to the product spaces.*

The properties of τ just considered include all those that are required earlier in the text (16, 17, 18).

IV. *Formal Power Series*

Formal power series have come strongly to the fore in recent years particularly in connection with local properties of varieties. They constitute also the natural bridge between analysis and algebraic geometry. The present treatment, admittedly sketchy and often without proofs rests in part upon a paper by W. Rückert [1]. See also the book of S. Bochner and W. T. Martin [1]. For recent work on the subject see notably Krull [2], Chevalley [1, 2], A. Weil [1] and Zariski [4, 7].

§ 1. Basic Concepts and Theorems

1. Let $u_1, \cdots, u_m$ be indeterminates and $f_s(u), f_{s+1}(u), \cdots,$ forms of $K_H[u]$ of degree $s, s+1, \cdots$. The expression

$$(1.1) \qquad f(u) = f_s(u) + f_{s+1}(u) + \cdots,$$

is a *formal power series* in $u_1, \cdots, u_m$. The first term $f_s(u) \neq 0$ is the *leading form* of the series and s is the *degree* of $f(u)$. Series of degree zero, i.e. with a constant term, are known as *units*, the others as *non-units*. Units will often be designated generically by $E(u)$. A series is *regular* in u_i whenever it is a non-unit and contains a term in u_i alone. The least degree k of such a term is the *degree* of f in u_i.

The term "regular" as applied here is used almost in the sense opposite to the one attributed to it in connection with polynomials or forms. The context will generally indicate which is meant and no confusion will arise.

Series are added and multiplied in the manner familiar in analysis, thus giving rise to the *ring* of formal power series written $K[[u_1, \cdots, u_m]]$ or $K[[u]]$. It is an integral domain with unity element and the quotient field is written $K((u_1, \cdots, u_m))$ or $K((u))$. The product of two units is a unit and every unit $E(u)$ has an inverse $E^{-1}(u)$ which is a unit: $E^{-1}(u)$ is an element of $K[[u]]$ such that $E(u)E^{-1}(u) = 1$. Hence units form a commutative group. If $\varphi(u) = E(u)\psi(u)$, φ and $\psi \in K[[u]]$, φ and ψ are said to be *associated*, written $\varphi \sim \psi$. Since units form a group, this is a relation of equivalence.

(1.2) If $\varphi_1(u), \varphi_2(u), \cdots,$ is a sequence of elements of $K[[u]]$ whose degrees $s_1, s_2, \cdots$ tend to infinity then the infinite addition $\varphi_1(u) + \varphi_2(u) + \cdots$ has meaning and yields a definite element of $K[[u]]$ written naturally as an infinite sum $\varphi_1(u) + \varphi_2(u) + \cdots$.

The preceding remarks become more significant in terms of a well known metrization of $K[[u]]$ which is familiar in valuation theory. If $\varphi \in K[[u]]$ is of degree r define its norm as $||\varphi|| = 2^{-r}$. Then for both $\varphi, \psi \in K[[u]]$ set their distance as $d(\varphi, \psi) = ||\varphi - \psi||$. We verify at once that the basic distance properties hold:

I. $d(\varphi, \psi) \leq 0$ and it is $= 0$ when and only when $\varphi = \psi$.

II. $d(\varphi, \psi) + d(\psi, \omega) \geq d(\omega, \varphi)$ (triangle axiom).

It follows that $d(\varphi, \psi)$ turns $K[[u]]$ into a metric space. What we have said regarding an infinite sequence and its sum is equivalent to the property that every Cauchy sequence of the metric space $K[[u]]$ converges to an element of the space. That is to say:

(1.3) *The metric space $K[[u]]$ is complete.*

(1.4) *Under the topology of $K[[u]]$ finite sums and products are continuous.* (Proof elementary.)

(1.5) As an application of infinite sums in $K[[u]]$ let $\psi(v_1, \cdots, v_k) \in K[[v]]$ and suppose that

$$\psi(v) = \psi_s(v) + \psi_{s+1}(v) + \cdots,$$

where the decomposition is like (1.1). If $\varphi_1(u), \cdots, \varphi_k(u)$ are non-units of $K[[u]]$ then $\psi_h(\varphi_1, \cdots \varphi_k)$, $h > 0$, is a non-unit of $K[[u]]$ whose degree $\rightarrow \infty$ with h. If $s = 0$ then of course $\psi_0 \in K$. As a consequence

$$\psi_s(\varphi_1, \cdots, \varphi_k) + \psi_{s+1}(\varphi_1 \cdots, \varphi_k) + \cdots$$

is a perfectly definite element of $K[[u]]$ which is to be denoted by $\psi(\varphi_1, \cdots, \varphi_k)$. It is a unit of $K[[u]]$ when and only when $\psi(v)$ is a unit of $K[[v]]$. Notice that the relation $\psi(\varphi_1, \cdots, \varphi_k) = 0$ is also well defined.

(1.6) The elements $\psi(\varphi_1, \cdots, \varphi_k)$ form a ring, which is a subring of $K[[u]]$ and is naturally designated by $K[[\varphi_1, \cdots, \varphi_k]]$ or $K[[\varphi]]$. It is an integral domain and its units and non-units are units and non-units of $K[[u]]$ also.

2. Fundamental theorems.

(2.1) **The Weierstrass preparation theorem.** *If $f(u) \in K[[u]]$ is regular and of degree s in u_m then*

$$\text{(2.1a)} \qquad f(u) \sim u_m^s + A_1 u_m^{s-1} + \cdots + A_s,$$

where the A_i are non-units of $K[[u_1, \cdots, u_{m-1}]]$ and the polynomial in u_m at the right is unique.

Let a polynomial such as occurs in (2.1a) be called *special in u_m*. It is clear that the theorem may be expressed more technically as follows:

(2.2) *A series regular and of degree $s > 0$ in u_m is associated with a special polynomial in u_m whose degree in u_m is s.*

(2.3) *Remarks.* I. The relation (2.1a) stands for an identity

$$\text{(2.3a)} \qquad f(u) = E(u)(u_m^s + A_1 u_m^{s-1} + \cdots + A_s).$$

It is therefore applicable to a ring $K[[\varphi]]$ of non-unit elements of $K[[u]]$ such as defined in (1.5).

II. Let $f_s(u)$, $s > 0$, be the leading form of $f(u)$. By means of a non-singular linear transformation of variables one may turn f_s into a form regular in u_m. Then f will have become of degree s in u_m. Hence in the new system f will be equivalent to a special polynomial of degree s in u_m. Moreover by identifying the leading forms in (2.3a) one sees that here A_h is of degree $\geq h$.

(2.4) **The implicit function theorem.** *Consider a system*

$$f_i(u_1, \cdots, u_p, v_1, \cdots, v_q) = 0, \quad i = 1, 2, \cdots, q \tag{2.4a}$$

where the f_i are non-units of $K[[u; v]]$ and the determinant of the first degree terms in the v_j is not zero when $u_1 = \cdots = u_p = 0$. The system has a unique solution

$$v_j = \varphi_j(u), \quad j = 1, 2, \cdots, q \tag{2.4b}$$

where the φ_j are non-units of $K[[u]]$. (Bochner-Martin, p. 7.)

(2.5) *Noteworthy special case: The relations*

$$\begin{cases} u_i = \Sigma a_{ij} v_j + g_i(v_1, \cdots, v_q) \\ i = 1, 2, \cdots, q;\ a_{ij} \in K; |a_{ij}| \neq 0, \quad g_i \in K[[v]], \end{cases} \tag{2.5a}$$

where the g_i are of degree at least two, have a unique solution of the form (2.4b). *Moreover in this solution the determinant of the coefficients of the first degree terms in the φ_j is $\neq 0$.*

The asserted property of the φ's is readily obtained by substituting their series in (2.5a) and comparing coefficients of like powers of the u_i.

We may think of (2.4b) as defining a transformation T from the variables u_i to the variables v_j. A transformation (2.5a), with $|a_{ij}| \neq 0$, is said to be *regular*. If T, T' are regular so is TT', and property (2.5) implies also the regularity of T^{-1}. Hence regular transformations form a group. In point of fact the properties which will mainly interest us are those which are invariant under regular transformations.

(2.6) A non-unit $f(u)$ is said to be *reducible* whenever it is associated with a product of two non-units: $f(u) \sim f'(u) \cdot f''(u)$, where f', f'' are non-units. When this does not hold f is said to be *irreducible*.

(2.7) **The unique factorization theorem.** *Every non-unit $f(u)$ admits a finite decomposition*

$$f(u) \sim g^p(u) \cdots h^q(u)$$

where $g, \cdots, h$ are irreducible and unique to within unit factors (See Bochner-Martin, p. 193).

(2.8) *Real or complex fields.* Suppose that the groundfield K is one or the other of these two fields. Then if the initial functions in the three propositions which we have just considered are convergent in a certain neighborhood of the origin, all the functions that occur in their statements are likewise convergent in a suitable neighborhood of the origin. This provides of course powerful analytical content for these theorems. In the case of the real field it is also useful to bear in mind that the series which occur are all real.

§ 2. Algebroid Varieties

3. As a basis for the local study of algebraic varieties we shall develop a fairly parallel theory of algebroid varieties. The treatment will only be carried far enough to cover our later requirements.

While we shall deal with the same basic set of parameters u_i as before, the only properties that will interest us are those left invariant under regular transformations.

One may introduce in $K[[u]]$, ideals, prime and primary ideals as in all rings. Such ideals will be referred to as *algebroid*. The first important property is:

(3.1) **Theorem.** *Every algebroid ideal* $\mathfrak{a}$ *is Noetherian.* (See I, 1.3.)

We will show that the Hilbert base property holds. Let $f \in \mathfrak{a}$ and let φ be its leading form. It is seen at once that the set $\{\varphi\}$ is a homogeneous ideal $\mathfrak{a}_H$ of the homogeneous ring $K_H[u]$. By the base theorem for the latter $\mathfrak{a}_H$ has a finite base $\{\varphi_1, \cdots, \varphi_q\}$ where φ_i is the leading form of an $f_i \in \mathfrak{a}$. Thus

$$\varphi = \Sigma\gamma_{i1}\varphi_i, \quad \gamma_{i1} \in K_H[u]$$

and hence with $f^{(1)} = f$ and if s_1 is the degree of $f^{(1)}$ then

$$f^{(2)} = f^{(1)} - \Sigma\gamma_{i1}f_i$$

is of degree $s_2 > s_1$. Similarly one may form

$$f^{(3)} = f^{(2)} - \Sigma\gamma_{i2}f_i$$

of degree $s_3 > s_2$, and more generally there is for each ν an $f^{(\nu)}$ and a relation

$$f^{(\nu+1)} = f^{(\nu)} - \Sigma\gamma_{i\nu}f_i, \quad \gamma_{i\nu} \in K_H[u]$$

where if s_ν is the degree of $f^{(\nu)}$ then the forms $\gamma_{i\nu}$ are so chosen that $\Sigma\gamma_{i\nu}\varphi_i$ is the leading form of $f^{(\nu)}$. Thus first $s_{\nu+1} > s_\nu$. Moreover if δ_i is the degree of φ_i then $\gamma_{i\nu}$ is of degree $s_\nu - \delta_i$. Since $s_\nu - \delta_i \to +\infty$ with ν,

$$g_i = \Sigma\gamma_{i\nu} \in K[[u]].$$

We verify then at once that

$$f^* = f - \Sigma g_i f_i \in K[[u]]$$

is of infinite degree. Hence $f^* = 0$ and $\{f_i\}$ is a finite base for $\mathfrak{a}$.

It follows from (3.1) (see I, 1.6) that every ideal $\mathfrak{a}$ of $K[[x]]$, has a canonical decomposition

$$\mathfrak{a} = \mathfrak{q}_1 \cap \mathfrak{q}_2 \cap \cdots \cap \mathfrak{q}_s \tag{3.2}$$

where the $\mathfrak{q}_i$ are primary ideals such that if $\mathfrak{p}_i$ is the prime ideal of $\mathfrak{q}_i$ then the $\mathfrak{p}_i$ are distinct and unique.

We shall only consider ideals of non-units and no further mention of this assumption will be made later. All our ideals are then subideals of the maximal ideal $\mathfrak{m}$ of all non-units.

(3.3) We will now define the algebroid concepts. Take a ring $K[[v_1, \cdots, v_r]] = K[[v]]$ and a prime ideal $\mathfrak{b}$ of $K[[v]]$. If $\varphi_1, \cdots, \varphi_m$ are residue classes of non-units of $K[[v]]$ mod $\mathfrak{b}$, then the set $(\varphi_1, \cdots, \varphi_m)$ is defined as an *algebroid point* M_φ, or merely M, and the φ_i are the *coordinates* of M. The totality of all algebroid points is the *algebroid space* $\mathfrak{U}^m$.

Let $f(u) \in K[[u]]$ and let us define what we mean by $f(M) = f(\varphi_1, \cdots, \varphi_m)$. Let $\psi_i(v)$ be an element of the class of φ_i mod $\mathfrak{b}$, and let $\omega_i(v) \in \mathfrak{b}$. Let also $f(u)$ admit the decomposition (1.1). Then $\tau_h(v) = f_h(\psi + \omega) - f_h(\psi) \in \mathfrak{b}$ and its degree $\to \infty$ with h. Hence $\tau(v) = \Sigma\tau_h(v) \in \mathfrak{b}$ or $f(\psi + \omega) - f(\psi) \in \mathfrak{b}$. Thus the class of $f(\psi)$ mod $\mathfrak{b}$ is fixed and it is by definition $f(\varphi)$ or $f(M)$. It may be thought of as the value of the series f at the algebroid point M. In particular if $f(\psi) \in \mathfrak{b}$ then $f(M) = 0$ and f is said to *contain* the algebroid point M.

Consider now an ideal $\mathfrak{a}$ of $K[[u]]$ itself. The totality of all algebroid points contained in every series of $\mathfrak{a}$ is the *algebroid variety* $\mathfrak{V}(\mathfrak{a})$ of the ideal $\mathfrak{a}$. The variety is defined as *irreducible* if $\mathfrak{V}(\mathfrak{a}) = \mathfrak{V}(\mathfrak{p})$ where $\mathfrak{p}$ is a prime ideal, and it is defined as *reducible* otherwise. The qualification "algebroid" is often omitted where the meaning is otherwise clear.

Suppose that the ideal $\mathfrak{a}$ has the canonical decomposition (3.2) and among the $\mathfrak{p}_i$ let $\mathfrak{p}_1, \cdots, \mathfrak{p}_\sigma$ be a set such that none is contained in the intersection of the rest. Then

$$\mathfrak{V}(\mathfrak{a}) = \mathfrak{V}(\mathfrak{p}_1) \cup \cdots \cup \mathfrak{V}(\mathfrak{p}_\sigma). \tag{3.4}$$

The $\mathfrak{V}(\mathfrak{p}_i)$, $i = 1, 2, \cdots, \sigma$, are the *components* of $\mathfrak{V}(\mathfrak{a})$.

In view of (3.4) we shall mainly concentrate upon irreducible algebroid varieties.

The following property is immediate:

(3.5) *The algebroid ideal consisting of all the series containing a given algebroid point M is prime.*

We will denote this ideal by $\mathfrak{p}(M)$ and its (irreducible) variety by $\mathfrak{V}(M)$.

4. Consider now a prime ideal $\mathfrak{p}$ and its variety $\mathfrak{V}$. We shall discuss more or less together the notions of general point and dimension for $\mathfrak{V}$ The treatment will rest upon normal systems patterned after those of (III, 6, 7, 8) for algebraic varieties.

Since $\mathfrak{p}$ consists of non-units, its elements have a least degree s_m. Let $f(u) \in \mathfrak{p}$ be of degree s_m. Then f is irreducible. For if $f \sim gh$ then since $\mathfrak{p}$ is prime one of the factors say $g \in \mathfrak{p}$ and as g is of degree $< s_m$ this is ruled out.

Let $f_{s_m}(u)$ be the leading form of $f(u)$ and apply a linear transformation to the u_i such that $f_{s_m}(u)$ becomes regular in u_m. Then

$$f(u) \sim f^{(m)}(u) = u_m^{s_m} + A_{m1}\, u_m^{s_m-1} + \cdots + A_{ms_m},$$

where the right hand side is a special polynomial in u_m and irreducible in $K[[u_1, \cdots, u_{m-1}]][u_m]$ and A_{mh} is of degree $\geq h$ (2.3, II).

Let $K[[u_1, \cdots, u_i]] = K^i[[u]]$, and $\mathfrak{p} \cap K^i[[u]] = \mathfrak{p}^i$. Here $\mathfrak{p}^i$ is a prime ideal of $K^i[[u]]$. We may repeat the same reasoning as above for $\mathfrak{p}^{m-1}$ and $K^{m-1}[[u]]$, etc. At each step there will be required an appropriate linear transformation and they combine to a transformation of the initial coordinates u_i with the following property due to Rückert: At the step $m - j + 1$ there is obtained a special polynomial $f^{(j)}$

$$f^{(j)}(u_1, \cdots, u_j) = u_j^{s_j} + A_{j1}u_j^{s_j-1} + \cdots + A_{js_j}$$

where the A_{ji} are non-units of $K^{j-1}[[u]]$, A_{jh} is of degree $\geq h$, and $f^{(j)}$ is irreducible in $K^{j-1}[[u]][u_j]$. The process stops at an $f^{(r+1)}(u)$ such that $\mathfrak{p}^r = 0$.

The points of the variety $\mathfrak{V}(\mathfrak{p})$ will all satisfy the *normal* system analogous to (III, 6.1) for algebraic varieties:

$$(4.1) \qquad f^{(j)}(u_1, \cdots, u_j) = 0, \quad j = r + 1, \cdots, m.$$

As a first application consider any series $g(u)$. We have upon dividing u_m^k by $f^{(m)}(u)$ as to u_m:

$$u_m^k = \varphi_{k,m}(u)f^{(m)}(u) + \varepsilon_{k0}(u) + \varepsilon_{k1}(u)u_m + \cdots + \varepsilon_{k,s_m-1}(u)u_m^{s_m-1}$$

where $\varphi_{k,m}(u) \in K[[u]]$, $\varepsilon_{ki} \in K^{m-1}[[u]]$, and the degrees of $\varphi_{k,m}$ and $\varepsilon_{ki} \to \infty$ with k. From this follows

$$(4.2) \qquad g(u) = \varphi_m(u)f^{(m)}(u) + \xi_0(u) + \xi_1(u)u_m + \cdots + \xi_{s_m-1}u_m^{s_m-1}$$

where $\varphi_m \in K[[u]]$ and $\xi_i(u) \in K^{m-1}[[u]]$. Proceeding similarly with the $\xi_i(u)$, etc., we will arrive at a relation

$$(4.3) \qquad \begin{cases} g(u) = \Sigma\varphi_j(u)f^{(j)}(u) + \psi(u) \\ \varphi_j \in K^j[[u]],\ \psi(u) \in K^r[[u]][u_{r+1}, \cdots, u_m]. \end{cases}$$

Note that if one applies this process to a series $g(u) \in K^h[[u]]$ then in (4.3) j runs only up to h and $\psi \in K^r[[u]][u_{r+1}, \cdots, u_h]$. Applying this to the coefficients of u_j in $f^{(j)}(u)$ we find that we may reduce them mod $f^{(r+1)}, \cdots, f^{(j-1)}$ to $K^r[[u]][u_{r+1}, \cdots, u_{j-1}]$.

To sum up we may state the following two properties:

(4.4) *One may assume in* (4.3) *that* $f^{(j)}(u) \in K^r[[u]][u_{r+1}, \cdots, u_j]$.

(4.5) *Every series* $g(u)$ *of* $K[[u]]$ *is equal* mod $\mathfrak{p}$ *to an element of the ring* $K^r[[u]][u_{r+1}, \cdots, u_m]$.

(4.6) Let now $\bar{u}_j$ denote the residue class mod $\mathfrak{p}$ of the coordinate u_j. The $\bar{u}_j$ are the coordinates of an algebroid point M. As M annuls every series of $\mathfrak{p}$ and only these, M is a *general algebroid point* of the variety $\mathfrak{V}$, in the same sense as for algebraic varieties: if the series $g(u) \in K[[u]]$ is annulled by M then it is annulled by every algebroid point of $\mathfrak{V}$.

Since $f^{(j)}(u) \in \mathfrak{p}$, $M(\bar{u})$ satisfies (4.1). Since $f^{(j)}(u)$ is a special polynomial in u_j, of $K^j[[u]]$, we may state:

(4.7) *The coordinate* $\bar{u}_s$, $s > r$, *of* M *is integral algebraic over* $K^{s-1}[[\bar{u}]]$. *Hence all the coordinates* $\bar{u}_{r+i}$ *are integral algebraic over* $K^r[[u]]$.

5. By making use of the general algebroid point $M(\bar{u})$ of $\mathfrak{V}$ one may paraphrase the argument of (III, 7, 8) and obtain most of the following comprehensive results:

(5.1) **Theorem.** *There exists in a prime ideal* $\mathfrak{p}$ *a set of series*

$$g_{r+i}(u_1, \cdots, u_{r+i}) = c_{0i}u_{r+i}^{e_i} + c_{1i}u_{r+i}^{e_i-1} + \cdots, \qquad (i = 1, 2, \cdots, m-r) \tag{5.1a}$$

with the following properties:

I. $c_{hi} \in K^r[[u]][u_{r+1}, \cdots, u_{r+i-1}]$ *and is a non-unit for* $h \neq 0$; $c_{0i} \in K^r[[u]]$.

II. $g_{r+i}(\bar{u}_1, \cdots, \bar{u}_{r+i-1}, u_{r+i})$ *is irreducible in*

$K^r((\bar{u}))(\bar{u}_{r+1}, \cdots, \bar{u}_{r+i-1})[u_{r+i}]$.

An equivalent form of II *is*:

II′. *To within a factor in* $K^r[[u]][u_{r+1}, \cdots, u_{r+i-1}]$, $g_{r+i}(u)$ *is a polynomial in* u_{r+i} *of* $\mathfrak{p} \cap K^r[[u]][u_{r+1}, \cdots, u_{r+i}]$, *with leading coefficient not in* $\mathfrak{p}$, *and of least degree in* u_{r+i}. *It divides therefore in* $K^r((u))(u_{r+1}, \cdots, u_{r+i-1})[u_{r+i}]$ *every other such polynomial of* $\mathfrak{p}$.

III. *If* $c(u_1, \cdots, u_r) = \Pi c_{0i}$ *then a n.a.s.c. in order that a series* $g \in \mathfrak{p}$ *is that it satisfy a relation*

$$c^\alpha g = \Sigma \gamma_i(u) g_i(u). \tag{5.1b}$$

IV. *Since* $M(\bar{u})$ *satisfies the system*

$$g_{r+i}(u_1, \cdots, u_{r+i}) = 0, \quad i = 1, 2, \cdots, m-r \tag{5.1c}$$

so does every point of the variety $\mathfrak{V}$. *For this reason we refer to this system as a normal system of equations for* $\mathfrak{V}$.

The only points in the statement which are not covered in (III, 7, 8) are the assertions as to c_{0i} and the necessity in property III.

Regarding c_{0i}, one arrives at g_{r+i} first by obtaining $g_{r+i}(\bar{u}_1, \cdots, \bar{u}_{r+i-1}, u_{r+i})$ with a leading coefficient $d(\bar{u}_1, \cdots, \bar{u}_{r+i-1}) \in K^r[[\bar{u}]][\bar{u}_{r+1}, \cdots, \bar{u}_{r+i-1}]$. Since $d(\bar{u})$ is integral algebraic over $K^r[[\bar{u}]]$ one may multiply $g_{r+1}(\bar{u}_1, \cdots, \bar{u}_{r+i-1}, u_{r+i})$ throughout by the product of the conjugates of $d(\bar{u})$ and as a result the new leading coefficient $c_{0i}(\bar{u}) \in K^r[[\bar{u}]]$, hence $c_{0i}(u)$ has the property asserted under I.

Passing now to the necessity of property III, let $g \in \mathfrak{p}$, and let Π_s denote this necessity for a $g(u_1, \cdots, u_s)$. Since there is no $g(u_1, \cdots, u_r) \neq 0$ in $\mathfrak{p}$, Π_r holds trivially, so we assume $m > r$ and Π_{m-1} and prove Π_m. We have now a relation (4.2). Upon dividing the polynomials $f^{(m)}(u)$, $\xi_0 + \cdots + \xi_{s-1}u_m^{s-1}$ in u_m of (4.2) by $g_m(u)$ as to u_m (note that by II′, $f^{(m)}(u)$ is divisible by $g_m(u)$ as polynomials of $K^r((u))(u_{r+1}, \cdots, u_{m-1})[u_m]$), there results a relation

$$(5.2) \qquad c^\beta g = \delta(u)g_m + \delta_0(u) + \delta_1(u)u_m + \cdots + \delta_{e-1}(u)u_m^{e-1},$$

where $\delta \in K[[u]]$, $\delta_i \in K^{m-1}[[u]]$ and e is the degree of g_m in u_m. From this follows

$$(5.3) \qquad c^\beta(\bar{u})g(\bar{u}) = 0 = \delta_0(\bar{u}) + \delta_1(\bar{u})\bar{u}_m + \cdots + \delta_{e-1}(\bar{u})\bar{u}_m^{e-1}.$$

Now (4.5) yields $\delta_i(\bar{u}) \in K[[\bar{u}_1, \cdots, \bar{u}_r]][\bar{u}_{r+1}, \cdots, \bar{u}_{m-1}]$. Since the degree of (5.3) in $\bar{u}_m$ is $< e$, by the irreducibility property II, $\delta_i(\bar{u}) = 0$, hence $\delta_i(u) \in \mathfrak{p}^{m-1} \subset \mathfrak{p}$. Applying now Π_{m-1} to the $\delta_i(u)$ and substituting in (5.2), Π_m follows.

Remark. In the preceding argument we have used in an essential manner property (4.7), i.e. in the last analysis the existence in $\mathfrak{p}$ of the special polynomials $f^{(s)}(u)$ of (4).

6. One will surmise that the number r depends solely upon the ideal $\mathfrak{p}$ and its variety $\mathfrak{V}$, and is in some sense the dimension of $\mathfrak{V}$. This is indeed the case and the most convenient way to prove it is by means of E. Noether's property as it appears in (III, 11.1).

Let "chain", "length of a chain", etc., have the same meaning for algebroid as for algebraic varieties (III, 11).

(6.1). **Theorem.** *The length of the longest chain beginning with the variety* $\mathfrak{V}$ *of* (5.1) *is* $r + 1$.

Thus no matter how the general point $M(\bar{u})$ arises the number r is the same and depends solely upon the variety $\mathfrak{V}$. It is therefore natural to refer to r as the *dimension* of $\mathfrak{V}$ or of its ideal. It is indicated by denoting the variety as $\mathfrak{V}^r$. As in the algebraic case r is the number of algebroidally independent coordinates among those of any general point of the variety.

Let $\mathfrak{V}' \subset \mathfrak{V}$ where $\mathfrak{V}'$ is irreducible and $\neq \mathfrak{V}$, and let $\mathfrak{p}'$ be the ideal of $\mathfrak{V}'$. Thus $\mathfrak{p} \subset \mathfrak{p}'$, $\mathfrak{p} \neq \mathfrak{p}'$. It follows that some series $g(u)$ is in $\mathfrak{p}'$ but not in $\mathfrak{p}$.

The notations being those of (5.1), $g(\bar{u})$ is algebraic over $K^r((\bar{u}))$ and hence it satisfies an irreducible equation

$$\varphi(\bar{u}) = A_0 g^\sigma(\bar{u}) + A_1 g^{\sigma-1}(\bar{u}) + \cdots + A_\sigma(\bar{u}) = 0,$$
$$A_i \in K^r[[\bar{u}]], \quad A_\sigma(\bar{u}) \neq 0.$$

Thus

$$\varphi(u) = A_0(u) g^\sigma(u) + \cdots + A_\sigma(u) \in \mathfrak{p}.$$

Since $g(u) \in \mathfrak{p}'$ and $\mathfrak{p} \subset \mathfrak{p}'$, necessarily $A_\sigma(u) \in \mathfrak{p}'$, and since $A_\sigma(\bar{u}) \neq 0$, $A_\sigma(u)$ is in $\mathfrak{p}'$ but not in $\mathfrak{p}$. This means that the prime ideal $\mathfrak{p}'' = \mathfrak{p}' \cap K^r[[u]] \neq 0$. It follows that upon applying to $\mathfrak{p}''$ the normalization of (4.1) we will come to a last function $f^{(h)} \neq 0$ with at most r variables. Hence if $\bar{r}(\mathfrak{V})$ is the least r for any choice of variables u_i, necessarily $\bar{r}(\mathfrak{V}') < \bar{r}(\mathfrak{V}) \leq r$.

Evidently $\bar{r}(\mathfrak{V}) \geq 0$ whatever $\mathfrak{V}$. By the result just proved if $\mathfrak{V} = \mathfrak{V}_1, \mathfrak{V}_2, \cdots, \mathfrak{V}_s$ is a chain beginning with $\mathfrak{V}$ then $\bar{r}(\mathfrak{V}_1) > \bar{r}(\mathfrak{V}_2) > \cdots > \bar{r}(\mathfrak{V}_s) \geq 0$ and so $0 \leq \bar{r}(\mathfrak{V}_s) \leq r - s + 1$, hence $s \leq r + 1$.

Let $(6.1)_r$ denote property (6.1) for r. Since for $r = 0$ the system (5.1c) reduces to $u_1 = \cdots = u_m = 0$, we have then $\mathfrak{p} = \mathfrak{m}$ and $\mathfrak{V}(\mathfrak{p}) = \mathfrak{V}(\mathfrak{m}) = O$, the origin. The only possible chain is then the origin itself and so $(6.1)_0$ holds.

Consider now $(6.1)_1$. The ideal $\mathfrak{p} \neq \mathfrak{m}$, hence $\mathfrak{V}(\mathfrak{p}) \neq 0$. Since it contains O, they form together a chain of two links, the maximum possible. Thus $(6.1)_1$ holds.

Assume now $r > 1$ and that $(6.1)_{r-1}$ holds. Let the variables $u_1, \cdots, u_r$ undergo if necessary a linear transformation such that $c(u_1, \cdots, u_r)$ is regular in all of them. Then $u_r \neq c(u_1, \cdots, u_r)$. Take now $u_1^*, \cdots, u_{r-1}^*$ indeterminate and $u_r^* = 0$. Then $c(u^*) \neq 0$. Hence one may solve one at a time the relations

$$g_{r+i}(u_1^*, \cdots, u_{r+i}^*) = 0$$

for the u_{r+i}^*. They will not all be zero and they will be the coordinates of a certain algebroid point M^*. For the variety $\mathfrak{V}(M^*) = \mathfrak{V}^*$ clearly $\bar{r}(\mathfrak{V}^*) = r - 1$. Since $g_i(M^*) = 0$, $c(M^*) \neq 0$, we infer from (5.1b) that if $g \in \mathfrak{p}$ then $g(M^*) = 0$. Hence $\mathfrak{p} \subset \mathfrak{p}^*$ the prime ideal of $\mathfrak{V}^*$ and so $\mathfrak{V}^* \subset \mathfrak{V}$. Since u_r is in $\mathfrak{p}^*$ but not in $\mathfrak{p}$, $\mathfrak{p}^* \neq \mathfrak{p}$ and so $\mathfrak{V}^* \neq \mathfrak{V}$. By $(6.1)_{r-1}$ there is a chain of length r beginning with $\mathfrak{V}^*$. Hence there is one of length $r + 1$ beginning with $\mathfrak{V}$. This completes the proof of (6.1).

(6.2) When $\mathfrak{V}$ is reducible its dimension r, also the dimension of its ideal, is by definition the largest dimension of the components of $\mathfrak{V}$. A pure variety is one whose components all have the same dimension.

It is a mere exercise to prove:

(6.3) *If* $\mathfrak{V}, \mathfrak{V}'$ *are distinct irreducible varieties then* dim $(\mathfrak{V} \cap \mathfrak{V}') <$ dim $\mathfrak{V}$, dim $\mathfrak{V}'$.

(6.4) *The Hilbert zero theorem. If a series* $f(u)$ *contains the variety* $\mathfrak{B}(\mathfrak{a})$ *of the ideal* $\mathfrak{a}$ *then some power* $f^{\rho} \in \mathfrak{a}$.

In view of the decomposition (3.2) it is sufficient to prove the theorem for a primary ideal $\mathfrak{q}$. Let $\mathfrak{p}$ be the prime ideal of $\mathfrak{q}$ and M a general point of the variety $\mathfrak{B}(\mathfrak{p})$. Since $f(M) = 0$, $f \in \mathfrak{p}$, hence some $f^{\rho} \in \mathfrak{q}$ which proves (6.4).

(6.5) *Differentials.* When K is of characteristic zero the definition of differentials in the field $K((u))$ or in the quotient field of the integral domain $K[[u]]/\mathfrak{p}$, $\mathfrak{p}$ a prime ideal, follows essentially the same pattern as for the similar algebraic situation and need not detain us here.

(6.6) *Monoidal systems.* If the characteristic of K is zero, it will be seen by reference to (III, 7) that the reduction to a monoidal system utilized for algebraic varieties (see III, 8) may be carried out for algebroid varieties. With a suitable choice of variables the monoidal system will assume the form

$$(6.7)\qquad \begin{cases} g(u) = u_{r+1}^{s} + a_1(u)u_{r+1}^{s-1} + \cdots + a_s(u) = 0, \\ \lambda_k(u) = b(u_1, \cdots, u_r)u_{r+k+1} - b_k(u_1, \cdots, u_{r+1}) = 0, \\ \qquad k = 1, 2, \cdots, m - (r+1), \end{cases}$$

where $g(u)$ is an irreducible special polynomial with coefficients in $K^r[[u]]$, $b \in K^r[[u]]$ and $b_k \in K^r[[u]][u_{r+1}]$. Of course (5.1) still holds with (6.7) in place of (5.1a) and (5.1b) replaced by

$$(6.8)\qquad b^{\alpha}h = \gamma(u)g(u) + \Sigma\gamma_k(u)\lambda_k(u), \quad \gamma, \gamma_k \in K^r[[u]],$$

as the condition that $h \in \mathfrak{p}$.

Even when the groundfield K has a characteristic $p \neq 0$, the algebroid variety $\mathfrak{B}$ may possess a monoidal representation. It will then be called *monoidal*. Thus when the characteristic is zero every algebroid variety is monoidal.

Consider now a fixed choice of the parameters u_i and relative to this choice series $f^{(r+1)}(u), \cdots, f^{(m)}(u)$, where as in (4) f^{r+i} is a special polynomial in u_{r+i} of the ring $K^r[[u]][u_{r+1}, \cdots, u_{r+i}]$. Let $\mathfrak{b}$ be the ideal generated by the $f^{(i)}(u)$ and let us consider only ideals over $\mathfrak{b}$. Suppose that $\mathfrak{a}$ is such an ideal with the monoidal representation (6.7). Since any series $h(u)$ is, mod $\mathfrak{b}$, an element $h'(u)$ of $K^r[[u]][u_{r+1}, \cdots, u_m]$, and since $K^r[[u]]$ is an integral domain, referring to (III, 10.11) we may apply with but few changes, the reasonings of (III, 10) and obtain the following result:

(6.9) *Let the ideal* $\mathfrak{a}$ *contain the ideal* $\mathfrak{b}$. *Let* $\mathfrak{a}$ *be monoidal with representation* (6.7), *and let* g *admit a decomposition*

$$g = g_1^{\nu_1} \cdots g_s^{\nu_s}$$

where the g_i *are irreducible special polynomials of the same nature as* g

itself. The series h which satisfy a relation (6.8) *with g replaced by* g_i, *and those which satisfy a relation* (6.8) *with g replaced by* $g_i^{\nu_i}$ *form an associated pair of a prime ideal* $\mathfrak{p}_i$ *and primary ideal* $\mathfrak{q}_i$. *There take place the relations* $\mathfrak{a} = \mathfrak{q}_1 \cap \cdots \cap \mathfrak{q}_s$, $\mathfrak{V}(\mathfrak{a}) = \mathfrak{V}(\mathfrak{p}_1) \cup \cdots \cup \mathfrak{V}(\mathfrak{p}_s)$ *where the* $\mathfrak{V}(\mathfrak{p}_i)$ *are all distinct. Since they all have now the same dimension r,* $\mathfrak{V}(\mathfrak{a})$ *is a pure r-dimensional algebroid variety.*

(6.10) *Remark on the complex field.* If K is the complex field and one only admits convergent series, everything goes through as before. Owing to the base theorem the variety $\mathfrak{V}(\mathfrak{a})$ of an ideal $\mathfrak{a}$ is determined by a finite system of relations

(6.11) $$f_1(u) = 0, \cdots, f_s(u) = 0.$$

Hence there will be a region of convergency common to all the $f_i(u)$. For (u) in the region we will thus obtain *analytical* points of $\mathfrak{V}(\mathfrak{a})$, namely the points of the affine space KA_u^m which satisfy (6.11). The variety $\mathfrak{V}(\mathfrak{a})$ is called a *complex algebroid variety.*

7. Local rings. A local ring is a Noetherian ring $\mathfrak{R}$ with unit element and hence with units (elements whose inverses are in $\mathfrak{R}$) whose non-units form an ideal $\mathfrak{m}$ (necessarily maximal and prime). These rings whose importance is growing constantly, will be barely touched upon here and merely insofar as they are required later. For more ample information see Krull [2] and Chevalley [1], whose writings we follow in substance.

Immediate properties are:

(7.1) *The ideals of* $\mathfrak{R}$ *admit a canonical decomposition.*

(7.2) *If* $\mathfrak{a}$ *is an ideal of* $\mathfrak{R}$ *then* $\mathfrak{R}^* = \mathfrak{R}/\mathfrak{a}$ *is a local ring with* $\mathfrak{m}^* = \mathfrak{m}/\mathfrak{a}$ *as ideal of non-units* (see van der Waerden [1], II, p. 21).

Evidently also:

(7.3) *A power series ring is a local ring.*

Let $\mathfrak{R}$, $\mathfrak{m}$ be as above. As a basis for topologizing the ring we prove:

(7.4) $$\mathfrak{n} = \cap\, \mathfrak{m}^\rho = 0.$$

Let us show first that

(7.5) $$\mathfrak{n} \cdot \mathfrak{m} = \mathfrak{n}.$$

We have at once $\mathfrak{n} \cdot \mathfrak{m} \subset \mathfrak{n}$ so that we only need to show that $\mathfrak{n} \subset \mathfrak{n} \cdot \mathfrak{m}$. There is a canonical decomposition

$$\mathfrak{n} \cdot \mathfrak{m} = \mathfrak{q}_1 \cap \cdots \cap \mathfrak{q}_s,$$

and it is sufficient to show that $\mathfrak{n} \subset \mathfrak{q}_i$. Let $\mathfrak{p}_i$ be the prime ideal of $\mathfrak{q}_i$. There are two possibilities:

(a) $\mathfrak{p}_i = \mathfrak{m}$. Then $\mathfrak{m}^\sigma \subset \mathfrak{q}_i$ for some σ and hence, owing to the definition of $\mathfrak{n}$; $\mathfrak{n} \subset \mathfrak{m}^\sigma \subset \mathfrak{q}_i$.

(b) $\mathfrak{p}_i \neq \mathfrak{m}$. Since $\mathfrak{m}$ is maximal, we do not have $\mathfrak{m} \subset \mathfrak{p}_i$. Hence there is an element m of $\mathfrak{m}$ not contained in $\mathfrak{p}_i$. If n is any element of $\mathfrak{n}$, then $mn \in \mathfrak{q}_i$ and since m is not in $\mathfrak{p}_i$, necessarily $n \in \mathfrak{q}_i$, hence $\mathfrak{n} \subset \mathfrak{q}_i$.

Thus always $\mathfrak{n} \subset \mathfrak{q}_i$ and hence $\mathfrak{n} \subset \mathfrak{n} \cdot \mathfrak{m}$, which proves (7.5).

Let now $\{n_1, \cdots, n_r\}$ be a base for $\mathfrak{n}$. From (7.5) follows

$$n_i = \Sigma m_{ik} n_k; \qquad i, k = 1, 2, \cdots, r, \ m_{ik} \in \mathfrak{m}.$$

Hence if

$$d = | m_{ik} - \delta_{ik} |, \quad (\delta_{ii} = 1; \quad \delta_{ik} = 0 \text{ for } i \neq k),$$

then $dn_i = 0$ for every i. It is seen at once that d is a unit. Therefore $n_i = 0$, and hence $\mathfrak{n} = 0$ which is (7.4).

Let now $\alpha \in \mathfrak{R}$ and define its norm $||\alpha||$ as follows: for a unit α, $||\alpha|| = +\infty$; $||0|| = 0$; if α is a non-unit and $\neq 0$ then by (7.4) there is a ρ such that α is in $\mathfrak{m}^\rho$ but not in $\mathfrak{m}^{\rho+1}$ and we take $||\alpha|| = 2^{-\rho}$. The usual norm properties are readily verified and as a consequence $d(\alpha, \beta) = ||\alpha - \beta||$ metrizes $\mathfrak{R}$, which is thus turned into a metric space. In this topology:

(7.6) *Every ideal $\mathfrak{a}$ of the local ring $\mathfrak{R}$ is closed. Thus in particular every ideal of the power series ring $K[[u]]$ is closed.*

Referring to (7.2) and in its notations by (7.4): $\cap\, \mathfrak{m}^{*\rho} = 0$. This means that if $b \in \mathfrak{R}$ is in every ideal $\mathfrak{a} + \mathfrak{m}^\rho$ then $b \in \mathfrak{a}$, which implies (7.6).

This completes the general material that we shall require in the sequel regarding local rings.

§ 3. Local Properties of Algebraic Varieties

8. We shall now apply the algebroid theory to the study of local properties of algebraic varieties. This will be done by associating a definite algebroid space with the individual points of the variety.

Given a point P in KP^m_x, let the coordinates x_i be so chosen that P is the point $(1, 0, \cdots, 0)$, i.e. the origin for the affine coordinates X_i. Everything will revolve around the properties of the ring $K[[X]]$ and of its ideals.

We are only interested in the properties of $K[[X]]$ which are invariant under regular transformations of the coordinates X_i. Now a projective transformation preserving the coordinates of the point P has the general form

$$\rho x_0' = x_0 + \Sigma a_j x_j, \quad \rho x_i' = \Sigma a_{ij} x_j; \quad i, j > 0; \quad |a_{ij}| \neq 0.$$

The associated transformation of the affine coordinates X_i is

$$X_i' = \frac{\Sigma a_{ij} X_j}{1 + \Sigma a_j X_j} = E(X) \Sigma a_{ij} X_j,$$

and so it is regular in the X_i. Thus it falls under the allowed category. As a consequence our results will not depend upon the choice of coordinates for KP^m provided that those of the point P remain $(1, 0, \cdots, 0)$.

The algebroid varieties of the algebroid space $\mathfrak{X}^m$ will now be referred to as *branches*, written $\mathfrak{B}$, or $\mathfrak{B}^r$ if dim $\mathfrak{B} = r$. A general algebroid point of $\mathfrak{B}$ will be called a *parametric point* of the branch.

The term "branch" is borrowed from the classical case where K is the real field and one has branches of a curve, of a surface, etc. A $\mathfrak{B}^1$ is generally merely a curvilinear arc (K real) through P. The "places" of a curve discussed at length in the next chapter, fall under this category.

There is nothing to prevent us from considering the algebroid points as points of the affine space KA_X^m. As a consequence the algebroid space $\mathfrak{X}^m$ is embedded in KA_X^m, or for that matter in the projective space KP_x^m. This gives meaning to statements such as: the parametric point M is in the algebraic variety V'' or "$\mathfrak{B} \subset V$."

Let now V^r be an algebraic variety of KP^m through the point P and let $\mathfrak{a}$ be its ideal in $K[X]$, i.e. as a variety of KA_X^m. Since the polynomials of $\mathfrak{a}$ all vanish at the origin they are non-units of $K[[X]]$. Hence they span in $K[[X]]$ an algebroid ideal $\mathfrak{a}^*$ and the latter is merely the closure of $\mathfrak{a}$ as a subset of $K[[X]]$. We apply to $\mathfrak{a}^*$ the canonical decomposition (3.2) into primary algebroid ideals, with $\mathfrak{p}_i$, $\mathfrak{q}_i$ as loc. cit. Among the $\mathfrak{p}_i$ let $\{\mathfrak{p}_1, \cdots, \mathfrak{p}_\sigma\}$ be the set of those such that none is contained in the intersection of the rest. To the $\mathfrak{p}_i$, $i \leq \sigma$, there correspond the branches $\mathfrak{B}_i = \mathfrak{B}(\mathfrak{p}_i, P)$ whose set $\mathfrak{B}(V^r, P)$ is the *neighborhood* of the point P in V^r. The branches $\mathfrak{B}_i$ are the *local components* of V^r at the point P. When V^r is a complex variety the ordinary points of $\mathfrak{B}(V^r, P)$ (see 6.10) make up a true neighborhood of P in V^r.

Simple examples where $\mathfrak{B}(V^r, P)$ has more than one branch are readily given. Thus at a multiple point of a plane curve Γ where there are k distinct tangents there are k branches (see below).

The dimension of the algebroid variety $\mathfrak{B}(V^r, P)$ is by definition the *local dimension of* V^r *at the point* P. It may well vary from point to point. Thus let S and l be a plane and a line in KP^3, where l is not in S and let Q be their intersection. If $V = l \cup S$, then dim $V = 2$. At every point of S the local dimension is likewise two. However at the points of l other than Q the local dimension is unity. It may be noted that at the point Q there are two local components of V, but only one at the other points.

9. Now let V^r be irreducible and as before let $\mathfrak{a}$ be its ideal in $K[X]$ and $\mathfrak{a}^*$ the closure of $\mathfrak{a}$ in $K[[X]]$. While $\mathfrak{a}$ is prime this need not be the case regarding a^*.

The central property regarding the local components is the following:

(9.1) **Theorem.** *Every branch of the irreducible variety V^r over an algebraically closed groundfield is r-dimensional. Hence V^r has the local dimension r at every point.*

We shall actually prove the more complete property:

(9.2) *The ideal $\mathfrak{a}^*$ of V^r in $K[[X]]$, K algebraically closed, has a canonical* *decomposition* $\mathfrak{a}^* = \mathfrak{q}_1 \cap \cdots \cap \mathfrak{q}_s$ *where the prime ideals* $\mathfrak{p}_i$ *associated with the* $\mathfrak{q}_i$ *are all r-dimensional. If the groundfield is of characteristic zero then* $\mathfrak{q}_i = \mathfrak{p}_i$ *and so the canonical decomposition is* $\mathfrak{a}^* = \mathfrak{p}_1 \cap \cdots \cap \mathfrak{p}_s$.

Property (9.2) also implies:

(9.3) *The number of local components of* V^r *at the point* P *is* s. *Hence the ideal* $\mathfrak{a}^*$ *of* V^r *in* $K[[X]]$ *is certainly not prime when* $s > 1$.

As an example let the groundfield K be algebraically closed and of characteristic zero. We will show in the next chapter that an irreducible curve Γ with a k-tuple point P with distinct tangents has then k local components at P. Examples with any value of k are readily produced, and they correspond to a non-prime algebroid ideal $\mathfrak{a}^*$, although the algebraic ideal $\mathfrak{a}$ is prime.

We shall require two normal forms for V^r, both in affine coordinates, that of (III, 6):

$$F_{r+i}(X_1, \cdots, X_{r+i}) = 0, \quad i = 1, 2, \cdots, m - r \tag{9.4}$$

where F_{r+i} is irreducible and regular in X_{r+i}, and the monoidal form of (III, 8.1):

$$\begin{cases} F(X_1, \cdots, X_{r+1}) = 0; \\ \Lambda_k = HX_{r+1+k} - H_k = 0, \quad k = 1, 2, \cdots, m - r - 1; \\ F, H_k \in K^{r+1}[X], \ H \in K^r[X]. \end{cases} \tag{9.5}$$

Moreover F is irreducible and regular in X_{r+1}.

We recall also that by (III, 8.5a) the ideal $\mathfrak{a}$ consists of those and only those polynomials $G(X) \in K[X]$ which satisfy a relation

$$H^\rho G = BF + \Sigma B_k \Lambda_k; \ B, B_k \in K[X]. \tag{9.6}$$

An important observation must be made here when the groundfield K is of characteristic $p > 0$. Namely if X_i^0 are the initial coordinates then (see III, 22) the X_i of (9.5) are obtained from them by relations

$$X_i = \Sigma \mu_{ij} X_j^0 \tag{9.7}$$

where $\mu = ||\mu_{ij}||$ is "almost" any such matrix of elements of K. On the other hand the X_i of (9.4) are derived from a succession of $m - r$ transformations of types

$$\begin{cases} X_i^h = \Sigma \mu_{ij}^{h-1} X_j^{h-1}; \ i, j = 1, 2, \cdots, m - h + 1, \\ X_i^h = X_i^{h-1}; \ i = m - h + 2, \cdots, m; \ h = 1, 2, \cdots, m - r \end{cases} \tag{9.8}$$

where again μ^{h-1}, the matrix of the coefficients at the right in (9.8), is almost any such matrix of elements of K. Since $\mu^{m-r} \cdots \mu^1$ is almost any μ, we conclude that in (9.4) and (9.5) one may assume that the coordinates are the same.

10. We will first require a certain new ring. For convenience let us set $\mathfrak{R} = K[X]$, $\mathfrak{R}^* = K[[X]]$.

The new ring is needed because while $\mathfrak{R}^*$ is a local ring $\mathfrak{R}$ is not. In fact the units of $\mathfrak{R}$ are merely the elements of K and its non-units are all the polynomials of positive degree. Thus X_1 and $X_1 + 1$ are non-units. Hence 1 is an element of the ideal spanned by the non-units of $\mathfrak{R}$, and so $\mathfrak{R}$ is not a local ring.

The basic observation is that the elements of the field $K(X)$ of the form $R = A/B$, where A and B are polynomials and $B(O) \neq 0$, do form a ring $\mathfrak{R}'$. This is precisely the ring that we need. Notice that its elements may also be written more conveniently

$$(10.1) \qquad R = \frac{A}{1 - C}; \quad A, C \in \mathfrak{R}, \quad C(O) = 0.$$

Now if $\mathfrak{a}$ is an ideal of $\mathfrak{R}$, its elements span in $\mathfrak{R}'$ an ideal $\mathfrak{a}' = \mathfrak{R}'\mathfrak{a}$. Conversely if $\mathfrak{a}'$ is an ideal of $\mathfrak{R}'$ and R above is in $\mathfrak{a}'$ then $(1 - C)R = A \in \mathfrak{a}'$ also. Thus $\mathfrak{a}'$ contains polynomials and their totality constitutes an ideal $\mathfrak{a}$ of $\mathfrak{R}$ such that $\mathfrak{a}' = \mathfrak{R}'\mathfrak{a}$. As a consequence a base $\{G_i\}$ for $\mathfrak{a}$ is likewise one for $\mathfrak{a}'$. Thus $\mathfrak{R}'$ is Noetherian. It also has an element unity. Furthermore if $\mathfrak{m}$ is the ideal $(X_1, \cdots, X_m)$ of $\mathfrak{R}$ then the ideal $\mathfrak{m}' = \mathfrak{R}'\mathfrak{m}$ is the set of all the non-units of $\mathfrak{R}'$, and incidentally $\mathfrak{m}^* = \mathfrak{R}^*\mathfrak{m}$ is the ideal of the non-units of $\mathfrak{R}^*$. Hence $\mathfrak{R}'$ is a local ring.

Returning again to the representation (10.1), using the relation in $\mathfrak{R}^*$

$$(1 - C)(1 + C + C^2 + \cdots) = 1,$$

we may imbed isomorphically $\mathfrak{R}'$ in $\mathfrak{R}^*$ by identifying the element R of $\mathfrak{R}'$ with the element $A(1 + C + C^2 + \cdots)$ of $\mathfrak{R}^*$. This imbedding is seen at once to assign to $\mathfrak{R}'$ its natural local ring topology as defined in (7).

Henceforth $\mathfrak{R}'$ is identified with its image in $\mathfrak{R}^*$. We will have $\mathfrak{R} \subset \mathfrak{R}' \subset \mathfrak{R}^*$, and the imbeddings are topological.

Let us observe finally that $\mathfrak{R}'$ is in a sense the smallest local ring over $\mathfrak{R}$.

11. We are now well equipped for the proofs of our theorems. Referring to (6.9), to prove Theorem (9.1), and also the part of (9.2) which corresponds to an arbitrary groundfield, it is sufficient to prove the analogue of (9.6) or rather of (III, 8.5) for series:

(11.1) *A n.a.s.c. for a series* $G(X) \in K[[X]]$ *to be in the ideal* $\mathfrak{a}^*$ *is that it satisfy a relation*

$$(11.1a) \qquad H^\rho G = BF + \Sigma B_k \Lambda_k; \quad B, B_k \in K[[X]],$$

where ρ *is the fixed exponent of* (9.5) (see III, 7.7).

The proof rests upon the following lemma, in which the rings $\mathfrak{R}$, $\mathfrak{R}'$, $\mathfrak{R}^*$ are as in (10):

(11.2) **Lemma.** *Let* $c \in \mathfrak{R}$ *and let* $\mathfrak{b}$ *be an ideal of* $\mathfrak{R}$. *The elements* α *of* $\mathfrak{R}$ *such that* $c\alpha \in \mathfrak{b}$ *form an ideal* $\mathfrak{a}$. *The n.a.s.c. in order that* $c\alpha^* \in \mathfrak{R}^*$ *be in the ideal* $\mathfrak{b}^* = \mathfrak{R}^*\mathfrak{b}$ *is that* $\alpha^* \in \mathfrak{a}^* = \mathfrak{R}^*\mathfrak{a}$.

To obtain (11.1) all that is necessary is to choose $c = H^\rho$ and

$$\mathfrak{b} = (F, \cdots, \quad \Lambda_k, \cdots).$$

We proceed to the proof of the lemma. Sufficiency is clear by a limiting process, so that we only need to consider necessity.

Preliminary remark: Since $\mathfrak{R}'$ is a local ring an ideal $\mathfrak{d}'$ in $\mathfrak{R}'$ is closed in $\mathfrak{R}'$. From this follows that $\mathfrak{R}^*\mathfrak{d}' \cap \mathfrak{R}' = \mathfrak{d}'$, i.e. the elements of $\mathfrak{d}'$ extended to $\mathfrak{R}^*$ which are in $\mathfrak{R}'$ make up $\mathfrak{d}'$.

Suppose now that $c\alpha^* \in \mathfrak{b}^*$. Since α^* may be indefinitely approximated by polynomials, one may choose, for any $n > 0$, a polynomial $\alpha_n \in \mathfrak{R}$ such that $\alpha_n - \alpha^* \in \mathfrak{m}^{*n}$. Then

$$\begin{aligned} c\alpha_n &= c\alpha^* + c(\alpha_n - \alpha^*) \in (\mathfrak{R}^*\mathfrak{b} + \mathfrak{R}^*c\mathfrak{m}^{*n}) \cap \mathfrak{R}' \\ &= \mathfrak{R}^*(\mathfrak{b} + c\mathfrak{m}^n) \cap \mathfrak{R}' = \mathfrak{R}^*\mathfrak{R}'(\mathfrak{b} + c\mathfrak{m}^n) \cap \mathfrak{R}' \\ &= \mathfrak{R}'(\mathfrak{b} + c\mathfrak{m}^n). \end{aligned}$$

Thus the polynomial $c\alpha_n$ is in the extension of the ideal $\mathfrak{b} + c\mathfrak{m}^n$ of $\mathfrak{R}$ into $\mathfrak{R}'$. It follows that there is a polynomial of $\mathfrak{R}$ of the form $e = 1 - d$, $d(0) = 0$, such that $ec\alpha_n \in \mathfrak{b} + c\mathfrak{m}^n$. Hence there is a $\mu \in \mathfrak{m}^n$ such that $c(e\alpha_n - \mu) \in \mathfrak{b}$. Therefore $e\alpha_n - \mu \in \mathfrak{a}$, $e\alpha_n \in \mathfrak{a} + \mathfrak{m}^n$. Since e is a unit of $\mathfrak{R}^*$ we have $\alpha_n \in R^*\mathfrak{a} + \mathfrak{m}^{*n}$. Thus α^* is arbitrarily near $\mathfrak{R}^*\mathfrak{a} = \mathfrak{a}^*$ and since $\mathfrak{a}^*$ is closed it contains α^*. This completes the proof of the lemma, hence also of (11.1). As we have seen this proves Theorem (9.1) and the part of (9.2) referring to a general groundfield K.

Let generally $F(X)$ admit in $\mathfrak{R}^* = K[[X]]$ the following factorization into distinct irreducible factors:

(11.3) $$F = \gamma\Phi_1^{\nu_1} \cdots \Phi_s^{\nu_s}, \ \gamma \in K.$$

The pair $\mathfrak{p}_i$, $\mathfrak{q}_i$ corresponds to Φ_i. By reference to (III, 10) it will be seen that $\mathfrak{q}_i \neq \mathfrak{p}_i$ when and only when $\nu_i > 1$. Now if K is of characteristic zero the irreducible polynomial $F(X)$ of $K^{r+1}[X]$ has only simple roots in X_{r+1} in any field over $K^r(X)$. Hence every $\nu_i = 1$ and the rest of (9.2) follows.

12. The results just proved may be completed in certain points.

(12.1) *The parametric points* M_i *of the branches* $\mathfrak{B}_i^r$ *of an irreducible* V^r *are general points of the variety.*

The branches $\mathfrak{B}_i^r$ of center P are in one-one correspondence with the factors Φ_i of (11.3). We may suppose that $\mathfrak{B}_i^r$ corresponds to Φ_i and it will then have the normal representation

(12.2) $$\Phi_i(X_1, \cdots, X_{r+1}) = 0; \quad \Lambda_k(X) = 0, \quad k = 1, 2, \cdots, m - r - 1.$$

Since F is regular in X_{r+1}, the Φ_i are special polynomials in X_{r+1} of the ring $K^{r+1}[[X]]$. The parametric point M_i will have for coordinates X_i a solution of the above system in which the X_i, $i \leq r$, are indeterminates. Hence the algebraic transcendency of M_i is at least r.

On the other hand if $G \in \mathfrak{a}$, the prime ideal of V^r in $K[X]$, then from (9.6) and since Φ_i divides F and $H(M_i) \neq 0$, there follows $G(M_i) = 0$. Hence $M_i \in V^r$. Therefore transc $M_i = r$ and M_i is a general point of the variety.

(12.3) *If a hypersurface W^s contains a local component of the irreducible variety V^r then it contains V^r itself.*

For if W contains $\mathfrak{B}_i^r$ it contains M_i and hence V^r by (12.1).

13. The simplest type of branch corresponds to a representation (12.2) in which $H = 1$ and Φ_i is of degree one in X_{r+1}. Such a branch will have a representation

$$(13.1) \qquad X_{r+i} = H_i(X_1, \cdots, X_r) \in K[[X]], \quad i = 1, 2, \cdots, m - r.$$

The branch is then said to be *linear.*

(13.2) *The intersection of a linear branch $\mathfrak{B}^r$ with a hypersurface G which is not in the prime ideal $\mathfrak{p}$ of $\mathfrak{B}^r$ is pure $(r - 1)$-dimensional.*

In view of (13.1) one may replace G mod $\mathfrak{p}$ by a series $G_1(X_1, \cdots, X_r) \neq 0$ and assume G_1 irreducible. At the cost of a linear transformation on the X_i, $i \leq r$, one may also assume that G_1 is regular in X_r and hence that it is a special polynomial in X_r. Thus the intersection will have the monoidal representation

$$G_1(X_1, \cdots, X_r) = 0, \quad X_{r+i} - H_i(X_1, \cdots, X_r) = 0, \quad i = 1, 2, \cdots, m - r.$$

Hence it is a $\mathfrak{B}^{r-1}$ and (13.2) follows.

The point P is said to be *non-singular* whenever its neighborhood consists of a single linear branch and it is *singular* otherwise.

Let P be non-singular and let as before $\mathfrak{a}^*$ denote the ideal of V^r in $K[[x]]$. The fact that there is a single linear branch $\mathfrak{B}^r$ and that it is represented by the system (13.1) means that

$$(13.3) \qquad K[[X]]/\mathfrak{a}^* = K^r[[X]].$$

Conversely let (13.3) hold. Then $\mathfrak{a}^*$ is prime since its quotient ring is an integral domain. Hence there is only one branch $\mathfrak{B}^r$ centered at P. In view of (13.3) the coordinates of a parametric point of $\mathfrak{B}^r$ satisfy a system (13.1) so that $\mathfrak{B}^r$ is linear. Hence P is non-singular. Thus:

(13.4) *A n.a.s.c. in order that the point P be non-singular for V^r is that with a proper numbering of the coordinates there take place the relation* (13.3).

Let again P be non-singular. Upon applying a regular transformation from $X_1, \cdots, X_r$ to $v_1, \cdots, v_r$, (13.1) is replaced by

$$(13.5) \qquad X_i = \varphi_i(v_1, \cdots, v_r), \quad i = 1, 2, \cdots, m$$

where $\varphi_i \in K[[v]]$ and the Jacobian matrix (coefficient matrix of the terms of the first degree)

$$\left\| \frac{\partial \varphi_i}{\partial v_j} \right\| (0, \cdots, 0)$$

is of rank r. In view of this one may solve (13.5) by the implicit function theorem as

(13.6) $$v_j = \psi_j(X) \in K[[X]], \quad j = 1, 2, \cdots, r,$$

and (13.5) and (13.6) together imply the relation

(13.7) $$K[[X]]/\mathfrak{a}^* = K[[v]].$$

One refers to (13.5) as a *parametric representation at the point* P and to the v_i as the *parameters* of this representation.

It is not difficult to see that the v_j behave like local coordinates in the following sense. Let $\mathfrak{b}^*$ be an ideal of $K[[X]]$ defining an algebroid variety $\mathfrak{W}$. If $G \in \mathfrak{b}^*$ then $G(X) = G(X(v)) = G(v) \bmod \mathfrak{a}^*$. The $G(v)$ generate an ideal $\mathfrak{b}^{**}$ of $K[[v]]$ and its algebroid variety is the intersection $\mathfrak{W} \cap V^r$. Thus the "ideal theory" of $K[[v]]$ is merely the ideal theory of the intersections of V^r with the algebroid varieties of $K[[X]]$.

From (13.2) we deduce the following noteworthy result:

(13.8) **Theorem.** *The intersection of an irreducible* V^r *without singularities with a hypersurface* G *which is not in the ideal of* V^r, *is a pure* V^{r-1}.

For the intersection is $(r - 1)$-dimensional in each point and hence it has no components of dimension $< r - 1$.

Remark. The extension of the "local coordinate" scheme to products of varieties is quite automatic. We will prove however the following interesting result:

(13.9) *Let* V^r, W^s, r *and* $s > 0$, *be irreducible and let* A, B *be non-singular points of* V^r, W^s *with parameters* v_i, w_j. *Then* (A, B) *is a non-singular point of* $V^r \times W^s$ *and it has for parameters the* v_i *and* w_j *together.*

Let X_i, Y_j be affine coordinates with origins at A, B in the spaces KP^m_x, KP^n_y of the two varieties, and let $\mathfrak{a}^*$, $\mathfrak{b}^*$ be their prime ideals in $K[[X]]$, $K[[Y]]$. From (13.3) and

$$K[[Y]]/\mathfrak{b}^* = K^s[[Y]]$$

follows readily

(13.10) $$K[[X; Y]]/(\mathfrak{a}^* \times \mathfrak{b}^*) = K[[X_1, \cdots, X_r, Y_1, \cdots, Y_s]],$$

where $\mathfrak{a}^* \times \mathfrak{b}^*$ is the ideal spanned by $\mathfrak{a}^*$, $\mathfrak{b}^*$ in the ring $K[[X; Y]]$. Hence (A, B) is an ordinary point of $V^r \times W^s$. From (13.10) follows that $X_1, \cdots, X_r, Y_1, \cdots, Y_s$ are local parameters for the point and so the same holds for the v_i and the w_j.

(13.11) *Remark.* One will compare the present characterization of non-singular points wholly independent of differentials with the characterization of (II, 21) in terms of differentials for characteristic zero. For the latter the prime ideal $\mathfrak{a}$ of V^r in $K[X]$ contains polynomials F_{r+i}, $i = 1, 2, \cdots, m - r$ such that

$$\frac{D(F_{r+1}, \cdots, F_m)}{D(X_{r+1}, \cdots, X_m)} \neq 0.$$

By the implicit function theorem the system

$$F_{r+i}(X) = 0, \quad i = 1, 2, \cdots, m - r$$

has then a unique solution for the X_{r+i} such as (13.1). Hence there is a unique branch $\mathfrak{B}^r$ of V^r centered at P and it is linear. Thus the earlier definition implies the present one. The converse also holds but is not so easily proved and we shall not stop to do so here.

§ 4. ALGEBRAIC VARIETIES AS TOPOLOGICAL SPACES

14. When the groundfield K is the complex field topology allied with analysis plays a fundamental role. In this direction there are very important modern investigations notably by W. D. Hodge, for which the reader is referred to his book [1]. For earlier contributions see also S. Lefschetz [1, 2]. We shall merely discuss here a few of the fundamental concepts closely related to power series representations.

We first define a *parametric n-cell* as an *n-cell* U^n (topological image of the open spherical region in Euclidean n-space) together with a topological mapping (parametrization) t of U^n into a spherical region of an Euclidean number space referred to coordinates $u_1, \cdots, u_n$ or *parameters* of the cell. A temporary convenient notation is (U^n, t, u_i). An *analytical n-manifold* is a connected space with a covering by parametric n-cells $\{(U^n_\alpha, t_\alpha, u_{\alpha i})\}$ with the following property: If x_0 is in both U^n_α and U^n_β, then the $u_{\alpha i}$ of the points of a certain neighborhood of x_0 are analytical functions of the corresponding $u_{\beta j}$ with non-vanishing Jacobian at x_0. From well known properties of the Jacobian follows that this condition is symmetrical in the two overlapping cells.

An analytical M^1 is known as an *analytical arc*. It is an analytical arc of M^n whenever the arc may be covered by parametric cells $(U^1_\lambda, t_\lambda, v_{\lambda j})$ each contained in a U^n_α and so that $v_{\lambda j}$ is one of the parameters $u_{\alpha i}$.

If the parameters $u_{\alpha i}$ can be chosen throughout so that the Jacobians of the definition of M^n have *constant* sign, then M^n is *orientable*; otherwise it is *non-orientable*.

Let n be even, say $n = 2m$ and let a *complex* parametric $2m$-cell V^m be now defined as the topological image of a spherical region in the space S^m of m complex variables $v_1, \cdots, v_m$. Except for this let manifolds be defined as before. The resulting structures are called *complex m*-manifolds written M^m_c.

Let $\{(V^m_\alpha, t_\alpha, v_{\alpha j})\}$ be the coverings which serve to define M^m_c and let

$v_{\alpha j} = v'_{\alpha j} + iv''_{\alpha j}$. Then t_α is a topological image of a spherical region of the Euclidean space of the variables $v'_{\alpha j}$, $v''_{\alpha j}$. The real Jacobians of these mappings are up to a constant factor

$$\left|\frac{D(v_{\alpha 1}, \cdots, v_{\alpha m})}{D(v_{\beta 1}, \cdots, v_{\beta m})}\right|^2 > 0.$$

Hence:

(14.1) *A complex m-manifold is a real analytical orientable 2m-manifold.*

Let us notice finally that:

(14.2) *If the manifolds are compact one may assume that the coverings are finite.*

For further information on all the concepts just developed the reader may consult the author's books [3] and [4].

15. Returning now to varieties let us merely observe that when the groundfield is complex, all the properties of power series discussed earlier in this chapter remain true even if one imposes the additional restriction that they have a positive radius of convergency.

A complex projective m-space S^m is the continuous image of a closed spherical region in an Euclidean $2m$-dimensional space and hence S^m is compact. Moreover S^m is arcwise connected: any two points may be joined by an arc (in this case a rectilinear segment). Finally it may certainly be covered by complex parametric $2m$-cells turning S^m into a complex m-manifold M_c^m. Its topology turns all the varieties of S^m into topological spaces under the topology induced by that of M_c^m. Let us now prove:

$(15.1)_r$ *An irreducible V^r of S^m is connected.*

Since K is algebraically closed an irreducible V^0 is a point so that $(15.1)_0$ holds. Now, referring to Picard [1], p. 429, $(15.1)_1$ holds: irreducible complex algebraic curves are connected. (His proof only given for plane curves is readily extended to curves in any space). Assuming now $(15.1)_{r-1}$, $r > 1$, we shall prove $(15.1)_r$. By (III, 20.1) one may find a hyperplane l which intersects V^r in an irreducible V^{r-1} which is therefore connected by $(15.1)_{r-1}$. If P is any point of V^r a hyperplane l' through P intersects V^r in a pure $r - 1$ dimensional variety one of whose components say V'^{r-1} contains P. Now V'^{r-1} is intersected by l in some point Q. Since V'^{r-1} is connected, P is in a connected set which meets the fixed connected set V^{r-1}. Hence V^r is connected.

Suppose now that V^r has no singularities. Referring to (13) every point of V^r is contained in a complex parametric $2r$-cell. The totality of these cells gives rise to a covering under which V^r becomes an M_c^r. It is also readily shown that V^r is a closed set. Since S^m is compact so is V^r. Hence:

(15.2) *A complex irreducible V^r without singularities is a compact complex r-manifold.*

V. *Algebraic Curves, Their Places and Transformations*

With the present chapter we take up the thorough study of algebraic curves. An intensive use of formal power series in one variable will enable us to carry over to the algebraic domain a large part of the technique and classical results of algebraic functions of a single complex variable. There are also noteworthy contacts with the theory of valuations whose importance, owing to the work of Zariski, is increasing by leaps and bounds in algebraic geometry.

For a more complete treatment of the subject matter of this and the next chapter, the reader is referred to the excellent book of R. J. Walker [2].

Hereafter the groundfield K is assumed to be *algebraically closed* and of *characteristic zero*.

§ 1. Formal Power Series in One and Two Variables

1. If $f(x,y)$ is an element of the power series ring $K[[x,y]]$ then

$$f(x, y) = x^a f_1(x, y), \quad a \geq o, \qquad f_1(0, y) \neq 0, \tag{1.1}$$

that is to say the series $f_1(x, y)$ is regular in y. The Weierstrass preparation theorem assumes therefore the form:

(1.2) *Whatever* $f(x, y) \in K[[x, y]]$ *we have*

$$f(x, y) \sim x^a(y^n + A_1(x)y^{n-1} + \cdots + A_n(x)) \tag{1.2a}$$

where the $A_i(x)$ *are non-units of* $K[[x]]$ *and* n *is the degree of* $f_1(x, y)$ *in* y *in* (1.1).

The special polynomial

$$g(x, y) = y^n + A_1(x)y^{n-1} + \cdots + A_n(x)$$

is an element of the integral domain $K[[x]][y]$. In this ring factorization to within units is unique. We have at once:

(1.3) *The factors of a special polynomial* $g(x, y)$ *are equivalent to special polynomials.*

By combining with (1.1) we find:

(1.4) *A finite system of relations*

$$f_1(x, y) = 0, \cdots, f_p(x, y) = 0, \quad f_h \in K[[x,y]]$$

is equivalent to a single relation

$$x^a g(x, y) = 0$$

where g is a special polynomial in y.

2. Formal power series in one variable present a shift of emphasis from rings to fields. For while no simplification is possible for a quotient of series in two or more variables, this is not at all the cases for quotients of series in one variable. Indeed a quotient of two elements of $K[[x]]$ may be written

$$\frac{f(x)}{g(x)} = \frac{x^p E_1(x)}{x^q E_2(x)} = x^r E(x)$$

where r may well be negative. Thus rather than mere series in non-negative powers, we are led here naturally to consider series of the form

(2.1) $$f(x) = a_{-h}x^{-h} + a_{-h+1}x^{-h+1} + \cdots, a_i \in K$$

with the obvious laws of combination. The natural collection which they form is the field $K((x))$ and it comes at once to the fore.

Consider now the algebraic extension $K(x, y)$ of $K(x)$ by the solution y of $y^n - x = 0$. Instead of y we write as usual $x^{1/n}$ and thus also $K((x^{1/n}))$ for $K((y))$. Thus $K((x^{1/n}))$ is the field of all the formal power series in $x^{1/n}$ with coefficients in K. Let $K\{x\}$ denote the union of all the fields $K((x^{1/n}))$ for $n = 1, 2, \cdots$. Let $y, y' \in K\{x\}$, say $y \in K((x^{1/n}))$, $y' \in K((x^{1/n'}))$. Then both are in $K((x^{1/nn'}))$ and there follow definitions for zero, $y + y'$, yy', y/y' in the obvious way and readily shown to be unique. Hence $K\{x\}$ is again a field over K and since it contains K it is also of characteristic zero.

(2.2) *Differentials.* Let dx be an indeterminate. Then if $u \in K\{x\}$, where

$$u = a_p x^{p/n} + a_{p+1}x^{(p+1)/n} + \cdots$$

we define its differential in the natural way and show that these differentials behave throughout $K\{x\}$ in the usual manner.

§ 2. Puiseux's Theorem

3. This is the central proposition regarding formal power series in one variable. Its statement is:

(3.1) **Theorem.** *The field $K\{x\}$ is algebraically closed.*

Let $f(x, y) \in K\{x\}[y]$, that is to say

$$f(x, y) = A_0(x)y^n + A_1(x)y^{n-1} + \cdots + A_n(x)$$

where the $A_i(x)$ are elements of $K\{x\}$ i.e. fractional power series in x. The theorem asserts that

$$f(x, y) = A_0(x)\prod_{i=1}^{n}(y - y_i(x)),$$

where the $y_i(x)$ are likewise fractional power series in x. By a classical argument all that is necessary is to prove that $f(x, y)$ has a root in y which is in $K\{x\}$. In carrying out the proof there is no restriction in assuming that: (a) the $A_i(x)$ have no negative exponents; (b) $A_0(x) = 1$; (c) the $A_i(x)$ are integral power series in x. The assertion as to (a) is obvious, and as regards (b) and (c), they may always be achieved by a suitable transformation $y \to y/A_0(x)$, $x \to x^p$.

We may then take

$$(3.2) \qquad f(x, y) = y^n + A_1(x)y^{n-1} + \cdots + A_n(x),\ A_i(x) \in K[[x]].$$

It is clear that Puiseux's theorem will follow if we can prove:

(3.3) *With f as in* (3.2) *if $f(0, a) = 0$ then $f(x, y)$ has a root $y_1(x) \in K\{x\}$ such that $y_1(0) = a$.*

Upon making the change of variables $y \to y + a$, the situation will be as before save that $a = 0$. Thus (3.3) will be reduced to

$(3.4)_n$ *With f as in* (3.2) *if $f(0, 0) = 0$ then $f(x, y) = 0$ has a root $y_1(x) \in K\{x\}$ such that $y_1(0) = 0$.*

This is the property which we shall now prove. Since $(3.4)_1$ is obviously true we assume $(3.4)_k$ for every $k < n$ and prove $(3.4)_n$. Moreover if $A_n(x) = 0$, $(3.4)_n$ holds and so we assume $A_n(x) \neq 0$.

We are seeking then a solution of the form

$$(3.5) \qquad y = tx^{\mu} + t_1x^{\mu+\mu_1} + t_2x^{\mu+\mu_1+\mu_2} + \cdots,$$

where $t, t_1, \cdots, \in K$ and are $\neq 0$, and the exponents $\mu, \mu_1, \cdots$, are positive fractions with the same denominator. Let

$$(3.6) \qquad y = x^{\mu}y', \qquad y' = t + t_1x^{\mu_1} + \cdots,$$

$$f(x,y) = \Sigma C_{\alpha\beta}x^{\alpha}y^{\beta}, \quad C_{\alpha\beta} \in K,$$

where the least β is zero and the greatest is n.

If (3.5) is to be a solution upon substituting y from it in $f(x, y)$ the lowest degree terms in x must cancel in

$$(3.7) \qquad f(x, tx^{\mu}) = \Sigma C_{\alpha\beta}t^{\beta}x^{\alpha+\mu\beta}.$$

Let us mark in a cartesian plane the points $M(\alpha, \beta)$. The lowest degree terms in (3.7) correspond to the points M on some line l: $x + \mu y = \nu$ such that no point M is below l. Moreover to have some cancellation of terms l must contain at least two of the points. This leads to the classical *Newton polygon* (Fig. 1). This is a polygonal line resting upon the two axes, concave towards the origin, whose vertices are points M and such that no such points are below it. The condition that the line l must satisfy is merely to be one of the sides of the polygon. Let us choose for l the side QR of the figure. If (γ_i, δ_i) are the vertices on QR we will have

$$f(x, tx^{\mu}) = x^{\nu}\{g(t)t^{\delta_0} + x^{\varepsilon}h(x, t)\},$$

$$g(t) = \Sigma C_{\gamma_i\delta_i}t^{\delta_i-\delta_0},$$

where δ_0 is the least δ_i. It is clear that

$$\text{I. } g(0) \neq 0; \qquad \text{II. } \delta_0 \leq n.$$

Moreover if (γ_1, δ_1) and (γ_2, δ_2) are any two vertices on QR then

$$\gamma_1 + \mu\delta_1 = \gamma_2 + \mu\delta_2,$$

hence

$$\mu = -\frac{\gamma_1 - \gamma_2}{\delta_1 - \delta_2} = \frac{p}{q},$$

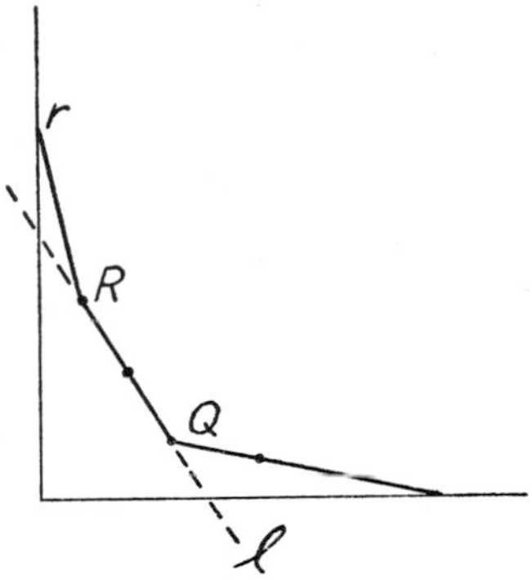

FIG. 1

where the last fraction is merely μ reduced to its simplest expression. It follows that $\delta_1 - \delta_2 = 0 \bmod q$. Hence in particular

$$g(t) = g_1(t^q) \in K[t^q].$$

We must now choose for t a root of $g(t) = 0$ and by I it is $\neq 0$. Making the substitution $y = x^\mu(t + y_1)$ and replacing x by x^q we find

$$\begin{aligned} x^{-\nu q} f(x^q, x^{\mu q}(t + y_1)) &= f_1(x, y_1) \\ &= (y_1 + t)^{\delta_0} g(y_1 + t) + x^{\varepsilon q} h(x^q, y_1 + t). \end{aligned}$$

To find the exponent μ_1 one must deal with f_1 as previously with f. There are now two possibilities:

Case I. $g(t) \neq c(t - b)^n$. Then $f_1 \in K[[x, y_1]]$ and the least degree n_1 of a term in y_1 alone in f_1 is certainly $< n$. By the preparation theorem $f_1 \sim f_1^*(x, y_1)$ where f_1^* is a special polynomial of degree n_1 in y_1. Hence by $(3.4)_{n_1}$, $f_1^* = 0$ has a solution $y_1 \in K\{x\}$ such that $y_1(0) = 0$ and this implies $(3.4)_n$.

Case II. $g(t) = c(t - b)^n$. Then $q = 1$ and so μ is an integer. Upon treating f_1 like f, etc., either: (a) we only have case II throughout, so that the μ_i are all integers and a root $y(x)$ is obtained in $K[[x]]$, yielding $(3.4)_n$, or else (b) at some stage case I occurs and $(3.4)_n$ holds once more. This completes the proof of (3.4) and hence of the theorem.

4. We shall now consider a certain number of special cases required later. At the outset let

$$f(x, y) = A_0 + A_1 y + \cdots + A_n y^n$$

where $A_i \in K\{(x-a)\}$ and has no negative powers. One may then write the Taylor expansion

$$f(x, y) = B_0 + B_1(y-b) + \cdots + B_n(y-b)^n,$$

where the B_k behave like the A_k. One must also bear in mind that $f(a, y)$ has the k-tuple root $y = b$ when and only when $B_h(a) = 0$ for $h < k$ and $B_k(a) \neq 0$.

(4.1) *If $f(a, y)$ has b for k-tuple root then $f(x, y) = 0$ has exactly k solutions in y which are in $K\{(x-a)\}$ and whose series begin with b. Hence if $A_n(a) \neq 0$, all the n solutions of $f(x, y) = 0$ which are in $K\{(x-a)\}$ are of non-negative order.*

Setting $f = f((x-a)+a, (y-b)+b)$ and referring to (3.3) there is one root $y_1(x) \in K\{(x-a)\}$ such that $y_1(a) = b$. Then $f_1 = f/(y - y_1(x))$ behaves like f with $k-1$ in place of k. The proof is then completed by an obvious induction.

(4.2) *Let the coefficients B_j all be in $K[[(x-a)]]$ and let $f(a, b) = 0$, $f_b \neq 0$. Then by (4.1) $f(x, y) = 0$ has a single solution $y_1(x) \in K\{(x-a)\}$ such that $y_1(a) = b$. This solution is actually in $K[[(x-a)]]$ and is merely the usual Taylor expansion of $y(x)$ such that $f(x, y) = 0$, $y(a) = b$.*

By direct substitution of a series $y = b + \alpha_0(x-a) + \alpha_1(x-a)^2 + \cdots$, in $f(x, y) = 0$, it is found that the coefficients $\alpha_0, \alpha_1, \cdots$, can be calculated uniquely one at a time and these coefficients turn out to be those of the Taylor series.

(4.3) *The equation $x - a = (y-b)E(y-b)$ has a unique solution $y - b = (x-a)E_1(x-a)$ in $K[[(x-a)]]$. (Implicit function theorem for one variable.)*

(4.4) *The equation $(y-b)^n = E(x-a)$ has n distinct solutions in $K[[(x-a)]]$ and they are all units. If one of them is $E_1(x-a)$ then all the others are represented by $\eta^r E_1(x-a)$, $r = 1, 2, \cdots, n-1$, where η is a primitive n^{th} root of unity in K.*

(4.5) *The equation $(y-b)^n = (x-a)^n E(x-a)$ has n distinct solutions in $K[[(x-a)]]$ such that $y(a) = b$.*

Setting $y - b = z(x-a)$, hence $z^n = E(x-a)$ and applying (4.4) yields (4.5).

(4.6) *The equation $(y-b) = (x-a)^n E(x-a)$ has in $K\{(y-b)\}$ the n solutions*

$$(x-a) = \eta^r (y-b)^{1/n} E_1(\eta^r (y-b)^{1/n})$$

where η is a primitive n-th root of unity in K.

Setting $y - b = t^n$, hence $t = \eta^r(y-b)$ and applying (4.5) the required result follows.

(4.7) *If* $f(x, y) \in K[x, y]$ *is irreducible the equation in* y: $f(x, y) = 0$ *has no multiple roots in* $K\{x\}$.

Suppose that there is a multiple root $\alpha(x) \in K\{x\}$. Then $\alpha(x)$ is also a root of $f_y(x, y) = 0$. Hence f and f_y have a common factor $y - \alpha(x) \in K\{x\}[y]$. By applying Euclid's algorithm if f and f_y have a common factor it is in $K(x)[y]$. Now we may assume that the degree m of f in $y > 1$ and f_y is of degree $m - 1$ in y. Hence the common factor would have to be of smaller degree than m in y and consequently f would be reducible in $K(x)[y]$, hence also in $K[x, y]$, contrary to assumption. Hence (4.6) holds.

5. Application to the complex field. Let the groundfield K be the complex field and let

$$f(x, y) = A_0(x)y^m + A_1(x)y^{m-1} + \cdots + A_m(x)$$

be a polynomial in y with coefficients $A_i(x)$ analytic and holomorphic at $x = \alpha$ and $A_0(\alpha) \neq 0$. It is then known from function theory that there are m roots $y_i(x)$, $i = 1, 2, \cdots, m$ analytic in x in the neighborhood of α and tending to the m roots $\beta_1, \cdots, \beta_m$ of $f(\alpha, y) = 0$ as $x \to \alpha$. Moreover as x describes a small circle around the value α, the $y_i(x)$ are distributed into circular systems of the following nature: if the notations are properly chosen then $\{y_1, \cdots, y_n\}$ will be one of the circular systems and its elements undergo a cyclic permutation as x turns once around α. Furthermore as $x \to \alpha$ the $y_i(x)$, $i = 1, 2, \cdots, n$ tend to the same β_j say β_1. It follows that the y_i of the cyclic system are holomorphic functions of $(x - \alpha)^{1/n}$ in the neighborhood of α, and hence

$$y_i(x) = \beta_1 + \Sigma\gamma_j[\omega^i(x - \alpha)]^{j/n}, \quad \omega^i = e^{2\pi i/n},$$

where the series is convergent for small $x - \alpha$. Thus the m roots $y_i(x)$ are represented by m convergent fractional power series in $x - \alpha$ for x near α. Since this is precisely the number of formal power series solutions known to exist from Puiseux's theorem, we conclude that the Puiseux's series represent actual analytic solutions.

If $A_0(\alpha) = 0$ and α is say a root of multiplicity k then we would replace y by $y^* = y/(x - \alpha)^k$ and proceed as before. We may thus state:

(5.1) *When the groundfield is the complex field the Puiseux series solutions represent analytic solutions.*

Application. Let

$$f(x, y) = ax + by + \cdots, \; b \neq 0,$$

where all the coefficients are real. As we have seen the unique solution $y(x)$ of $f(x, y) = 0$ which $\to 0$ with x is given by the McLaurin expansion calculated in the customary way and whose coefficients are now all real. Thus the solutions of $f = 0$ near the origin are all given by a real power series

$$y = \alpha x + \beta x^2 + \cdots$$

convergent in a certain vicinity of the origin. That is to say on the real curve $f(x, y) = 0$ the origin has an analytic arc for neighborhood. This will hold of course if $A(a, b)$ is any point of the curve such that $f_y \neq 0$. The expansion will then express $y - b$ in powers of $x - a$.

Notice that the situation is the same in the complex domain save that the neighborhoods are now 2-cells (simply connected regions).

§ 3. THE PLACES OF AN ALGEBRAIC CURVE

6. Let $f(x)$ be an irreducible algebraic curve of degree m in KP^2 and $A(\alpha)$ any point of the curve. Choose the coordinates such that f is regular in x_2 and that $\alpha_0 \neq 0$. Upon passing to affine coordinates we have a curve $F(X, Y)$ where F is of degree m and contains a term in Y^m. The point A is now in KA^2 and has coordinates written (b, c). In particular $F(b, Y) = 0$ has finite roots, one of which is c. By reference to (3.3) $F(X, Y) = 0$ has a certain number of solutions

$$(6.1) \qquad Y = c + \Sigma c_j (X - b)^{n_j/n}, \qquad 0 < n,\ 0 < n_1 < n_2 < \cdots,$$

where $n, n_1, \cdots,$ have no common factor. Setting $X - b = t^n$ we may say that the pair of expressions

$$(6.2) \qquad X = b + t^n, \qquad Y = c + \Sigma c_j t^{n_j}$$

are the coordinates of a point M_t of f depending upon the indeterminate t. Since transc $X =$ transc $t = 1$, M_t is a general point of the curve. The projective coordinates of M_t are given by

$$(6.3) \qquad \rho x_0 = 1, \quad \rho x_1 = b + t^n, \quad \rho x_2 = c + \Sigma c_j t^{n_j}.$$

7. The result just obtained suggests that we consider general points of f with coordinates in the integral power series field $K[[t]]$. Such a point M_t will have coordinates x_i given by a system

$$(7.1) \quad \rho x_i = a_i + \Sigma a_{ij} t^{n_j};\ i = 0, 1, 2;\ 0 < n_1 < n_2 < \cdots;\ a_i, a_{ij} \in K.$$

It is manifestly no restriction to assume that the a_i are not all zero. Thus $A(a_0, a_1, a_2)$ is a point of KP^2. As a matter of fact

$$f(\rho x_0(t), \quad \rho x_1(t), \quad \rho x_2(t)) = 0 = t^{ms}(f(a_0, a_1, a_2) + \alpha_1 t + \cdots).$$

Since all the terms of the series at the right must vanish $f(a_0, a_1, a_2) = 0$ so that A is a point of the curve.

Since M_t is a general point of f we have:

(7.2) *A n.a.s.c. for a curve g to contain f is that $g(t) = g(x(t)) = 0$.*

From analytical considerations we are justified in considering as *equivalent* two points M_t, $M_{t'}$ such that the representation analagous to (7.1) for $M_{t'}$ is derived from (7.1) by a regular transformation $t = t'E(t')$. Since these transformations form a group we have here a true relation of equivalence. We will also say that the representations corresponding to M_t, $M_{t'}$ are *equivalent*. A class π of equivalent representations is known as a *place* of the curve f. The point A is the same for all equivalent representations of a given place, and is referred to as the *center* of the place.

We shall now reverse the procedure and go back from (7.1) to (6.3). We will suppose the coordinates so chosen that f is not a line through one of the vertices of the triangle of reference and that furthermore $a_0 \neq 0$. Since $x_0(t)$ is then a unit we may divide the $x_i(t)$ by it and thus replace (7.1) by a representation

$$(7.3) \qquad \rho x_0 = 1, \ \rho x_1 = b + t^m E(t), \quad \rho x_2 = c + t^{m'} E_1(t),$$

where $m, m' > 0$. By (4.4) we can write $E(t) = E_2^m(t)$. Then by (4.3) if τ is a new indeterminate the relation $\tau = tE_2(t)$ has a solution $t = \tau E_3(\tau)$. Substituting in (7.3) and writing t for τ we obtain a representation equivalent to (7.3)

$$(7.4) \qquad \rho x_0 = 1, \quad \rho x_1 = b + t^{nd}, \quad \rho x_2 = c + \Sigma c_j t^{n_j d}.$$

Here $n, n_1, \cdots$ are all positive and have no common factor. If we had permuted the role of x_0 and x_1 or x_2 we would have arrived at a similar representation with some of the coordinates permuted. Any one of these is known as a *normal* representation.

Whenever $d = 1$, i.e. all the exponents in a normal representation are relatively prime, we say that the representation is *irreducible*, otherwise that it is *reducible*. Any representation is said to be *reducible* [*irreducible*] if it is equivalent to a normal reducible [irreducible] representation.

From the representation (7.4) for π we deduce the normal irreducible representation (6.3). The place π' which it defines still has the same center A as π and we agree to identify π' with π. Thus:

(7.5) *Every place has a normal irreducible representation. Moreover, the passage from a normal irreducible to a normal reducible representation is by an operation* $t \to t^d$. *The number* d *is then the H.C.F. of the exponents in the normal reducible representation.*

(7.6) By a *parameter for a place* π we shall mean, unless otherwise stated, a parameter in an irreducible representation for π.

8. A notion of fundamental importance in relation to the places is that of the *order* of an element R of the function field K^f at a place π. Let π be taken in the irreducible representation (6.3). Then

$$R(t) = R(x_0(t), x_1(t), x_2(t)) = t^\omega E(t).$$

Evidently $\omega = \omega(R, \pi)$ is not affected by passing to an equivalent representation for π. It depends then solely upon π and R, and $\omega(R, \pi)$ is precisely the order of R at the place π.

(8.1) *There is an element* R *of* K^f *whose order* $\omega(R, \pi)$ *is unity and hence an element, for instance* R^k, *whose order has any preassigned integral value* k.

Let α be the least positive order for any $R \in K^f$ and let S be of order α. We must show that $\alpha = 1$.

At all events if $T \in K^f$ is of order β and if γ is the H.C.F. of α and β, there exist integers p, q such that $p\alpha + q\beta = \gamma$. Hence $\omega(S^pT^q) = \gamma \leq \alpha$. Since $\alpha \leq \gamma$, the two are equal and so α divides β. Thus α divides every $\omega(R)$. Since $\dfrac{x_1}{x_0} - b \in K^f$, n in (6.3) is divisible by α: $n = m\alpha$.

Suppose now $\alpha > 1$. Since the representation (6.3) is irreducible the n_i are not all divisible by α. Thus there exist elements of K^f, such as $\dfrac{x_2}{x_0} - c$, in whose t series the exponents are all positive but not all divisible by α. Let z be such an element. The first exponent in $z(t)$ is $\omega(z)$ and is divisible by α. Hence

$$z(t) = a_1t^{m_1\alpha} + \cdots + a_kt^{m_k\alpha} + t^q(b_0 + b_1t + \cdots)$$
$$a_i,\ b_i \in K; \qquad a_1b_0 \neq 0; \qquad q > m_k\alpha.$$

Let $\rho(z) = q - m_1\alpha > 0$. Among all functions such as $z(t)$ let z be one for which $\rho(z)$ assumes its least value. Then z^m is of the type of z. Its order is $mm_1\alpha$ and in its series the lowest exponent not divisible by α is the exponent of $(t^{m_1\alpha})^{m-1} \cdot t^q$ or $m_1\alpha(m-1) + q$. Hence $\rho(z^m) = \rho(z)$. On the other hand the first term in the series for z^m is

$$a_1^m t^{m_1 m\alpha} = a_1^m\left(\frac{x_1}{x_0} - b\right)^{m_1}.$$

Hence

$$z^m - a_1^m\left(\frac{x_1}{x_0} - b\right)^{m_1} \in K^f$$

is of positive order and

$$\rho\left(z^m - a_1^m\left(\frac{x_1}{x_0} - b\right)^{m_1}\right) < \rho(z^m) = \rho(z).$$

Since this contradicts the assumption that $\rho(z)$ is minimum, we must have $\alpha = 1$ and property (8.1) follows.

(8.2) Suppose that instead of the normal irreducible representation (6.3) we had taken the reducible one (7.4). There would result orders $\omega'(R) = d\omega(R)$. Thus d is the H.C.F. of the orders $\omega'(R)$ calculated from a reducible normal representation whose exponents have likewise d as their H.C.F. Or expressed in another way, a representation is irreducible when and only when the related orders of the rational functions have no common factor.

An immediate consequence is the following :

(8.3) *All the irreducible representations of a given place π are equivalent.*

For suppose that π has the irreducible representation (6.3), and that say $b \neq 0$ allows for its reduction for instance to the equivalent form

(8.4) $$\sigma x_0 = a' + t^{n'd}, \quad \sigma x_1 = 1, \quad \sigma x_2 = c' + \Sigma c'_i t^{n'_i d},$$

where $n', n'_1, \cdots$, have no common factor. Then d divides all the orders of the rational functions. As a consequence $d = 1$, and (8.4) is an irreducible representation.

We may state with more precision:

(8.5) *All the irreducible representations of* π *in the form* (6.3) *are given by*

(8.5a) $$\rho x_0 = 1, \quad \rho x_1 = b + (\eta^r t)^n, \quad \rho x_2 = c + \Sigma c_i(\eta^r t)^{n_i},$$

where η *is a primitive nth root of unity in* K.

Let a second representation in the form (6.3) be

(8.6) $$\sigma x_0 = 1, \quad \sigma x_1 = b + t^{n'}, \quad \sigma x_2 = c + \Sigma c'_i t^{n'_i}.$$

One must be able to pass from (6.3) to (8.6) by a regular transformation $t \to tE(t)$. Hence $t^{n'} = t^n E^n(t)$. As a consequence $n' = n$, $E(t) = \eta^r$ and (8.5) follows.

Upon the notion of order one may base the following fundamental property:

(8.7) **Theorem.** *A birational transformation* T *of a curve* f *into a curve* g *establishes a one-one correspondence between their places.*

Let f be the same curve as before and let g be in KP^2_y. Let the place π of f have the representation (7.1) which is now assumed to be irreducible. Through this representation the function field $K^f = K^g$ is imbedded isomorphically as a subfield $\mathfrak{F}$ of $K((t))$. As a consequence the elements of K^g determined by y_1/y_0, y_2/y_0 are identified with elements of $\mathfrak{F}$, i.e. of $K((t))$. This gives rise to relations

(8.8) $$\sigma y_i = \alpha_i + \Sigma \alpha_{ij} t^{m_j}; \qquad \alpha_i, \alpha_{ij} \in K,$$

representing a place π^* of g determined from π through T. The representation (8.8) is irreducible since it maps K^g also isomorphically onto $\mathfrak{F}$ and assigns to its elements the same relatively prime orders as (7.1) for π. Furthermore it is an elementary matter to show that upon replacing (7.1) by an equivalent representation the same hold for (8.8) and π^*. Thus π^* is uniquely determined by π and we write $\pi^* = T\pi$. Since the process is manifestly reversible $\pi = T^{-1}\pi^*$ and (8.7) follows.

9. Let us say a few words regarding the so-called "field-values" at the place π. If $R \in K^f$ and

$$R(t) = t^s(\alpha + \beta t + \cdots)$$

then the field-value $\varphi(R, \pi)$ is an element of $K + \infty$ defined as follows: $\varphi(R, \pi) = 0$ when $s > 0$; $\varphi(R, \pi) = \infty$ when $s < 0$; $\varphi(R, \pi) = \alpha$ when $s = 0$. If $s \geq 0$ one may calculate $R(A)$ and one finds: $R(A) = R(x_0(0), x_1(0), x_2(0)) = (R(t))_{t=0} = \varphi(R, \pi)$. Thus whenever the field-value at the center may be calculated it is the same as at the place.

However, for instance when A happens to be a center of several places $\pi_1, \cdots, \pi_s$, the field-values $\varphi(R, \pi_i)$ may well be distinct.

§ 4. VALUATIONS

10. A new light is thrown upon the notion of order in relation to the theory of valuations.

The order $\omega(R)$ of R at π has the following properties:

I. *$\omega(R)$ is an integer or zero or ∞.*

II. *$\omega(R) = \infty$ when and only when $R = 0$.*

III. $\omega(RS) = \omega(R) + \omega(S)$.

IV. *$\omega(R) = 0$ when $R \in K - 0$.*

V. $\omega(R + S) \geq \min \{\omega(R), \omega(S)\}$.

VI. *$\omega(R)$ takes all integral values together with zero and infinity.*

The first five properties are immediate and VI is a consequence of (8.1) and II, IV. Note also that III and IV imply together:

VII. $\omega(R^{-1}) = -\omega(R)$; $\quad \omega(R/S) = \omega(R) - \omega(S)$.

It is a consequence of properties $I, \cdots, V$ that the operation $\mathfrak{V}(\pi)$ on the elements of K^f such that $\mathfrak{V}(\pi)R = \omega(R)$ is a so-called non-archimedean valuation of K^f (see van der Waerden [1] I, pp. 245–248). Property VI states that $\mathfrak{V}(\pi)$ maps K^f onto the additive group of the integers plus infinity.

In the sequel "valuation" will merely refer to those just described.

(10.1) **Theorem.** *There is a one-one correspondence between the set $\Pi = \{\pi\}$ of the places and the set $\mathfrak{W} = \{\mathfrak{V}\}$ of the valuations $\mathfrak{V}$ of K^f.*

Since a birational transformation $f \rightarrow g$ causes an identification of their function fields (10.1) yields, in an obvious way, another proof of (8.7).

To prove Theorem (10.1) it will be sufficient to establish the following two results:

(10.2) *Given any valuation $\mathfrak{V}$ there is a place π of f such that $\mathfrak{V} = \mathfrak{V}(\pi)$.*

(10.3) If $\pi \neq \pi'$ then $\mathfrak{V}(\pi) \neq \mathfrak{V}(\pi')$.

This last property will follow in turn from:

(10.4) *If $\pi \neq \pi'$ there exists an $R \in K^f$ such that $\omega(R, \pi) \neq \omega(R, \pi')$.*

Thus the proof of the theorem reduces to establishing (10.2) and (10.4). At the same time as (10.4) we shall obtain:

(10.5) *If $\pi \neq \pi'$ there exists an $R \in K^f$ such that its field-values at π and π' are distinct.*

If $R \in K^f$ then $\omega(R, \pi) = \mathfrak{V}(\pi)R$. Hence:

(10.6) *$\omega(R, \pi)$ is birationally invariant.*

11. We begin with the proof of (10.2), the most difficult part of our work. It rests upon:

(11.1) **Lemma.** *If $R \in K^f$ is such that $\mathfrak{V}(R) \geq 0$ then there is a unique element $\alpha \in K$ such that $\mathfrak{V}(R - \alpha) > 0$.*

If $R \in K$ the assertion is trivial. We suppose then that R is not in K. By property VI there is an element $t \in K^f$, certainly not in K, such that $\mathfrak{V}(t) = 1$. Since R is also transcendental, t satisfies a relation

$$a_0(R)t^n + a_1(R)t^{n-1} + \cdots + a_n(R) = 0,$$

where $a_i(R) \in K[R]$ and $a_0(R)a_n(R) \neq 0$.

A repeated application of property V yields now

$$\mathfrak{V}(a_n(R)) \geq \min\{\mathfrak{V}(a_i(R)) + n - i\},\ i < n.$$

On the other hand if

$$a_i(R) = \Sigma a_{ij} R^j, \quad a_{ij} \in K,$$

then since $\mathfrak{V}(R) \geq 0$ we have

$$\mathfrak{V}(a_i(R)) \geq \min\{\mathfrak{V}(a_{ij}R^j)\} = \min\ \{\mathfrak{V}(R^j)\} \geq 0.$$

Consequently $\mathfrak{V}(a_n(R)) > 0$. Since the groundfield K is algebraically closed, $a_n(x)$ is completely factorable in linear factors. Hence

$$a_n(R) = \beta\Pi(R - \beta_h), \quad \beta \in K - 0, \quad \beta_h \in K.$$

Hence

$$0 < \mathfrak{V}(a_n(R)) = \Sigma\mathfrak{V}(R - \beta_h).$$

Therefore for some h: $\mathfrak{V}(R - \beta_h) > 0$. Thus at least one $\alpha \in K$ exists such that $\mathfrak{V}(R - \alpha) > 0$. If likewise $\mathfrak{V}(R - \alpha') > 0$, $\alpha' \in K$ then by V:

$$\mathfrak{V}(\alpha' - \alpha) = \mathfrak{V}((R - \alpha) - (R - \alpha')) > 0$$

and hence by IV: $\alpha' - \alpha = 0$. Thus α is unique and the lemma follows.

Take now any $R \in K^f - 0$ and let $\mathfrak{V}(R) = r$. Then $\mathfrak{V}(t^{-r}R) = 0$ and hence there is a unique $\alpha_r \in K$ such that $\mathfrak{V}(t^{-r}R - \alpha_r) > 0$ or equivalently such that $\mathfrak{V}(R - \alpha_r t^r) > r$. Suppose that there has been found

(11.2) $$\rho_k(R) = \alpha_r t^r + \alpha_{r+1}t^{r+1} + \cdots + \alpha_k t^k$$

such that

(11.3)$_k$ $$\mathfrak{V}(R - \rho_k) > k.$$

Then $\mathfrak{V}(t^{-k-1}(R - \rho_k)) \geq 0$ and hence there is a unique α_{k+1} such that if $\rho_{k+1} = \rho_k + \alpha_{k+1}t^{k+1}$ then (11.3)$_{k+1}$ holds. We thus obtain a unique formal power series

(11.4) $$\rho(R) = \alpha_r t^r + \alpha_{r+1}t^{r+1} + \cdots$$

such that if $\rho_k(R)$ is given by (11.2) then (11.3)$_k$ holds for every $k \geq r = \mathfrak{V}(R)$. If we define $\rho_k(R) = 0$ for $k < r$ then (11.3)$_k$ will hold for every k.

(11.5) *The operation $\rho(R)$ on the elements of the function field K^f is an isomorphic imbedding of K^f preserving K, into the field of integral power series $K((t))$.*

Let R, $S \in K^f$ and $\alpha \in K$. Then we have at once:

(a) $$\rho(\alpha) = \alpha, \text{ i.e. } \rho \text{ preserves } K;$$

(b) $$\rho(R) = 0 \text{ implies that } R = 0.$$

The following three properties are to be established by showing that in each case the appropriate relation $(11.3)_k$ holds

(c) $$\rho(t^h R) = t^h \rho(R).$$

(d) $$\rho(R - S) = \rho(R) - \rho(S).$$

(e) $$\rho(RS) = \rho(R)\rho(S).$$

Proof of (c). From $(11.3)_k$ for R follows $\mathfrak{B}(t^h R - t^h \rho_k(R)) > h + k$ for every h and this implies (c), since $\rho_{k+h}(t^h R) = t^h \rho_k(R)$.

Proof of (d). We have at once

$$\rho_k(R - S) = \rho_k(R) - \rho_k(S)$$

and hence

$$\mathfrak{B}(R - S - \rho_k(R - S)) \geq \min \{\mathfrak{B}(R - \rho_k(R)),\quad \mathfrak{B}(S - \rho_k(S))\} > k,$$

which is $(11.3)_k$ in the present instance and so (d) holds.

Proof of (e). If $\mathfrak{B}(R) = r$ then $\mathfrak{B}(t^{-r} R) = 0$. In view of (c) one may replace in the proof of (e), R by $t^{-r}R$, hence assume $\mathfrak{B}(R) = 0$, and similarly $\mathfrak{B}(S) = 0$. Under the circumstances:

$$\sigma = \rho(R)\rho(S) = \gamma_0 + \gamma_1 t + \cdots.$$

Let us set

$$\sigma_k = \gamma_0 + \gamma_1 t + \cdots + \gamma_k t^k.$$

The proof of (e) reduces to showing that for every $k \geq 0$ we have

(11.6) $$\mathfrak{B}(RS - \sigma_k) > k.$$

We have at once

$$\begin{aligned} RS - \sigma_k &= RS - \rho_k(R)\rho_k(S) + t^{k+1}(\delta_0 + \delta_1 t + \cdots \delta_e t^e) \\ &= S(R - \rho_k(R)) + \rho_k(R)(S - \rho_k(S)) + t^{k+1}(\delta_0 + \cdots + \delta_e t^e) \end{aligned}$$

where $\delta_i \in K$. Since $\mathfrak{B}(S)$, $\mathfrak{B}(\rho_k(R)) \geq 0$ and $\mathfrak{B}(t^{k+1}(\delta_0 + \cdots)) \geq k + 1$, we find

$$\mathfrak{B}(RS - \sigma_k) \geq \min \{\mathfrak{B}(R - \rho_k(R)),\quad \mathfrak{B}(S - \rho_k(S)),\quad k + 1\} > k$$

which is (11.6), and so (e) holds.

From (e) follows now with R/S in place of R:

(f) $$\rho(R/S) = \rho(R)/\rho(S).$$

As a consequence of properties (d), (f), $\mathfrak{F} = \{\rho(R)\}$ is a subfield of $K((t))$. In view of (b), (*d*): $\rho(R) = \rho(S)$ implies $R = S$. In other words ρ establishes a one-one correspondence between the fields K^f and $\mathfrak{F}$. By (d), (f), ρ is an isomorphism and since it preserves K, (11.5) is proved.

Let now each element of K^f be identified with its image under ρ. In particular the elements of K^f determined by $X = x_1/x_0$, $Y = x_2/x_0$

will form a rational base for K^f. That is to say we will be able to write a system of relations

$$\text{(g)} \qquad \sigma x_0 = \Sigma a_i t^i, \quad \sigma x_1 = \Sigma b_i t^i, \quad \sigma x_2 = \Sigma c_i t^i$$

such that if $R(x_0, x_1, x_2) \in K_H(x)$ and we substitute in R the $x_i(t)$ for the x_i, then $R(t) = \rho(R)$. This means that (g) represents a place π of the curve f. Since the order $\omega(R) = \mathfrak{B}(R)$ and for some R: $\mathfrak{B}(R) = 1$, the representation is irreducible. Hence $\mathfrak{B}(R) = \omega(R, \pi)$. This proves (10.2).

12. We shall now prove jointly (10.4) and (10.5): distinct places π, π' have distinct valuations and do not always assign the same field values to each rational function.

Let us dispose at once of the case of distinct centers A, A' for π, π'. Let affine coordinates be chosen with both points in the affine plane. If $l = aX + bY + c$ is a line through A but not through A' then l defines an element $R \in K^f$ whose order is at least one at A and zero at A' and whose value is zero at A and $\neq 0$ at A'. Thus for both (10.4) and (10.5) we may suppose that π, π' have the same center A and we take A as affine origin. Let θ be an element of K^f of order one at π. If t is a parameter for π, we will have $\theta = tE(t)$. Let n be the order of θ at π'. If $n < 0$, one may replace θ by $\dfrac{\theta}{1+\theta}$ whose order at π is still one and whose order at π' is zero. Writing then t for θ we may suppose that $t \in K^f$ and that its order at π' is $n \geq 0$. Similarly we may choose a $t' \in K^f$ for π' whose order is unity at π' and $n' \geq 0$ at π.

Suppose first that say $n > 1$. Then $R = t'^n/t$ is of order $nn' - 1 > 0$ at π, and zero at π'. Hence $\mathfrak{B}(\pi) \neq \mathfrak{B}(\pi')$. Moreover the values of R are: zero at π and $\neq 0$ at π' and therefore distinct. This disposes of the present case.

Suppose now that $n = n' = 1$. We may then choose t (still $\in K^f$) as the common parameter for both π and π'. Let their representations be

$$\pi: \ X = \Sigma a_i t^{n_i}, \quad Y = \Sigma b_i t^{n_i};$$
$$\pi': \ X = \Sigma a'_i t^{n_i}, \quad Y = \Sigma b'_i t^{n_i}.$$

Since $\pi \neq \pi'$, the two series for X, or else the two for Y must differ. We may assume the coordinates so chosen that the two X series differ. Thus we will have:

$$\text{on } \pi\text{: } X = g(t) + t^n(c + dt + \cdots),$$
$$\text{on } \pi'\text{: } X = g(t) + t^n(c' + dt + \cdots),$$

where $g(t) \in K[t]$ and $c \neq c'$. Thus since t and $g(t) \in K^f$,

$$R = \frac{X - g(t)}{t^n} - c$$

is an element of K^f whose order is > 0 at π and zero at π'. Hence again $\mathfrak{B}(\pi) \neq \mathfrak{B}(\pi')$, and the values at π, π' are distinct. This completes the proof of (10.4), (10.5) hence also of theorem (10.1).

§ 5. MULTIPLE POINTS, INTERSECTIONS AND THE PLACES

13. In what follows we shall lean considerably upon the concept of *order* of a place. Let π be a place, t its parameter in an irreducible representation and let A be the center of π. The *order* $\omega(g)$ of a form g may be defined as for rational functions: $g(x(t)) = g(t) = t^s E(t)$ and by definition $\omega(g) = s$. It is also the order of the rational function g/x_i^e where e is the degree of g and $x_i(A) \neq 0$. We see at once that $\omega(g) \geq 0$, and $\omega(g) = 0$ when and only when $g(A) = 0$, i.e. when and only when g contains the point A. The order of π itself is the least possible positive order of a form g at π, i.e. it is the least order of a linear form $l(x)$ through A. A place of order one is said to be *linear*.

The order of a form is merely a projective but not a birational invariant. Projective invariance is however just what is required for multiple points and intersection properties.

Suppose that A is a p-tuple point. Let it be chosen as affine origin and such that the Y axis is not tangent to the curve F. Let d be the degree of F. Among the intersections of F with the Y axis p are absorbed by the point A itself and there are $d - p$ others. It follows then from the Puiseux theory that $F(X, Y) = 0$ has exactly p solutions $Y_i(X)$, $i = 1, 2, \cdots, p$ such that $Y_i(0) = 0$.

Since A is a p-tuple point

$$F(X, Y) = F_p(X, Y) + F_{p+1}(X, Y) + \cdots \tag{13.1}$$

where F_p is regular in Y. The tangents to the curve at the point A are (see II, 24):

$$F_p(X, Y) = 0 \tag{13.2}$$

and their slopes are the roots $m_1, \cdots, m_p$ of the polynomial $F(1, m)$.

Let us set $Y/X = Z$. Thus Z satisfies the equation

$$G(X, Z) = F_p(1, Z) + XF_{p+1}(1, Z) + \cdots = 0.$$

Since $G(0, Z) = F_p(1, Z)$, corresponding to m_i there is a solution of the form

$$Z(X) = m_i + \Sigma a_j X^{(n_j - n)/n}, \quad n < n_1 < \cdots.$$

Moreover the solutions corresponding to the same m_i are grouped in circular systems whose total number of elements is the multiplicity q of m_i as a root of $F_p(1, m)$. The particular solution above belongs to a circular system of n elements and $\Sigma n = q$. (We suppose $n, n_1, \cdots,$ relatively prime.)

To $Z(X)$ there corresponds the solution

$$(13.3) \qquad Y(X) = m_i X + \Sigma a_j X^{n_j/n}, \quad n < n_1 < \cdots,$$

of $F = 0$. It is a member of a circular system of n conjugate such solutions where again $\Sigma n = q$. Since the total number of solutions $Y_i(X)$ such that $Y_i(0) = 0$ of $F = 0$ thus obtained is $\Sigma q = p$, the maximum number, Puiseux's theory shows that all the solutions of $F = 0$ which vanish for $X = 0$ are those described.

Now to the circular system of (13.3) there corresponds a single place π with the normal irreducible representation

$$(13.4) \qquad \rho x_0 = 1, \quad \rho x_1 = t^n, \quad \rho x_2 = m_i t^n + \Sigma a_j t^{n_j}.$$

If the point A were not chosen as affine origin but merely not on x_0, and so with affine coordinates a, b we would have for π in place of (13.4) the representation (still normal and irreducible):

$$(13.5) \qquad \rho x_0 = 1, \quad \rho x_1 = a + t^n, \quad \rho x_2 = b + m_i t^n + \Sigma a_j t^{n_j}.$$

The order of π is manifestly n. We note here also that $q = \Sigma n$, where the sum is extended to the orders of all the places related to a given q-tuple tangent at A, and that evidently $\Sigma q = p$, the multiplicity of the point A itself.

14. We will now consider the tangents at the places. Starting with a general irreducible representation of π centered at $A(a_{00}, a_{10}, a_{20})$ we will have

$$\rho x_i = \Sigma a_{ij} t^{n_j}; \qquad i = 0, 1, 2,$$

and a line

$$l(x) = \Sigma u_i x_i.$$

Then

$$l(t) = \Sigma (u_i a_{ij}) t^{n_j}.$$

The line will contain the point A when and only when

$$(14.1) \qquad \Sigma u_i a_{i0} = 0.$$

Now the coefficients of $l(t)$ cannot be all zero for all the u_i which satisfy (14.1), for then $a_{ij} = \lambda_j a_{i0}$, $\lambda_j \in K$, for $j = 1, 2, \cdots$, and hence

$$\rho x_i = a_{i0}(1 + \lambda_1 t + \cdots) = a_{i0} E(t).$$

This means, however, that the parametric point $M_t(x_i(t))$ is the center A of π, which is ruled out since M_t must be a general point. We conclude then that there is an $h > 0$ and we take the smallest, such that

$$\Sigma u_i a_{ih} \neq 0,$$

for some solution (u) of (14.1). If $h > 1$ then as above

$$\rho x_i = a_{i0} E(t) + a_{ih} t^{n_h} + \cdots.$$

Hence dividing by $E(t)$ the situation will be the same save that $h = 1$. We suppose then $h = 1$. Thus the a_{i1} are not all zero; they are indeed the coordinates of a point $B \neq A$. For all lines l through A other than

AB, l is of order n_1 while AB is of order $> n_1$ at π. The line AB is known as the *tangent* to the place π. Its equation is

$$(14.2) \qquad |x_i, a_{i0}, a_{i1}| = 0, \qquad (i = 0, 1, 2).$$

For the normal representation (13.5) we see at once that $h = 1$, and A and B have the respective coordinates $(1, a, b)$ and $(0, 1, m_i)$. The two points are thus manifestly distinct. The equation of the tangent to π reduced to affine coordinates is found to be

$$Y - b = m_i(X - a)$$

and as it has the same slope as the tangent to f to which π is attached, the two tangents coincide.

Upon combining with the results of (13) we have:

(14.3) **Theorem.** *To a q-tuple tangent l at the p-tuple point A there corresponds a set of places centered at A, tangent to l, and whose orders have for sum the multiplicity q of the tangent. The sum of the orders of all the places centered at A is the multiplicity p of the point itself.*

Various corollaries and subordinate results may be mentioned. They are all immediate consequences of what precedes.

(14.4) *To a simple tangent l at A there corresponds a single linear place π centered at A and tangent to l. If m is the slope of the tangent then the corresponding solution $Y(X)$ of $F = 0$ is $Y(X) = mX + bX^2 + \cdots$. This is also a representation for π.*

(14.5) *A p-tuple point A with distinct tangents is the center of p distinct places, all linear, and each tangent to one of the tangents to the curve at A. By* (13.3) *the place π_i corresponding to the tangent slope m_i has a representation with parameter X : $Y = m_iX + a_iX^2 + \cdots$.*

(14.6) *A n.a.s.c. for a point A to be the center of a place of the curve f is that A be a point of f.*

(14.7) *The order of a place π of center A is the order at π, of every line through A other than the tangent to π itself.*

(14.8) *Remark on the ordinary points.* If A is an ordinary point

$$F = \alpha X + \beta Y + \cdots, \qquad \beta \neq 0.$$

Hence $F = 0$ has a single Puiseux solution $Y(X)$ such that $Y(0) = 0$ and it is merely the McLaurin expansion of $Y(X)$ obtained in the customary way:

$$Y = -\frac{\alpha}{\beta}X + \gamma X^2 + \cdots.$$

The place π of center A referred to as an *ordinary* place, has the representation

$$X = t, \quad Y = -\frac{\alpha}{\beta}t + \gamma t^2 + \cdots$$

and it is clearly linear.

(14.9) *General places.* Up to the present we have only admitted places whose centers are fixed points, i.e. of transcendency zero. There is no reason however to be so strict about it. For let $M(\xi)$ be a general point of the curve. Upon replacing the groundfield K by $L = \overline{K_H(\xi)}$, M becomes a fixed point. Moreover f continues to be irreducible in L and since L is algebraically closed the general theory applies. Since M is an ordinary point there is a single place π of center M and it is linear. We refer to π as a *general place* of the curve.

Notice that the process of (14.8) to obtain a representation for π does not require the introduction of elements other than those of $K_H(\xi)$. The algebraic closure was only needed to justify the procedure.

15. Let now g be a form prime to f so that it intersects f in a finite number of points. Let A be one of these.

(15.1) *The multiplicity of A as an intersection of f and g is equal to the sum of the orders of g at the places of f centered at A.*

Take again affine coordinates with the origin at A and in particular such that F and G are both regular in Y. It is no restriction to assume furthermore that their leading coefficients in Y are unity. If d is the degree of F there will be d Puiseux solutions $Y_i(X)$, $i = 1, 2, \cdots, d$, all in $K\{X\}$, and none with negative exponents. Taking the resultant of F and G relative to Y there is obtained

$$R(X) = X^{\mu}E(X) = \pm \Pi G(X, Y_i).$$

The axes having been properly chosen, G will not pass through the intersections, other than the origin, of F with the Y axis. We substitute again for each Y_i its series $Y_i(X)$ and inquire for the lowest degree term in $G(X, Y_i(X))$. If Y_i begins with a constant term, i.e. corresponds to places of F whose centers are on the Y axis but not at the origin, then $G(X, Y_i(X))$ will also begin with a constant term. On the other hand if $Y_i(X)$ is represented by (13.3) with π of (13.5) as its associated place, the result will be

$$\sigma(X) = G(X, m_iX + \Sigma a_jX^{n_j/n}).$$

Let $\delta(X)$ be the lowest degree term in $\sigma(X)$. Since there are n factors $G(X, Y_i(X))$ for the place π, they will contribute to the lowest degree terms in $R(X)$ the same power as $(\delta(X))^n$, which is the same as $\delta(t^n)$, i.e., in the last analysis the order ρ of $G(X, Y)$ at π.

By combining (15.1) with Bezout's theorem there follows:

(15.2) *If g is prime to f and d, d' are the orders of f, g then the sum of the orders of g at the places of f is dd'.*

(15.3) *Remark.* Owing to our concentrating upon the curve f, the present treatment of intersection multiplicities at a point is not symmetrical with respect to the two curves f and g. A symmetrical treatment may be given on the following pattern. First of all let us drop the condition that one or the other curve is irreducible and let a place π of a curve be defined as a place of any irreducible component of the curve. Then curves without common components have no common places. Suppose now that f and g are relatively prime. Let the affine origin A be an intersection of f and g and let π and ω be places of f and g of center A. There will correspond to each a circular system of solutions of $F(X, Y)$ and $G(X, Y)$ say for π and F:

$$Y_i = \sum_{j=1}^{\infty} a_j \eta^j X^{j/p}, \quad i = 1, 2, \cdots, p$$

and for ω and G:

$$Y'_h = \sum_{k=1}^{\infty} b_k \zeta^k X^{k/q}, \quad k = 1, 2, \cdots, q$$

where η and ζ are primitive p-th and q-th roots of unity in K. Since π and ω are distinct places $Y_i \neq Y'_h$ whatever i, h. Consider now the product

$$\varphi(\pi, \omega) = \prod_{i,h} (Y_i - Y'_h).$$

Since φ is symmetrical in both the Y_i and the Y'_h, it contains only powers of X itself and they are all positive. Hence $\varphi(\pi, \omega) = X^\nu E(X)$. The number $\nu(\pi, \omega)$ is positive and readily shown to be independent of the choice of axes. We define it naturally as the *intersection multiplicity* of the two places π and ω at A.

Now let $\pi_1, \cdots, \pi_\lambda$ and $\omega_1, \cdots, \omega_\mu$ be the distinct places of f and g with A for center. Under our hypothesis $\pi_i \neq \omega_j$. The place π_i occurs in an irreducible factor f_i of f which occurs in a factorization of f into prime powers, say to the power α_i. Similarly there is a β_j related to ω_j. If we set

$$\nu = \sum \nu(\pi_i, \omega_j)\, \alpha_i \beta_j, \tag{15.4}$$

then, on the strength of (I, 3.4) and (II, 27) we readily see that the number ν is precisely the intersection multiplicity of the two curves at A. In other words the intersection multiplicity is the sum of the intersection multiplicities of the pairs of places of the two curves centered at A, where each place is to be taken with the same multiplicity as the component of f or g to which it belongs.

In point of fact the treatment just given is quite general. It would hold for instance about as well for F and G special polynomials of the power series ring $K[[X, Y]]$:

$$F = Y^m + A_1(X) Y^{m-1} + \cdots + A_m(X),$$
$$G = Y^n + B_1(X) Y^{n-1} + \cdots + B_n(X).$$

Only unimportant and obvious modifications in the concept of place would be required to cover this case.

In a different direction we are now in a position to complement the theorem of Bezout in a noteworthy way. Suppose that π and ω are as before and that the axes X, Y are chosen not tangent to π or ω. Then X, Y have the same orders on π and on ω. Therefore the expansions Y_i, Y'_h assume the forms

$$Y_i = mX + \Sigma a_j \eta^j X^{j/p}, \; j > p;$$
$$Y'_h = m'X + \Sigma b_k \zeta^k X^{k/q}, \; k > q.$$

The tangents to π and ω at the origin are then $Y - mX$ and $Y - m'X$. We find now:

$$\varphi(\pi, \omega) = (m - m')X^{pq} + \cdots .$$

Hence if $m \neq m'$, i.e. if π and ω of orders p, q have distinct tangents then $\nu(\pi, \omega) = pq$ and conversely. Thus

(15.5) *If two places of orders p, q and with the same center are not tangent, their intersection multiplicity has its least value pq and conversely.*

Upon combining with (15.4) we obtain:

(15.6) *If the point A is r-tuple for the curve f and s-tuple for the curve g, then its intersection multiplicity for f and g is at least rs. It is exactly rs when and only when the two curves have no common tangent at the point A.*

§ 6. Rational and Birational Transformations and the Places

16. Let f and g be irreducible curves in KP_x^2 and KP_u^2, and suppose that there exists a rational transformation T of f onto g. Under our general theory T will be given by a system

$$\rho u_i = P_i(x), \quad i = 0,1,2 \tag{16.1}$$

where (*a*) the P_i are forms of $K_H[x]$, of the same degree, without common factor and hence not all divisible by f; (b) if $M(\xi)$ is a general point of f and $\eta_i = P_i(\xi)$ then $N(\eta)$ is a general point of g.

We are in the particular case where T maps a variety onto one of the same dimension. It induces then an isomorphic imbedding $K^g \subset K^f$ making K^f an algebraic extension of K^g of a certain degree μ. As one may expect the role of μ will be dominant here. We infer at once from our general theory (III, 19.5):

(16.2) *If T is a rational transformation of f onto g and μ is its degree, then for almost all points N of g, and for all its general points, the set $T^{-1}N$ consists of μ distinct points of f, and they are all general when N is general.*

Referring to (III, 16) since the groundfield is of characteristic zero, the transformation may be represented by a monoidal system:

$$\begin{cases} \varphi(u; x_0, x_1) = 0, \\ \psi(u; x_0, x_1)x_2 - \omega(u; x_0, x_1) = 0; \\ \varphi, \psi, \omega \in K_H^2[u; x]. \end{cases} \tag{16.3}$$

Moreover if $N(\eta)$ is a general point of g then $\varphi(\eta; x_0, x_1)$ is irreducible as a form of $(K_H(\eta))_H[x]$ and its degree is μ.

17. We shall now extend the transformation T to the places. Let the place π of f have the irreducible representation

$$\rho x_i = a_i + \Sigma a_{ij} t^{n_j}, \quad i = 0,1,2. \tag{17.1}$$

The point $A(a_0, a_1, a_2)$ is the center of π. Upon substituting in the relations (16.1) for T we find

$$\sigma u_i = b_i + \Sigma b_{ij} t^{m_j}. \tag{17.2}$$

where the b_i are not all zero so that $B(b_0, b_1, b_2)$ is a point of KP_u^2. Since the parametric point $M_t(x_i(t))$ is a general point of f, the point $N_t(u_i(t)) = TM_t$ is a general point of g. Hence (17.2) is a representation of a place π^* of g whose center is B. Hence B is a point of g. It is seen at once that if one replaces (17.1) by any other representation for π there results merely another representation for π^*. Hence π^* is uniquely determined by T and π. It is natural therefore to extend T to the set $\{\pi\}$ of all the places of f by defining $T\pi = \pi^*$. If A is not fundamental then the $P_i(a_0, a_1, a_2) = (P_i(t))_{t=0}$ are not all zero. Hence

$$b_i = P_i(a_0, a_1, a_2), \ B = TA.$$

Thus we may state:

(17.3) *One may extend the rational transformation T: $f \to g$ to a single-valued transformation of the places. If π is a place of f whose center A is not a fundamental point of T then the center of $T\pi$ is TA.*

One may extend T to *all* the points but it may cease then to be single-valued in a finite set of points of f. This is done as follows. For every π of center A take $T\pi^*$ and if its center is B then define TA as the set of points B. Since the number of places of center A is finite, the set TA is always finite. If A is not a multiple point then TA is unique, and if A is not fundamental then TA is the same as before. Hence the extension of T is consistent with the original definition of T. However, T as extended may well be multiple valued at the singular points, i.e., at a finite set of points.

Returning to our main problem let us take the coordinates u_i so that $b_0 \neq 0$ and choose as in (7) the parameter t so as to have a normal representation for π^* equivalent to (17.2):

$$\sigma u_0 = 1, \quad \sigma u_1 = b + t^{md}, \quad \sigma u_2 = c + \Sigma c_i t^{m_i d} \tag{17.4}$$

where $m, m_1, m_2, \cdots$, are positive and relatively prime.

As we have seen (8.2) the number d is independent of the normal representation and represents the lowest order $\omega(R,\pi)$ of the elements of K^g at π, also the $H.C.F.$ of the orders of the elements of K^g at the place π. We call d the *local degree* of T at π.

Upon making in (17.4) the change of parameter $t^d = t^*$ there results for π^* the normal irreducible representation

$$(17.5) \qquad \sigma u_0 = 1,\ \sigma u_1 = b + t^{*m},\ \sigma u_2 = c + \Sigma c_i t^{*m_i}.$$

Suppose that T is birational. Then $K^g = K^f$, hence $d = 1$. We may then take $t^* = t$. This time $TM_t = N_t$, $T^{-1}N_t = M_t$. Since π and π^* are uniquely determined by M_t and N_t, T extended to the places becomes one-one. As already noted in the proof of (8.7), the identification of K^f with K^g associated with T leaves the orders of the elements unchanged. Hence the valuations $\mathfrak{B}(\pi)$, and $\mathfrak{B}(T\pi)$ are the same, so that the one-one correspondence between the places is the one which is associated with (8.7) or (10.2). We may also complete (8.7) in the following manner:

(17.6) *The one-one correspondence between the places determined by a birational transformation is such that for almost all places π the center of π in f is imaged into that of $T\pi$ in g and conversely for g and T^{-1}.*

18. Returning to our earlier situation suppose again that $T\pi = \pi^*$, where π is given by (17.1) and π^* by (17.5). Thus π is one of the places making up $T^{-1}\pi^*$. We assign to π the multiplicity d where as before d is the local degree at π. We shall now prove:

(18.1) **Theorem.** *If π^* is a place of g then $T^{-1}\pi^*$ consists of μ places of f where μ is the degree of T and each place π of $T^{-1}\pi^*$ is to be counted d times, where d is the local degree of T at the place π.*

We may also add the following complement:

(18.2) *If B is the center of an ordinary place π^* of g and $B = TA$ (B is the sole image of A), where A is not a fundamental point of T, then A is the center of a place of $T^{-1}\pi^*$. Hence in view of* (16.2), *for almost all places π^* the μ places of $T^{-1}\pi^*$ are distinct.*

(18.3) The places π^* such that $T^{-1}\pi^*$ consists of fewer than μ distinct places are known as the *branch-places of T on g.* An example of a branch-place is the following: f is of degree $m > 1$ and without singularities; T is the projection of f from a point O not in f onto a line l which does not pass through O. The branch-places are the places of l centered at the intersections with l of the tangents from O to f.

(18.4) Let us first dispose of (18.2). Let π^* be given in the representation (17.5) and let N_{t^*} be its parametric point. The set $T^{-1}N_{t^*}$ will consist of μ points $M_1, \cdots, M_\mu$ whose coordinates are obtained by solving the system (16.3) for the x_i with the u_i replaced by the $u_i(t^*)$ from (17.5). Setting $x_0 = 1$, the first relation (16.3) assumes the form

$$\Phi(x_1;\ t^*) = 0,$$

where Φ is a polynomial of degree μ in x_1 with coefficients in $K[[t^*]]$ and μ distinct roots in x_1, which by Puiseux's theorem are in $K\{t^*\}$, say

$x_1^h(t^*)$, $h = 1, 2, \cdots, \mu$. For each there is a single solution for x_2, since the second relation of (16.3) is linear in x_2,

$$x_2^h = R(x_1^h),$$

where $R(x) \in K\{t^*\}(x)$. Accordingly we will have for the μ points M_h coordinates

$$(18.5) \qquad x_0^h = 1, \quad x_1^h = t^{*a/p}E_1(t^{*1/p}), \quad x_2^h = t^{*b/p}E_2(t^{*1/p}).$$

It is not ruled out that a, b may be negative. However, after clearing negative powers and setting $t^{*1/p} = t$, we obtain representations $x_i^h(t)$, $i = 0, 1, 2$ of the usual types for μ places imaged into π^* by T. It is also a consequence of the Puiseux theory that if $B = TA$ then there is a series $x_i(t)$ beginning with the coordinate x_i of A and so (18.2) will hold.

19. Passing now to the proof of (18.1), suppose then that π is such that $T\pi = \pi^*$. Since μ, d and the places have birational character we may replace our curves by birationally equivalent curves. This will now be done in a definite way in relation to π and π^*.

As we have seen (8.1) there is an element ζ of K^f of order one at π. Then there exists another θ such that $K^f = K(\zeta, \theta)$. We may assume that the order of θ at π is positive. For if it is negative we replace θ by θ^{-1} and if θ is of order zero then $\theta(A) = \alpha \neq 0$ and we replace θ by $\theta - \alpha$. It is also desirable to have ζ of degree μ over K^g. If it is not then some combination $\alpha\zeta + \theta$, $\alpha \in K - 0$ will be so and continue to be of order one at π. It may then take the place of ζ.

Let $F(X, Y) = 0$ be the irreducible equation ($F \in K[X, Y]$) satisfied by (ζ, θ). Since $K^f = K(\zeta, \theta)$, F is birationally equivalent to f and (ζ, θ) is a general point of F. This means that we can so choose f that it has a general point $M(\xi)$ with $\xi_0 \neq 0$ such that ξ_1/ξ_0 is of order one at π and ξ_2/ξ_0 of positive order there. Hence we may choose the element $t = \xi_1/\xi_0$ of $K_H(\xi)$ as parameter for π and π will then have a representation

$$(19.1) \qquad \rho x_0 = 1, \quad \rho x_1 = t, \quad \rho x_2 = \sum_{i>0} a_i t^i.$$

Furthermore since $t = \xi_1/\xi_0 = \zeta$ is still of degree μ over K^g the system (16.3) will have preserved all its former properties.

A similar treatment will now be applied to g and π^*. We first require an element t^* of K^g whose order at π^* is unity and whose order at π is positive. At all events there is a $\tau \in K^g$ of order one at π^*. Its expansion on π will be $\tau(t) = t^q(\alpha + \beta t \cdots)$, $\alpha \neq 0$, and we may choose τ so that $\alpha = 1$. If $q > 0$ we take $t^* = \tau$. If $q \leq 0$ then

$$t^* = \frac{\tau}{1 + \tau} - \frac{\tau^2}{1 + \tau^2}$$

will have the required behavior

Operating as above we may select g and a representation for π^*

(19.2) $$\rho u_0 = 1, \quad \rho u_1 = t^*, \quad \rho u_2 = \sum_{i=0}^{+\infty} b_i t^{*i}.$$

Since $\omega(t^*, \pi) > 0$ and is divisible by d, it is a number ed, $e > 0$. Hence on π^*; $t^* = t^{ed} E(t)$.

Let now $v \in K^g$ be of order s at π^*. Thus $v = t^{*s} E_1(t^*)$. Hence at $\pi : v = t^{sed} E_2(t)$. Thus all the orders $\omega(v,\pi)$ are divisible by ed. Hence $e = 1$, $t^* = t^d E(t)$. Hence by (4.6) there are d distinct solutions

(19.3) $$t = \eta^r t^{*1/d} E(\eta^r t^{*1/d}), \qquad r = 1, 2, \cdots d,$$

where η is a primitive dth root of unity in K. Hence from (19.1) the relations for the representative point of π:

$$\rho x_0 = 1, \quad \rho x_1 = \eta^r t^{*1/d} E(\eta^r t^{*1/d}), \quad \rho x_2 = \eta^r t^{*s/d} E'(\eta^r t^{*1/d}).$$

These are then the relations (18.5) corresponding to π and we see that there are exactly d such sets. Each corresponds to one of the μ points m_h. Hence the number of places such as π each counted d times is μ. This proves the theorem.

(19.4) *Involutions.* Let us consider as a single object the set of places of $T^{-1}\pi^*$, say $\gamma = \{\pi_1, \cdots, \pi_\mu\}$, where each place π_h is taken as often as its multiplicity. Take any place π of f. The place $\pi^* = T\pi$ is uniquely determined and so is the set $\gamma = T^{-1}\pi^*$ which contains π. Thus any one of the places π of γ enables one to determine all the other places of the set γ to which it belongs. The set $\{\gamma\}$ is thus in one-one correspondence with the set $\{\pi^*\}$ of the places of g. We refer to the collection $\{\gamma\}$ as an *involution* on the curve f, and to μ as its *degree*. The usual designation for such an involution will be I_μ.

§ 7. Space Curves

20. Practically everything that precedes is directly applicable to an irreducible curve Γ in KP^m. The few deviations of interest later are discussed below.

A place π of Γ may be taken in a general representation

(20.1) $$\rho x_i = a_{i0} + \Sigma a_{ij} t^{n_j}, \qquad 0 < n_1 < n_2 \cdots,$$

the center being the point $A(a_{i0})$. This representation may be reduced to a normal irreducible representation in a suitable coordinate system

(20.2) $$\rho x_0 = 1, \quad \rho x_1 = a_1 + t^n, \quad \rho x_i = a_i + \Sigma a_{ij} t^{n_j}$$
$$0 < n, \quad 0 < n_1 < n_2 < \cdots,$$

where $n, n_1, n_2, \cdots$, have no common factor. The order questions are dealt with as before.

As in (14) one may assume the representation such that the a_{i1} are the coordinates of a point $B \neq A$. Then a hyperplane through A:

$$l(x) = \Sigma u_i x_i, \qquad \Sigma u_i a_i = 0$$

is of least order n or n_1 at π and of greater order if it contains B or equivalently the line AB. For this reason the line AB is defined as the *tangent* to Γ at the place π.

21. Projections. We shall only consider those from a point. We take the point as the vertex A_m of the simplex of reference and the projection is into a hyperplane chosen as x_m. If Γ has the representation

$$(21.1) \qquad \begin{cases} f(y_0, y_1, y_2) = 0, \\ \rho x_i = P_i(y), \quad i = 0, 1, \cdots, m, \end{cases}$$

then the projection Γ' has the representation

$$(21.2) \qquad \begin{cases} f(y_0, y_1, y_2) = 0, \\ \rho x_i = P_i(y), \quad i = 0, 1, \cdots, m-1, \\ x_m = 0. \end{cases}$$

Since Γ is a curve the $P_i(y)$, $i \leq m - 1$ are not all zero and hence Γ' is a point or a curve. If Γ' is a point Γ is a line through A_m. If Γ is not a line through A_m, as we assume until further notice, the projection operation Pr is a rational transformation $\Gamma \to \Gamma'$ of a certain degree μ. Since Pr is birational when and only when $\mu = 1$, we can assert:

(21.3) *If Γ does not pass through the center of projection A_m, the projection* Pr *operating on Γ is birational when and only when at most a finite number of secants of Γ pass through A_m.*

22. Let us now examine the effect of the projection on the places. Taking the place π as before suppose first that its center $A \neq A_m$. Consider in relation to (20.1) the system

$$(22.1) \qquad \rho x_i = a_{i0} + a_{i1}t^{n_1} + \cdots; \qquad i \leq m - 1, \quad x_m = 0.$$

It does represent a place π' of Γ' whose center $A' = \text{Pr}A$. However the representation need not be irreducible. Such a representation may be obtained by a transformation $t \to \theta^{1/d}(1 + \alpha\theta^{1/d} + \cdots)$ but this will not affect the points A' and $B' = \text{Pr}B$, where B is the point a_{i1}. Now if the line AB does not contain A_m, necessarily $B' \neq A'$ and $A'B'$ is the tangent to Γ' at the place π'. Or explicitly:

(22.2) *If the tangent at the place π of Γ does not contain the center of projection then its projection is the tangent to the projection π' of π.*

If π is linear $n_1 = 1$ and if in addition $B' \neq A'$ then π' is also linear. Hence we may state:

(22.3) *If the place π is linear, its center is not the center of projection and its tangent does not pass through the center of projection then its projection π' will be linear.*

Suppose now that $A = A_m$. We then have in place of (22.1)

$$\rho x_i = a_{i1} + a_{i2}t^{n_2 - n_1} + \cdots .$$

From this we deduce as before the existence of a place π' which is the projection of π. The center is the projection B' of B, i.e. the intersection of the tangent AB at π with x_m. Hence:

(22.4) *If the center of π is at the center of projection then the center of π' is the intersection of the tangent at π with the space onto which the projection is made.*

The behavior of the points of Γ as place centers is cleared up by the following:

(22.5) *Every point of Γ is the center of a finite non-zero number of places of Γ.*

Since the required result is known for plane curves we may assume it for KP^{m-1}, $m > 2$, and prove it for KP^m.

Let A be a point of Γ. Referring to (II, 18.3) the secants of Γ through A make up a surface Φ. Since $m > 2$, KP^m contains points not on Φ and hence not on Γ. Take such a point as center of projection and coordinates such that it is the point A_m, the projection being onto x_m. The curves Γ, Γ' will then have representations (21.1) and (21.2). The projection is a rational transformation T of a certain degree μ.

By hypothesis $A' = \text{Pr}\, A$ is the center of a finite set $\pi'_1, \cdots, \pi'_s$ of places of Γ'. There exist then μ places $\pi_{i1}, \cdots, \pi_{i\mu}$ of Γ such that $\text{Pr}\, \pi_{ih} = \pi'_i$ and if A_{ih} is the center of π_{ih} then $\text{Pr}\, A_{ih} = A'$. Since A is the only point of Γ such that $\text{Pr}\, A = A'$, we have $A_{ih} = A$. Hence A is the center of the μs places π_{ih}. On the other hand if π is any place of Γ with its center at A, $\pi' = \text{Pr}\, \pi$ is a place of Γ' with the center A'. Hence π' is one of the places π'_i and π is a place π_{ih}. This proves (22.5).

23. One may now define the multiplicity of Γ at A as the sum of the orders of the places centered at A. A point of order p is known as a p-tuple point, also as a *simple* point, for $p = 1$. A simple point is characterized by the fact that it is the center of exactly one place π and that π is linear.

The relationship between the concepts of multiplicity and singularity is settled by the following proposition.

$(23.1)_m$ *A n.a.s.c. for a point A of Γ to be ordinary (non-singular) is that it be simple. Moreover when A is simple the tangent to the place of center A coincides with the tangent to the curve at A.*

Since $(23.1)_2$ holds we assume $(23.1)_{m-1}$, $m > 2$, and prove $(23.1)_m$. We may, of course, assume in addition that the curve Γ under consideration is not contained in any space of dimension less than m. The argument will rest very naturally for a good part on projections.

We return to the representation (21.2) for the projection. Let $\mathfrak{p}_H$ be the ideal of Γ and $\mathfrak{p}'_H \subset K_H^{m-1}[x]$ the ideal of Γ'. Let $A(\alpha)$ be a point of Γ other than A_m. Its projection is $A'(\alpha_0, \cdots, \alpha_{m-1})$, where we consider the x_i, $i < m$, as coordinates for the hyperplane x_m. Corresponding to any $f(x) \in \mathfrak{p}_H$ write down the relation

$$(23.2) \qquad l(f) = \sum_{j=0}^{m} x_j f_{\alpha_j} = 0.$$

If ρ is the number of linearly independent forms $l(f)$ then $\rho \leqq m - 1$. When $\rho = m - 1$ the point A is ordinary, otherwise it is singular (II, 21).

Let now $f'(x_0, \cdots, x_{m-1}) \in \mathfrak{p}'_H \subset \mathfrak{p}_H$. The analogue of (23.2) for f' and A' is

$$(23.3) \qquad l(f') = \sum_{j=0}^{m-1} x_j f'_{\alpha_j} = 0.$$

Let ρ' be the analogue of ρ for (23.3). Since $\mathfrak{p}'_H \subset \mathfrak{p}_H$ the relations (23.3) are included among the relations (23.2) and hence $\rho' \leqq \rho$.

24. *Suppose first that A is a simple point of Γ.* Thus A is the center of a single place π and π is linear. The secants through A are on a cone of dimension two. Together with the tangent at A the cone constitutes a variety V^2 and since $m > 2$ we may choose the center of projection not in V^2.

The representation of the projection being as before, the point A' of Γ' will be the center of a single place $\pi' = \mathrm{Pr}\,\pi$. Moreover since π is linear and its tangent does not contain the center of projection π' is likewise linear. Hence A' is simple for Γ' and so, by the hypothesis of the induction, A' is an ordinary point of Γ'. From this follows that ρ' has its maximum value $m - 2$.

Let Φ be the cone projecting Γ from A_m. The ideal of Φ is the prime ideal $\mathfrak{p}^*_H$ spanned by the forms of $\mathfrak{p}'_H$ in $K_H[x]$. Its base is therefore the same as for $\mathfrak{p}'_H$ and consists of a set $\{f'_1, \cdots, f'_\sigma\}, f'_h \in K_H^{m-1}[x]$. If $g(x) \in \mathfrak{p}^*_H$ we have then

$$g(x) = \Sigma \varphi_i f'_i, \quad \varphi_i \in K_H[x].$$

Hence at any point of $A_m A'$ except A_m:

$$l(g) = \sum_j \varphi_i(\alpha) f'_{i\alpha_j} x_j, \quad i = 1, 2, \cdots, \sigma; \; j = 0, 1, \cdots, m-1,$$

and therefore

$$l(g) = \Sigma \varphi_i(\alpha)\, l(f'_i).$$

Hence along the generator $A_m A$ of the cone, or more precisely at all points of $A_m A$ other than A_m, the tangent hyperplanes to the hypersurfaces of $\mathfrak{p}^*_H$ have the same intersections as the hyperplanes of KP^m represented by $l(f') = 0$, $f' \in \mathfrak{p}'_H$. The upshot of it is that relative to A and the cone the analogue ρ^* of ρ is the same as for (23.3), i.e.

$\rho^* = \rho' = m - 2$. Since dim $\Phi = 2$, A is an ordinary point of Φ. Let S^2 be the tangent plane to Φ at A. By projecting from some center of projection distinct from A_m and likewise not in V^2, there will be obtained a second cone Φ_1 with A as ordinary point and tangent plane S_1^2 at A. One may manifestly assume at the outset A_m exterior to $V^2 \cup S_1^2 \cup \Phi_1$. Since A is an ordinary point of Φ_1 and S_1^2 does not contain A_m, Φ_1 will be contained in some hypersurface $f(x)$ whose tangent hyperplane $l(f)$ at A does not contain A_m. Hence $f_{\alpha_m} \neq 0$.

Since $\Gamma \subset \Phi_1 \subset f$, and Γ is irreducible, $f \in \mathfrak{p}_H$. Thus (23.2) will contain at least one relation with $f_{\alpha_m} \neq 0$. Since in (23.3) every $f'_{\alpha_m} = 0$ we have $\rho \geq \rho' + 1 \geq m - 1$. Since $\rho \leq m - 1$, necessarily $\rho = m - 1$. Hence A is an ordinary point of Γ.

Regarding the tangents let us suppose that the tangent AB to the place π and the tangent AC to Γ at A are distinct. Then one may choose the center of projection A_m as before but in addition exterior to the plane BAC of the two tangents. Since the projection $A'B'$ of AB is the tangent to π' at A', under the hypothesis of the induction it is the tangent to Γ' at A'. Hence S^2 is the plane $A_mA'B' = A_mAB$. Hence S^2 does not contain AC. However, since A is an ordinary point both for Γ and for the cone Φ containing Γ, the tangent plane to Φ at A must contain the tangent AC to Γ at A. This contradiction shows that $AB = AC$, i.e., that Γ and π have the same tangent at A.

Suppose now that A is an ordinary point of Γ. Since $\rho = m - 1$, one may find $m - 1$ hypersurfaces $f_i(x)$, $i = 1, 2, \cdots, m - 1$ of $\mathfrak{p}_H$ such that the matrix

$$||f_{i\alpha_j}||$$

is of rank $m - 1$. The coordinates may then be so numbered that the determinant

$$D = |f_{i\alpha_j}| \neq 0 , \qquad i, j = 1, 2, \cdots, m - 1.$$

Without affecting this situation we may select the coordinate system so that $\alpha_0 \neq 0$. First if $\alpha_0 = 0$, $\alpha_m \neq 0$ a mere inter-change of x_0 and x_m achieves the desired effect. Suppose $\alpha_0 = \alpha_m = 0$. Then one of the other coordinates say $\alpha_h \neq 0$. Therefore the change of coordinates $x_0 \to x_0 + \lambda x_h$, $\lambda \in K$; $x_h \to x_h$ for $h > 0$, will replace α_0 by $\lambda\alpha_h$ and D by $D + \lambda D_1$ where

$$D_1 = \pm |f_{i\alpha_0} f_{i\alpha_1} \cdots f_{i\alpha_{h-1}}, f_{i\alpha_{h+1}}, \cdots f_{i\alpha_{m-1}}|.$$

We may then always choose $\lambda \neq 0$ such that $D + \lambda D_1 \neq 0$ and $\lambda\alpha_h \neq 0$. Hence our purpose will have been accomplished.

At this stage it is best to operate in affine coordinates. Since $\alpha_0 \neq 0$, A will be in KA^m. We choose A as the affine origin, denote the ratios x_i/x_0 by X_i as usual for $i < m$, but will write $x_m/x_0 = u$. Let also

$f_i(1, X_1, \cdots, X_{m-1}, u) = F_i(X_1, \cdots, X_{m-1}, u)$. Under our hypothesis if

$$\Delta(X;\ u) = | F_{iX_j} |$$

then $D = \Delta(0;\ 0) \neq 0$. Now we may write

$$F_i(X;\ u) = a_i(u) + \Sigma a_{ij}(u)X_j + G_i(X;\ u)$$

where $a_i(u)$, $a_{ij}(u) \in K[u]$, $a_i(0){=}0$, and G_i is a polynomial in the X_j which only contains terms of degree ≥ 2 in the X_j and whose coefficients are in $K[u]$. We have then $D = | a_{ij}(0) | \neq 0$. As a consequence the system

$$F_i = a_i(u) + \Sigma a_{ij}(u)X_j + G_i(X;\ u) = 0 \tag{24.1}$$

has a unique solution in the X_j in $K[[u]]$:

$$X_j = X_j(u) = \Sigma \alpha_{jk} u^k, \quad k = 1, 2, \cdots . \tag{24.2}$$

Since (24.1) may also be considered as a similar system with a_i, a_{ij}, $G_i \in K[X;\ u^{1/n}]$ for any $n = 1, 2, \cdots$, it follows that the solution (24.2) is likewise the only solution of (24.1) in elements of $K\{u\}$ with all exponents positive.

We have seen that there is at least one place π of center A. This place will have an irreducible representation

$$X_j = \Sigma \beta_{jk} t^{n_k}; \qquad u = \Sigma \gamma_k t^{n_k}, \qquad 0 < n_1 < n_2 < \cdots .$$

The right-hand sides are the coordinates of a general point M_t of Γ. As a consequence the γ_k cannot all be zero. For then M_t would be in the hyperplane $u = 0$, and hence Γ would be in it also. This would contradict, however, the assumption that Γ is contained in no space of dimension $< m$. Let h be the least index such that $\gamma_h \neq 0$. Writing n for n_h, we have then $u = t^n E(t)$. This relation has a solution $t = vE_1(v)$, where v is a solution of $u = v^n$. Hence π has an irreducible representation:

$$X_j = X_j(v) = \Sigma \delta_{jk} v^{m_k}, \quad u = v^n.$$

Since the right-hand sides are the coordinates of a point M_v of Γ they satisfy the relations (24.1). Hence

$$X_j(u) = \Sigma \delta_{jk} u^{m_k/n} \tag{24.3}$$

is a solution of (24.1) in $K\{u\}$ with all exponents positive. We have seen that (24.2) represents the only solution of this nature. Hence (24.3) reduces to (24.2), $n = 1$ and so (24.2) is a representation of π. Since $n = 1$ the place is linear. Thus there is only one place of center A; it is represented by (24.2) and it is linear. Thus A is a simple point. This completes the proof of (23.1).

(24.4) Our theorem still leaves us with no other tangents for a singular point A than those of the place or places of center A and their number is finite. Hereafter any one of these will be referred to as a *tangent at the point* A, and this will cause no ambiguity.

25. We shall now consider several complementary results required later.

(25.1) *The number of singular points of a curve* Γ *is finite. Hence almost all the places of* Γ *are linear.* (See II, 21.4.)

$(25.2)_m$ *There are at most a finite number of tangents to* Γ *passing through a given point* B *of* KP^m.

Since this holds for plane curves we may assume $(25.2)_{m-1}$, $m > 2$, and prove $(25.2)_m$.

Suppose that B is on an infinite number of tangents to Γ. The lines joining B to the points of Γ are on a surface Φ. If $B \in \Gamma$ the tangent or tangents to Γ at B, whose number is finite (24.4) form together with Φ a V^2 in KP^m. Since $m > 2$ one may select in KP^m a projection center O not in V^2, on at most one tangent through B, and a hyperplane H not containing O. Since O is not in V^2, by (22.9) there will be an infinite number of tangents to the projection Γ' of Γ in H through the projection B' of B. Since this contradicts the hypothesis of the induction (25.2), follows.

(25.3) *If* $m > 2$ *and* Γ *is not a plane curve there is at most a finite number of tangents of* Γ *meeting a given line* l *of* KP^m.

We may assume that Γ is not contained in a hyperplane of KP^m. If l meets an infinite number of tangents to Γ, these tangents cannot be contained in a finite number of planes. For in that case some hyperplane H_1 would contain an infinite number of the tangents and hence intersect Γ in an infinity of points. Hence H_1 would intersect Γ in a V^1. Since Γ is irreducible $V^1 = \Gamma$, i.e. $\Gamma \subset H_1$, contrary to assumption.

Take now the center of projection O in l. By (25.2) an infinity of tangents to Γ intersect l at points other than O, and no finite set of planes through l contains them all. Since H does not contain O the line l meets H at a single point B'. The projection Γ' of Γ in H will have an infinite number of tangents through B', in contradiction to (25.2). This proves (25.3).

§ 8. Reduction of Singularities

26. We propose to discuss the birational transformation of an irreducible curve to a space curve without singularities and also to a plane curve which has the simplest possible singularities: only double points with distinct tangents. One refers sometimes to such singularities as *ordinary* singularities.

The transformations to be applied are birational on the curves *alone* and not on the space which contains them. There is however a classical reduction of singularities of a plane curve due to Max Noether and which is obtained by means of a finite number of quadratic transformations of the plane of the curve. An excellent treatment of this reduction will be found in R. Walker, [2], p. 80. The reduced curves in this case have no other singularities than multiple points with distinct tangents. There is no doubt that to have multiple points and not merely double points would not cause any additional trouble later.

Since every irreducible curve has a plane birational model, we may start the reduction with a plane curve $f(y)$ in KP^2_y. We first prove:

(26.1) **Theorem.** *Every irreducible curve has a birational model in some KP^m which has no singular points.*

Let $S = \{P_i(y_0,y_1,y_2)\}$ be a set of $m+1$ forms of $K_H[y]$ of the same degree which do not all vanish on f. When does the associated system of type (21.1) represent a projective model Γ of f without singularities? The following are evidently n.a.s.c.:

(a) *If M is a general point of f then $\{P_i(M)\}$ is a homogeneous base for K^f.*

At all events property (a) is a n.a.s.c. for Γ to be a birational model of K^f. We will then say briefly: *S has the base property.*

(b) *No point of Γ is the center of more than one place of Γ.*

(c) *All the places of Γ are linear.*

If $S' = \{P'_j(y)\}$ is a second system such as S we will denote by SS' the system $\{P_iP'_j\}$. The analogue of Γ for SS' will be written Γ^*. If $\pi, \cdots,$ $M, \cdots,$ are places of f and their centers, the corresponding elements of Γ and Γ^* will be written $\omega, \cdots, N, \cdots,$ and $\omega^*, \cdots, N^*, \cdots$.

We shall agree that if we apply to the P_i a linear transformation $P_i \to \Sigma\lambda_{ij}P_j$, $\lambda_{ij} \in K$, $|\lambda_{ij}| \neq 0$ then S is unchanged. Similarly for S'. The result of such operations is merely to change the coordinates in the spaces of Γ and Γ^* and they will not affect the properties under discussion.

(d) *If S has the base property so does SS' (regardless of S').*

Since the P_i, P'_j do not all vanish on f, neither all the P_i nor all the P'_j will all vanish at the general point M of f. Hence we may choose them such that $P_0(M)P'_0(M) \neq 0$. Since S has the base property $\{P_i(M)/P_0(M)\}$ is a rational base for K^f. The corresponding set for SS' is merely obtained by adding the $P'_i(M)/P'_0(M)$. Hence it is still a rational base for K^f and (d) follows.

(e) *If $\omega, \bar{\omega}$ have distinct centers $N, \bar{N}$ then the centers $N^*, \bar{N}^*$ of $\omega^*, \bar{\omega}^*$ are likewise distinct.*

Let us compare the coordinates of N and N^*. Let t be a parameter for π. Then

$$P_i(y_0(t), y_1(t), y_2(t)) = t^\sigma(a_i + b_it + \cdots) \tag{26.2}$$

$$P'_j(y_0(t), y_1(t), y_2(t)) = t^{\sigma'}(a'_j + b'_jt + \cdots) \tag{26.3}$$

where neither all the a_i nor all the a'_j are zero. The coordinates of N are thus the a_i and those of N^* the $a_ia'_j$. Similarly they will be $\bar{a}_i$ and $\bar{a}_i\,\bar{a}'_j$

for $\bar{N}$ and $\bar{N}^*$. We can then find a linear combination $\Sigma\lambda_j P'_j$, $\lambda_j \in K$, such that both $\Sigma\lambda_j a'_j$ and $\Sigma\lambda_j \bar{a}'_j \neq 0$. This means that we may choose the P'_j so that say $a'_0\bar{a}'_0 \neq 0$. Since by assumption $N \neq \bar{N}$ the a_i and $\bar{a}_i$ are not proportional. Hence the $a'_0 a_i$ and $\bar{a}'_0\bar{a}_i$ are corresponding sets of coordinates of N^*, $\bar{N}^*$, such that neither consists solely of zeros and yet they are not proportional. Hence $N^* \neq \bar{N}^*$.

(f) *If ω is linear so is ω^*.*

Referring to (26.2) linearity for ω means that there exists a hyperplane $l = \Sigma\lambda_i x_i$ of order one at ω. This reduces to the following condition: there exist $\lambda_i \in K$ and not all zero such that

$$\Sigma\lambda_i a_i = 0, \qquad \Sigma\lambda_i b_i \neq 0.$$

This may also be interpreted as follows: the point B whose coordinates are the b_i must be distinct from the center $N(a_i)$ of ω.

Now for ω^* the same conditions imply that the center $N^*(a_i a'_j)$ is distinct from the point $B^*(a_i b'_j + b_i a'_j)$. Now we may choose S and S' so that $a_0 = a'_0 = 1$; a_i, $a'_j = 0$ for $i, j > 0$. Since ω is linear $B \neq N$ and hence the b_i, $i > 0$, are not all zero. We may still assume S so chosen that $b_1 \neq 0$. Then N^* has the coordinate $a_0 a'_0 \neq 0$ and all others are zero. As for B^* among the coordinates not zero at least one $a_1 b'_0 + b_1 a'_0 = b_1 \neq 0$. Hence $B^* \neq N^*$ and so ω^* is linear.

Let $\mu(S)$ denote the number of non-linear places of Γ and $\nu(S)$ the number of its pairs of distinct places with common center. Set also $\rho(S) = \mu(S) + \nu(S)$. It follows from (e), (f) that:

$$\rho(SS') \leq \rho(S).$$

Let us now consider only systems S which satisfy (a) and for which ρ, and hence μ, ν are finite. Since $\{x_i\}$ is of this type, such systems do exist. Let us choose in particular an S for which $\rho(S)$ has its minimum value. To prove our theorem it is sufficient to show that $\rho(S) = 0$. For then $\mu(S) = \nu(S) = 0$, so that (b), (c) hold in addition to (a).

Suppose then $\rho(S) > 0$ so that either $\mu(S) > 0$ or else $\nu(S) > 0$. Let $\mu(S) > 0$. Thus Γ has a non-linear place ω with center say N. It corresponds to π of f with center M. As we know, there is a rational function of order one at π, say

$$R = \frac{P'_1(y_0, y_1, y_2)}{P'_0(y_0, y_1, y_2)}. \tag{26.4}$$

Set $S' = \{P'_0, P'_1\}$ and let σ be the least order of any P_i at π. We may assume the numbering such that P_0 is of that order at π. If σ' is the order of P'_0 at π, then that of P'_1 is $\sigma' + 1$. Hence the analogue of σ for SS' is $\sigma + \sigma'$ and, since $P_0 P'_1$ is of order $\sigma + \sigma' + 1$ at π, $\bar{\omega}$ is linear. Hence $\mu(SS') < \mu(S)$, and $\rho(SS') < \rho(S)$, contrary to assumption. Hence all the branches of Γ are linear, or (c) holds.

Suppose now $\nu(S) > 0$. Thus Γ has two distinct places ω, $\bar{\omega}$ with the same center N. There exists a rational function R taking distinct values at ω, $\bar{\omega}$. Writing again R in the form (26.4) and passing as before to SS', we find that this time the coordinate ratios of the centers of ω^*, $\bar{\omega}^*$ are not the same, and so these centers are distinct. Hence $\nu(SS') < \nu(S)$, leading to the same contradiction as before.

It follows that $\rho(S) = 0$ and, as we have seen, this proves the theorem.

27. By means of suitable projections the reduction already obtained may be carried further and will yield the following theorems.

(27.1) **Theorem.** *Every irreducible algebraic curve has a non-singular model in a projective* 3-*space.*

(27.2) **Theorem.** *Every irreducible algebraic curve has a projective plane model which has no other singularities than double points with distinct tangents.*

Starting then with the non-singular curve Γ in a space KP^m already obtained as a model of the initial curve, if $m > 3$ we shall project Γ into subspaces without introducing singularities, or at the end for $m = 3$ without introducing others than those mentioned in (27.2). It is clear that we may assume Γ not in the hyperplane x_0.

Let O be the center of projection. New singularities may appear if and only if secants or tangents of Γ pass through O. Hence we must examine the loci of secants or tangents and more particularly their dimensions. If these are less than m the desired selection of O will be possible.

Let $N(x)$ and $N'(x')$ be two distinct points of Γ and $R(u_0, u_1)$ a point of a line $KP^1 = l$ referred to the coordinates u_i. In the space $KP^m_x \times KP^m_{x'} \times l_u$ the point $(N, N', R) = (x_i, x'_j, u_k)$ is a point of the irreducible product variety $W^3 = \Gamma \times \Gamma' \times l$ (III, 14.1). To the same point there corresponds if $N \neq N'$ and $x_0 x'_0 \neq 0$ a unique point Q of the line NN' given by

$$\rho z_i = u_0 x'_0 x_i + u_1 x_0 x'_i, \quad i = 0,1, \cdots, m. \tag{27.3}$$

The relations (27.3) define a rational transformation T of W^3 into a variety V of KP^m and V is irreducible and contains all the secants NN' such that neither N nor N' are in x_0. We shall prove the following properties:

(27.4) $\dim V = 3$.

(27.5) *V contains every secant of* Γ.

(27.6) *V contains also every tangent of* Γ.

Let us first derive a preliminary result. Assume for the present that N, N' are merely distinct points neither of which is in x_0, and let $L = K^2_h(x; x') = K(N, N')$. Then if u_0, u_1 are indeterminates

$$\text{transc}_L\, Q = \text{transc}\left(\frac{u_1}{u_0}\right) = 1$$

and therefore

$$\text{(27.7)} \qquad \operatorname{transc}_K Q = 1 + \operatorname{transc}_K (N, N').$$

This is the result which we had in view.

Proof of (27.4). Assuming again that N, N' are general points and algebraically unrelated, by (27.7) $\operatorname{transc}_K Q = 3$. This would not hold for $m = 2$ since then every point is of transcendency at most two.

Since V is a rational transform of W^3, $\dim V \leq 3$. Hence Q is a point of V of maximum transcendency for the variety. Therefore Q is a general point of V and so $\dim V = 3$. We denote then the variety by V^3.

Proof of (27.5). Take any two distinct points $A(a)$ and $A'(a')$. They are the centers of two places π and π'. We denote their parameters by t, t' and the related parametric points by N_t, $N_{t'}$.

Let now $\varphi(x)$ be any form of the prime ideal $\mathfrak{p}_H$ of V^3. Since N_t, $N_{t'}$ are general points of Γ they are not in x_0, and $A \neq A'$ implies $N_t \neq N_{t'}$. Hence there is a well defined secant $N_t N_{t'}$ and it is in V^3. It follows that

$$\varphi(\cdots, u_0 x_0(t') x_i(t) + u_1 x_0(t) x_i(t'), \cdots) = 0.$$

The left hand side is an element of $K_H(u)[[t, t']]$ and since it is zero the constant term

$$\varphi(\cdots, u_0 a_0' a_i + u_1 a_0 a_i', \cdots) = 0.$$

This means that φ and hence V^3 contains the secant AA' and this proves (27.5).

Proof of (27.6). Suppose that Γ is in none of the hyperplanes x_h and write relations such as (27.3) with x_0, x_0' replaced by x_h, x_h'. There results a new irreducible variety V_1^3 analogous to V^3 containing Q. Since $\operatorname{transc} Q = 3$, Q is general for V_1^3 also and hence $V_1^3 = V^3$. Thus in writing down the relations (27.3) defining V^3 we are free to choose any coordinate system such that x_0 does not contain the curve Γ.

Let A, π, N_t be as before and let the coordinates be so chosen that A is not in x_0, so that we may assume for the place π a representation (20.2). Since π is linear we may even choose the coordinates such that the representation is

$$\text{(27.8)} \qquad \rho x_0 = 1,\ \rho x_1 = a_1 + t,\ \rho x_i = a_i + b_i t + c_i t^2 \cdots .$$

The center A is the point $(1, a_1, \cdots)$. If B is the point $(0, 1, b_2, \cdots)$ then $B \neq A$ and AB is the tangent to Γ at the point A.

Take now a new indeterminate t' and let $N_{t'}$ be the point obtained by substituting t' for t in (27.8). Upon substituting in (27.3) the coordinates of N_t and $N_{t'}$ we obtain the coordinates of a point Q of the secant $N_t N_{t'}$

and hence $Q \in V^3$. Take $u_0 = 1 - u$, $u_1 = u$. Thus the following point is in V^3:

$$\rho z_i(t, t') = x_i(t) + u\left(\frac{x_i(t') - x_i(t)}{t' - t}\right)$$
$$= x_i(t) + u(b_i + \gamma(t, t')c_i + \cdots)$$

where the coefficients $\gamma(t, t')$ are symmetrical polynomials with integral coefficients and no constant term. It follows that the points obtained for $t = t' = 0$, or

$$\rho z_i = a_i + ub_i$$

are in V^3. Now the points thus obtained are all points of the line AB, i.e. of the tangent at A. Thus V^3 intersects this line in an infinite number of points, and hence in a V^1. Since AB is an irreducible curve $AB = V^1$ and hence $AB \subset V^3$. This proves (27.6).

Proof of (27.1). If $m > 3$ one may take a center of projections O exterior to V^3. The projection of Γ from O into a hyperplane H not containing O is an irreducible curve Γ' in H. Since O is not in V^3 every projecting line from O to Γ meets Γ in a single point and is not tangent to Γ. Hence the degree of the projection is unity and so Γ' is a birational model of Γ. Moreover the projection introduces no new singularities so that Γ' is likewise non-singular. The operation may be repeated until there is obtained a non-singular birational model in KP^3 and this proves (27.1).

28. As one will readily surmise the tangents are actually contained in a subvariety of V^3. That is to say

(28.1) *All the tangents to* Γ *are on a* V^2.

Let H be a hyperplane which does not contain Γ and N a general point of Γ. The tangent to Γ at N meets H in a point N' whose coordinate ratios are algebraic over $K(N)$, and hence in $K(N)$, since N' is uniquely determined by N. It follows that N' is the general point of a rational transform $V^k = \Delta$ of Γ where $k = 0$ or 1. Now $k = 0$ means that N' is fixed and that an infinite number of tangents of Γ go through N'. Hence $k = 1$ and so Δ is an irreducible curve. Let T be the rational transformation $\Gamma \to \Delta$ such that $N' = TN$. Its fundamental variety is a V^0, i.e. a finite number of points. Hence all but a finite number of tangents $\tau_1, \cdots, \tau_s$ to Γ meet Δ.

Let now N be any point of Γ and let Q be determined by (27.3) from N, N' as before. If N is not a fundamental point of T then by (27.7) transc $Q = 1 +$ transc $(N, N') = 1 +$ transc $N \leq 2$, and transc $Q = 2$ when N is general. This time the variety V contains no point of transcendency ≥ 2, and contains some of that transcendency. Hence dim $V = 2$ and so V is a V^2. Upon augmenting V^2 by the tangents τ_j we still have a V^2 containing all the tangents and this is (28.1).

29. Once in possession of (27.1) one may assume in proving (27.2) that Γ is a non-singular curve in KP^3 and that it is not in a plane, for then the ultimate reduction would already be achieved. The proof will rest here also upon the choice of a projection center avoiding certain loci of secants.

We first prove:

(29.1) *The multisecants of* Γ (*secants meeting* Γ *in more than two points*) *are on a variety of dimension at most two.*

Let us observe at the outset that if N, N' are points of Γ and the secant NN' meets Γ in further points $N'', \cdots, N^{(s)}$ then transc $(N, \cdots, N^{(j)}) =$ transc (N, N'), for $1 < j \leq s$. For by (25.3), the number of points $N'', \cdots, N^{(s)}$ is finite and hence they are algebraic over $K(N, N')$.

Let Γ', Γ'' be copies of Γ in spaces $KP^3_{x'}$, $KP^3_{x''}$. If $\mathfrak{p}_H$ is the prime ideal of Γ let $\mathfrak{p}'_H$, $\mathfrak{p}''_H$ be the corresponding ideals of $K_H[x']$, $K_H[x'']$ associated with Γ', Γ''. Writing KP^3_x for KP^3 let

$$\Sigma = KP^3_x \times KP^3_{x'} \times KP^3_{x''}.$$

Consider now the matrix

$$||x_i, x'_i, x''_i||$$

and let D^2_h, D^3_k; $h, k = 1, 2, \cdots$, denote in some order its determinants of orders two and three. The forms of $\mathfrak{p}_H$, $\mathfrak{p}'_H$, $\mathfrak{p}''_H$ together with the D^3_k span an ideal $\mathfrak{a}$ of $K^3_H[x; x'; x'']$ which determines a variety W of the product space Σ. The forms of $\mathfrak{a}$ together with the D^2_h span an ideal of the same ring, which determines a variety W' contained in W.

If (N, N'_0, N''_0) is a point of W and N', N'' are the images of N'_0, N''_0 in Γ, then N, N', N'' will be collinear. However, $NN'N''$ will only be a true multisecant of Γ if the three points are distinct, that is to say if the point $(N, N', N'') \in W - W'$. In view of (27.7) it is clear that we merely need to prove:

(29.2) dim $W \leq 1$ *or equivalently transc* $(N, N', N'') \leq 1$.

In proving this we may further assume that (N, N', N'') is not in W', i.e. that $NN'N''$ is a true multisecant of Γ.

We proceed with (29.2). Since transc $(N, N', N'') =$ transc (N', N''), we must show that the latter ≤ 1. At all events it is ≤ 2. Suppose then transc $(N,' N'') = 2$. This implies transc $N' =$ transc $N'' = 1$. Then also transc $N = 1$. For the alternative transc $N = 0$ implies that N is fixed. This is ruled out as follows. Projecting Γ from N on a plane H not containing N there results a plane curve g which is a rational transform of Γ. If M is the common projection of N', N'' and $\mathfrak{M}$ the field obtained by adjoining the coordinate ratios of M to K, then those of N', N'' are in the algebraic closure of $\mathfrak{M}$. Since both $\mathfrak{M}$ and its closure have transcendency unity over K, we must have transc $(N', N'') = 1$, whereas by assumption it is 2. This contradiction proves that the three points N, N', N'' are general for Γ.

Let L denote the algebraic closure of the field $K(N)$, and similarly for L' and N'. Since N is general it is not in the hyperplane x_0, and so in the projection just considered from N into H we may choose $H = x_0$. The equations of the projection will then be $g(x_1, x_2, x_3) = 0$, $x_0 = 0$, where $g \in L_H[x_1, x_2, x_3]$. The multiple points of the projection g are in LP^2 and hence they have transcendencies zero over L. From $\text{transc}_K\, L = 1$ and $\text{transc}_K\, (N', N'') = 2$, there follows $\text{transc}_L\, (N', N'') = 1$. Hence if M is as above, $\text{transc}_L\, M = 1$ and M is general for g. It follows that M is not a multiple point. As a consequence the tangent to g at M is the common projection of those to Γ at N' and N''. Hence these two tangents are coplanar and so they intersect. Hence N'' is one of the points in finite number whose tangents meet the tangent to Γ at the point N'. This means that the coordinates of N'' are in L' or $\text{transc}_{L'}\, N'' = 0$ and therefore $\text{transc}_K\, (N', N'') = 1$. Thus our original assumption is untenable and we must have $\text{transc}_K\, (N', N'') \leq 1$. This proves (29.2) and hence also (29.1).

To complete the argument we still require:

(29.3) *The secants NN' such that the tangents at N and N' intersect are contained in a variety of dimension ≤ 2.*

As above let N be general and let the projection be as before from N on x_0. If P is the intersection of the tangent to Γ at N with x_0, then the tangents to Γ which meet NP are projected into tangents to g from P, and the points such as N' are projected into the points of contact, in finite number, of the tangents to g from P. It follows once more that $\text{transc}_L\, N' = 0$, $\text{transc}_K\, (N, N') = \text{transc}_K\, N = 1$ and as before this yields (29.3).

Proof of (27.2). Let V_1 be the variety containing all the multisecants, V_2 the variety of (29.3), V_3 the variety containing all the tangents to Γ. Thus the union V of the V_i is of dimension ≤ 2 in KP^3. Hence one may take a center of projection O not on V and project Γ from O on a plane not containing O. Let g be the projection. Since Γ has only linear places and O is not on V_3, g has likewise only linear places. Since O is not on V_1, no multisecants pass through O, and so g has only double points for singularities. Finally, since O is not on V_2, the tangents at the double points are distinct. Moreover, g is a birational transform of Γ and hence of f. For, if g were not, almost all points of g would be the projections of at least two points of Γ. Thus g would contain an ordinary point M projection of two points N, N' of Γ and, as we have seen, the tangents to Γ at N, N' would then meet, which requires $O \in V_2$ contrary to assumption. Thus g satisfies all the requirements of (27.2) whose proof is now complete.

VI. Linear Series

The notion of linear series arises in substance when one considers the collection of the intersections with the basic plane curve f, of the curves of a linear family, for instance all the lines or conics of the plane. The major birational properties of algebraic geometry center around this fundamental concept.

Needless to say throughout the chapter the groundfield K continues to be algebraically closed and of characteristic zero.

§ 1. Divisors and Their Classes

1. As we shall be concerned mainly with rational functions and their orders, properties which have birational character, we may as well take as birational model a plane irreducible curve f. We denote its order by m.

Let $R \in K^f$, $R \neq 0$, and let π be a place of the curve. We call π a *zero* [a *pole*] *of order* ν of R whenever R is of order ν [of order $-\nu$] at π. Take a representation P/Q of R where P, Q are forms of equal degree μ of $K_H[x]$. Let $\omega(P, \pi)$, $\omega(Q, \pi)$ be the orders of P and Q at π, where each is zero at almost all places. Then (sum of the orders of the zeros) — (sum of the orders of the poles) $= \Sigma\omega(P, \pi) - \Sigma\omega(Q, \pi) = 0$, since each sum is $m\mu$. Hence:

(1.1) *For any non-zero element R of K^f the sum of the orders of the zeros is equal to the sum of the orders of the poles.*

A complementary result is:

(1.2) *When R has no zeros, and hence no poles, then R is in K.*

Under the hypothesis and in the above notations P and Q have the same zeros $\pi_1, \cdots, \pi_r$ and with equal orders $\omega(\pi_i)$ such that

$$\Sigma\omega(\pi_i) = m\mu.$$

Let π_0 be a place which is not a π_i so that $P(\pi_0) \neq 0$, $Q(\pi_0) \neq 0$. Then $P^* = P(\pi_0)Q - Q(\pi_0)P$ is a form of order μ with π_i as a zero of order at least $\omega(\pi_i)$, and in addition with the zero π_0 of order at least one. Hence the sum of the orders of the zeros of P^*, i.e. of the multiplicities of its intersections with F exceeds $m\mu$. Therefore $P^* = 0 \bmod F$. Hence

$$R = P(\pi)/Q(\pi) \in K.$$

From (1.2) follows:

(1.3) *Two elements of K^f with the same zeros and poles and the same orders in each differ only by a factor in K.*

2. Consider now all the places π of f as generators of an additive group $\mathfrak{G}$. Any element D of $\mathfrak{G}$ is an expression, called a *divisor*;

$$D = \rho_1\pi_1 + \cdots + \rho_n\pi_n = \Sigma\rho(\pi)\pi,$$

where $\rho(\pi)$ is integral-valued and zero at almost all places. The meaning of $D \pm D'$, $D = 0$ is obvious. The number $n = \Sigma\rho_i$ is the *degree* of D and the divisor D is *effective* whenever every $\rho_i \geq 0$.

Noteworthy divisors are the following:

I. Corresponding to $R \in K^f$ and not in K: (a) D' the divisor of its zeros; the π_i are the zeros of R and the ρ_i their orders; (b) D'' the divisor of the zeros of R^{-1} or divisor of the poles of R; (c) the divisor $D = D' - D''$ or divisor of R itself. Notice that D' and D'' are effective but D is not.

II. Let $P(x) \in K_H[x]$ be a form not divisible by f. Let π_i be its intersection places with f with intersection multiplicities ρ_i. Then $D = \Sigma\rho_i\pi_i$ is the divisor of the zeros of P and it is effective. If μ is the order of P then the degree of D is $m\mu$.

III. The divisors of an involution I_μ on f. Referring to (V, 19.4) I_μ results from a rational transformation $T: f \rightarrow g$, wherein $K^g \subset K^f$ and K^f is of degree μ over K^g. The set of places $\pi_1, \cdots, \pi_\mu$ of f making up $T^{-1}\pi$ (π a place of g) with multiplicities ρ_i have for sum an effective divisor $D = \Sigma\rho_i\pi_i$ of degree μ. The salient property of these divisors is that each is uniquely determined by any one of its places. One may also remember that almost all the divisors of I_μ consist of μ distinct places (the multiplicities are then unity).

An arbitrary collection of places and multiplicities is not very promising from the standpoint of geometry. Hence we can have but little interest in the full additive group of the divisors. A much more fruitful line of attack appears when divisors are compared in relation to the elements of the function field.

We shall say that two divisors D, D' are *equivalent* written $D \sim D'$, whenever $D - D'$ is the divisor of an element R of K^f. It is at once seen that this is a true equivalence relation. It gives rise therefore to equivalence classes $\mathfrak{C}$ and then to an automatic definition of the additive group of the classes. In point of fact we need only to retain that the operations $\mathfrak{C} \pm \mathfrak{C}'$ have a meaning. Note also this consequence of (1.1):

(2.1) *All the divisors of the same class have the same degree n. The number n is also referred to as the degree of the class.*

Since everything introduced in the section rests upon the function field we may state:

(2.2) *The divisors and their classes as well as the operations $+$, $-$ on the divisors and classes have birational character.*

§ 2. Linear Series: First Properties

3. Let $R_0, \cdots, R_r$ be $r + 1$ linearly independent elements of K^f and let

(3.1) $$R^\lambda = \Sigma \lambda_i R_i, \qquad (\lambda_i \text{ indeterminate}).$$

Let $\omega_0(\pi)$ be the least order of any R_i at the place π. This number is zero for almost all places. The order of R^λ itself at π is $\omega_0(\pi) + \omega_\lambda(\pi)$ where $\omega_\lambda(\pi) \geq 0$ and again $\omega_\lambda(\pi) = 0$ at almost all places. We refer to the effective divisor

$$A^\lambda = \Sigma \omega_\lambda(\pi)\pi$$

as the *variable divisor* of R^λ.

Take any fixed effective divisor A_0 and set $D^\lambda = A_0 + A^\lambda$. The divisors D^λ belong to a fixed class. The collection $\{D^\lambda\}$ is known as a *linear series*. The degree n of D^λ is the *degree* of the series and r is its *dimension*. Following Brill and Noether the series is denoted by g_n^r.

The correspondence $D^\lambda \longleftrightarrow R_\lambda$ is one-one. Since one may consider R_λ as a point M_λ of KP_λ^r this correspondence turns g_n^r into a projective space and it is in fact this space which we have in view when we consider g_n^r. Upon replacing the set $\{R_i\}$ by $r + 1$ linearly independent linear combinations of the R_i:

$$R_i' = \Sigma a_{ij} R_j, \quad a_{ij} \in K, \quad |a_{ij}| \neq 0,$$

R_λ is unchanged. The effect on KP_λ^r is a change of coordinates.

One may evidently write $R_i = P_i/P$, where $P, P_i \in K_H[x]$. Then A^λ is the variable intersection of

(3.2) $$P^\lambda = \Sigma \lambda_i P_i$$

with f. Upon multiplying the P_i by the same Q intersecting in a divisor containing A_0, and still calling P_i the new polynomials we will have the following situation: P^λ has for intersection divisor $A + A^\lambda$ where A is fixed and A^λ variable; $A = A_0 + A_1$ and $D^\lambda = A_0 + A^\lambda$. One may then say that g_n^r is generated by P^λ.

It may also be observed that if one considers the P_i as forms in the indeterminates x_i then they are linearly independent mod f.

A series g_n^s represented by a subspace of g_n^r is said to be *contained in* g_n^r. A series which is contained in no other series but itself is said to be *complete*.

Since series and their inclusions are defined in terms of the function field we may state:

(3.3) *Under a birational transformation a series [a complete series] g_n^r goes into a series [a complete series] g_n^r for the transformed curve.*

4. Consider now a g_n^r generated say by (3.2).

Corresponding to any $h \leq r$ consider h points $M_1, \cdots, M_h$ of the curve f and in relation to these the system

$$\mathscr{E}_h: \Sigma\lambda_i P_i(M_j) = 0, \qquad j = 1, 2, \cdots, h.$$

If we take for M_1 any point which is not fixed for P^λ there results a system $\mathscr{E}_1$ whose coefficient matrix is of rank one and it defines in the space KP^r_λ a linear subspace S^{r-1}.

Suppose that there have been obtained $h - 1$ points $M_1, \cdots, M_{h-1}$ such that the corresponding system $\mathscr{E}_{h-1}$ has a coefficient matrix of rank $h - 1$ and so defines an S^{r-h+1} of KP^r_λ. We may then select M_h not an M_j, $j < h$, and not contained in all the P^λ satisfying $\mathscr{E}_{h-1}$. The resulting system $\mathscr{E}_h$ will have a coefficient matrix of rank h. In particular for $h = r$ we may select r points $M_1, \cdots, M_r$ such that the coefficient matrix of $\mathscr{E}_r$ is of rank r and so determines a single point S of KP^r_λ.

It is clear that in the above construction one may choose the M_i so as to avoid any preassigned finite set of points of f. In particular, one may choose for the M_i ordinary points of f. Thus M_i will be the center of a single place π_i and the r places thus obtained will be distinct. We have thus proved the following useful property:

(4.1) *Corresponding to g^r_n, $r > 0$, and its generating system* (3.2) *one may select r distinct points $M_1, \cdots, M_r$, where each M_i is the center of a single place π_i and with the following two equivalent properties:* (a) *the matrix*

$$\| P_i(M_j) \|, \quad i = 0, 1, \cdots, r; \quad j = 1, 2, \cdots, r$$

is of rank r; (b) *there is a unique divisor of g^r_n containing all the places π_i.*

Let now π be a place of f with parameter t and let ρ be the least order of any P_i at π. Thus

$$P_i(t) = t^\rho(\alpha_{i0} + \alpha_{i1}t + \cdots),$$

where the α_{i0} are not all zero. If P^λ is to be of order $\rho + \sigma$ at π, the λ_i must satisfy the linear system of σ relations

$$\Sigma\lambda_i\alpha_{ih} = 0, \quad h = 0, 1, \cdots, \sigma - 1.$$

Notice that among these relations the first certainly has coefficients not all zero. Let as before A^λ denote the variable part of the intersection divisor of P^λ.

(4.2) *If the variable divisor A^λ is to contain a preassigned divisor B of degree ν the λ_i must satisfy a system of ν linear relations whose coefficient matrix is not zero. Hence in the space KP^r_λ these special P^λ will correspond to the points of a subspace S of dimension s where $r - \nu \leq s < r$.*

In fact for at least one divisor π of B there will result a system of relations such as above with the α_{i0} not all zero, and the asserted property follows.

An immediate consequence of (4.2) is:

(4.3) *If the places* $\pi_1, \cdots, \pi_q$ *are not in the fixed divisor of* g_n^r *then there exists a divisor* D^λ *of* g_n^r *which does not contain the* π_i.

For if g_n^r is generated by P^λ, the P^λ containing π_i make up a hyperplane S_i in KP_λ^r and all that is necessary is to take $(\lambda_0, \cdots, \lambda_r)$ exterior to all the S_i.

(4.4) *For any* g_n^r *necessarily* $r \leq n$.

This is trivial for $r = 0$, and when $r > 0$, by (4.1) some divisor of g_n^r contains r distinct places.

(4.5) *Application. An irreducible curve* f *of degree* m *possesses at most* $N = \dfrac{(m-1)(m-2)}{2}$ *distinct double points with distinct tangents.*

The proof will rest upon the series cut out by the curves $\varphi(x)$ of degree $m - 2$ passing through the double points.

Since (4.5) holds manifestly for $m = 1, 2$ we will assume $m > 2$, so that there are curves φ of degree $m - 2$. A form of degree $m - 2$ has a number of coefficients equal to

$$\frac{m(m-1)}{2} = N + m - 1.$$

Since passage through a point imposes a single linear relation upon the coefficients there will exist a curve φ passing through any preassigned set of $N + m - 2$ points. In particular if there are more than N double points there will exist curves φ through $N + 1$ of them say $M_1, \cdots, M_{N+1}$. Among these curves there will be $1 + r = m - 2 + \varepsilon$, $\varepsilon \geq 0$, linearly independent say $\varphi_0, \cdots, \varphi_r$ and they will also be linearly independent mod f since f is irreducible and the degree of the φ_i is $< m$. According to (V, 14.5), M_i is the center of two linear places π_{2i-1}, π_{2i}. Let $\Delta = \Sigma\pi_j$, so that Δ is of degree $2N + 2$. Thus $\varphi^\lambda = \Sigma\lambda_i\varphi_i$ has an intersection divisor $\Delta + D^\lambda$ where D^λ is of degree $n = m(m-2) - 2N - 2 = m - 4$. Since $n \geq 0$, $m = 3$ is already ruled out and so (4.5) holds for cubic curves. Assuming then $m \geq 4$, φ^λ generates a g_n^r with $n - r = -1 - \varepsilon < 0$, which contradicts (4.4) and this proves (4.5).

(4.6) Let us make here a remark useful later. If there are exactly N double points with distinct tangents say $M_1, \cdots, M_N$ then defining g_n^r as above we find this time by the same calculation $n - r = -\varepsilon$, hence $\varepsilon = 0$. That is to say an irreducible f with N double points contains *a* g_n^n.

5. (5.1) *If* $g_n^r, g_n^{r'}$ *have a common divisor D then both are contained in a* $g_n^{r''}$, *where evidently* $r'' \geq r, r'$. *If neither of the given series contains the other then* $r'' > r, r'$.

Let the two series be generated by

$$P = \Sigma\lambda_i P_i, \quad P' = \Sigma\lambda'_j P'_j.$$

We may suppose the P_i, P'_j so chosen that D is cut out by P_0, P'_0. That is to say D is the D^λ corresponding to $\lambda_0 = 1$, $\lambda_1 = \cdots = \lambda_r = 0$ and similarly for the second series. Since we may replace the P_i by $P_i P'_0$ and the P'_i by $P_0 P'_i$, we may assume at the outset that $P_0 = P'_0$, and hence that the P_i, P'_j have the same degree. Among the $P'_1, \cdots, P'_{r'}$ a certain number $s \leq r'$ may be linear combinations mod f of the P_j. These linear combinations will form with P_0 a set of $s + 1$ forms linearly independent mod f. We may choose the notations so that these forms are $P_0, \cdots, P_s$ and that $P'_i = P_i$, $i \leq s$. Then the forms P'_{s+h}, $h > 0$, will be linearly independent of the P_i mod f. If we define $P_{r+h} = P'_{s+h}$ then

$$P^\mu = \mu_0 P_0 + \cdots + \mu_{r''} P_{r''}, \quad r'' = r + r' - s,$$

generates a $g_n^{r''}$ containing the two given series. For g_n^r corresponds to the μ_i such that $\mu_{r+h} = 0$, $h > 0$, and $g_n^{r'}$ to the μ_i such that $\mu_{s+1} = \cdots = \mu_r = 0$. If neither of the two series contains the other $s < r, r'$ and hence $r'' > r, r'$. This completes the proof of (5.1).

(5.2) *Every g_n^r determines a unique complete linear series g_n^s which contains it. In particular every effective divisor D (since it is a g_n^0) determines a unique complete linear series of which it is an element, and which is written* $|D|$.

(5.3) *A complete g_n^r consists of all the effective divisors of an equivalence class.*

All the divisors of g_n^r are in a fixed class $\mathfrak{C}$. Suppose that $\mathfrak{C}$ contains an effective divisor D_1 which is not in g_n^r. Let $D_0 \in g_n^r$. Since $D_0 \sim D_1$, $D_1 - D_0$ is the divisor of an element P_1/P_0, $P_i \in K_H[x]$ of the function field K^f and the divisor of zeros of P_i is $D_i + A$. Hence the divisor of zeros of $P^\lambda = \lambda_0 P_0 + \lambda_1 P_1$ is $D^\lambda + A$ where D^λ is effective. Hence $\{D^\lambda\}$ is a g_n^1 with both D_0 and D_1 as elements. Clearly $g_n^r \neq g_n^1$; $g_n^r \subset g_n^1$ is also excluded since g_n^r is complete and $g_n^1 \subset g_n^r$ is ruled out since g_n^r does not contain D_1. Hence there is a g_n^s, $s > r$, containing g_n^r, a contradiction which proves (5.3).

(5.4) *Sum and difference of linear series.* Let g_n^r, $g_{n'}^{r'}$ be two linear series and $\mathfrak{C}$, $\mathfrak{C}'$ their classes. The class $\mathfrak{C} + \mathfrak{C}'$ is known and its complete series is called the *sum* $g_n^r + g_{n'}^{r'}$. Similarly for the *difference* $g_n^r - g_{n'}^{r'}$ provided that the class $\mathfrak{C} - \mathfrak{C}'$ contains effective divisors. This will certainly be the case whenever there exist effective divisors $D \in g_n^r$, $D' \in g_{n'}^{r'}$ and A such that $D = D' + A$.

6. (6.1) **Theorem of Bertini for algebraic curves.** *In a g_n^r, $r > 0$, without fixed places almost all the divisors consist of n distinct places.*

Let g_n^r be generated by (3.2) where the P_i are linearly independent mod f. The relations

$$f(x) = 0, \quad P^\lambda = \Sigma \lambda_i P_i = 0 \tag{6.2}$$

define an irreducible correspondence $\mathfrak{C} : f \to KP^r_\lambda$. For f is irreducible in $K_H[x]$ and if (ξ) is a general point of f then $P^\lambda(\xi)$ is irreducible over $(K_H(\xi))_H[\lambda]$ since it is of degree one in the λ_i. Given $M^\lambda \in KP^r_\lambda$ there correspond to it, without exception a finite number of points of f, namely its intersections with P^λ, which is always prime to f. Hence by (III, 18.6) to almost every M^λ there correspond distinct points of f each counted with multiplicity unity, and hence distinct places each counted with the same multiplicity one (V, 15.1) and this is precisely (6.1).

(6.3) *Application to the class.* Let as before f be irreducible and let its order $m > 1$. The first polar of the point $M^\lambda(\lambda_0, \lambda_1, \lambda_2)$ is

$$f^\lambda = \Sigma \lambda_i f_{x_i}.$$

To begin with the f_{x_i} are linearly independent. For suppose $f^\lambda = 0$ for some point M^λ. Then this will hold in every coordinate system. Let the system be so chosen that M^λ is the point $(1, 0, 0)$. Then $f^\lambda = f_{x_0} = 0$. Thus f does not contain x_0. Since it is of the form $f(x_1, x_2)$ and irreducible it must be of degree one, contrary to assumption.

Since the f_{x_i} are of degree $< m$ they are also linearly independent mod f. Let D^λ be the variable part of the intersection divisor of f^λ and n its degree. Thus f^λ generates a g^2_n. The points on f where the f_{x_i} all vanish are the double points $B_1, \cdots, B_\delta$. In order that f^λ have in one of the places of center B_i order above the minimum the λ_j will have to satisfy a certain linear relation. Hence for almost all M^λ the divisor D^λ will not contain a place of center B_i and, furthermore by Bertini's theorem its n places $\pi_1, \cdots, \pi_n$ will be distinct. Hence (III, 5, Example III) for almost all points M^λ of KP^2_x their centers $C_1, \cdots, C_n$ will be ordinary distinct points of f and they are the contacts of the tangents from M^λ to f. Hence n is the class of the curve f. To calculate it take one of the double points B and let π, π' be the places of center B. Choose coordinates such that B is $(1, 0, 0)$ and the tangents at B the lines x_1, x_2. Then

$$f = \alpha x_0^{m-2} x_1 x_2 + \cdots, \quad \alpha \neq 0$$

$$f^\lambda = \alpha x_0^{m-2}(\lambda_1 x_2 + \lambda_2 x_1) + \cdots.$$

Hence for almost all M^λ the curve f^λ is not tangent to f at B. It follows that f^λ is of order one at π, π'. Hence π, π' each enter with coefficient unity in the fixed part of the intersection divisor of f^λ. Hence

$$n = m(m-1) - 2\delta.$$

This is a special case of one of a classical set of formulas given by Plücker and relating various characters of an algebraic curve: order, class, number of inflexions, of bitangents, of double points and of cusps.

§ 3. BIRATIONAL MODELS AND LINEAR SERIES

7. Given a set of forms $P_i \in K_H[x]$, $i = 0, 1, \cdots, s$, of the same degree and not all divisible by f, we may on the one hand consider the linear series g_n^r generated by

$$P^\lambda = \Sigma \lambda_i P_i \tag{7.1}$$

and on the other the associated rational transformation T: $f \rightarrow KP_y^s$:

$$\rho y_i = P_i(x), \quad i = 0, 1, \cdots, s. \tag{7.2}$$

To replace the P_i by another set of $s + 1$ linearly independent linear combinations of themselves is the same as to apply a projective transformation in KP_y^s and will not affect our treatment. Taking advantage of this choose the P_i so that the first $r + 1$ are linearly independent mod f and the rest divisible by f. This amounts to selecting coordinates in KP_y^s such that $\Gamma = Tf$ is in the subspace $y_{r+i} = 0$, $i = 1, 2, \cdots, s - r$. At the same time it assigns to g_n^r the generating system $\lambda_0 P_0 + \cdots + \lambda_r P_r$. In other words one may as well take $s = r$. Since the case $r = 0$ offers no interest we assume also $r \geq 1$. Finally since the fixed part of the divisors of g_n^r plays no role in the sequel we shall suppose that there is none, or in our earlier notations that $D^\lambda = A^\lambda$.

Since T is a rational transformation of f onto Γ it has a certain degree μ. A n.a.s.c. for Γ to be a birational model is that $\mu = 1$. We wish to translate this property into a property of g_n^r.

Let the place π^* of Γ have in its inverse $\mathrm{T}^{-1}\pi^*$ the places $\pi_1, \cdots, \pi_\rho$ of f, where π_h has multiplicity n_h. Thus $B = \Sigma n_h \pi_h$ is a divisor of the involution I_μ on f associated with the rational transformation T.

Referring to (V, 17), and recalling that for π_h the local degree is n_h, one may select parameters t for π_h and t^* for π^* such that $t^* = t^{n_h}$.

Since g_n^r has no fixed places there exists a $P^{\lambda'} = Q$ whose divisor $D^{\lambda'}$ contains no places of D^λ and in particular none of the π_h. Thus P^λ/Q defines an element $R^\lambda \in K^f$ which is also in K^Γ, since P^λ/Q is of the form

$$\frac{\Sigma \lambda_i y_i}{\Sigma \lambda'_i y_i}.$$

It is clear that D^λ is the divisor of zeros of R^λ as an element of K^f. On the other hand since $R^\lambda \in K^\Gamma$ it has a certain order α at the place π^* of Γ: $R^\lambda(t^*) = t^{*\alpha} E(t^*)$. As a consequence on π_h: $R^\lambda(t) = t^{\alpha n_h} E(t^{n_h})$. Since π_h is a zero of R^λ we have $\alpha > 0$. Hence π_h enters in D^λ with the positive coefficient αn_h and D^λ contains αB.

Let now $B_1, \cdots, B_k$ be the distinct divisors of the involution I_μ which contain the places of D^λ. We have just shown that if B_i contains the place π of D^λ then D^λ contains $\alpha_i B_i$, $\alpha_i > 0$. Since distinct B_i have no common places

$$D^\lambda = \Sigma \alpha_i B_i. \tag{7.3}$$

That is to say every divisor of g_n^r is an exact sum of divisors of I_μ. The series g_n^r is then said to be *compounded with the involution* I_μ.

When $\mu = 1$, $I_\mu = I_1$ is merely the collection of places of f and f and Γ are birationally equivalent. The series g_n^r is thus not compounded with any I_μ, $\mu > 1$. Such a series is said to be *simple*.

Thus if Γ is not a birational model of f, g_n^r is compounded with an I_μ, $\mu > 1$. Conversely let this be the case and suppose that nevertheless T is birational. Let π be an ordinary place of f. Then the divisors of g_n^r containing π make up a g_n^{r-1} with π as its sole fixed part. Hence T cannot be compounded with an I_μ, $\mu > 1$.

To sum up we may state:

(7.4) **Theorem.** *A n.a.s.c. in order that the curve* Γ *associated with* g_n^r, $r > 0$, *be a birational model of* f *is that* g_n^r *be simple.*

Returning to the case where g_n^r is compounded with an involution I_μ, and referring to (7.3) the divisor $D'^\lambda = TD^\lambda$ has for degree $n' = \Sigma\alpha_i$. Since the B_i have the common degree μ we have $n = \mu n'$. As we have a $g_{n'}^r$ in Γ, by (4.4): $r \leq n'$. Hence the useful inequality

$$\mu \leq \frac{n}{r}, \tag{7.5}$$

which limits the degree of an involution with which g_n^r might be compounded.

(7.6) *Normal curves.* Every algebraic curve Γ of order n which is a model of K^f in KP^r may be generated by a system (7.1) such that $P^\lambda = \Sigma\lambda_i P_i$ cuts out a simple g_n^r. We say that Γ is a *normal* curve of KP^r whenever: (a) Γ is not contained in a $KP^{r'}$, $r' < r$; (b) there is no curve Δ of order n in some $KP^{r+s} \supset KP^r$ contained in no KP^u, $u < r + s$, whose projection into KP^r is Γ. If such a curve exists coordinates may be so chosen for KP^{r+s} that KP^r is the space $y_{r+i} = 0$, $i = 1, 2, \cdots, s$. Thus if Δ is the curve

$$\rho y_i = P_i(x_0, x_1, x_2), \quad i = 0, \cdots, r + s \tag{7.7}$$

then Γ is the curve represented by the first $r + 1$ relations (7.7), and by $y_{r+i} = 0$, $i = 1, 2, \cdots, s$. Now on Δ the image of g_n^r is the series cut out by the hyperplane $\lambda_0 y_0 + \cdots + \lambda_r y_r$ and it is contained in the g_n^{r+s} cut out by all the hyperplanes of KP^{r+s}. Thus when Γ is not normal g_u^r is not complete. The converse is immediate. Hence:

(7.8) *A necessary and sufficient condition in order that a curve* Γ *of* KP^r *be normal is that the hyperplanes of the space cut out on* Γ *a complete* g_n^r.

§ 4. Rational, Elliptic and Hyperelliptic Curves

8. Rational curves.

(8.1) **Theorem.** *A n.a.s.c. for the rationality of a curve f is that it possess a linear series of type g_n^n. Then all its complete series are of that type.*

A series g_n^n can only be complete since its dimension is the largest possible for its degree (4.4). Supposing f rational we may assume that it is the line x_0. Then the forms $\psi_n(x_1, x_2)$ of order n cut out a series of degree n. Since the $n + 1$ monomials $x_1^k x_2^{n-k}$ are manifestly linearly independent mod x_0, the dimension of the series is n and so it is a g_n^n. Since there is a ψ_n cutting out any preassigned divisor of degree n, the family $\{g_n^n\}$ thus obtained is the totality of all the complete series on a rational f. Thus all but the sufficiency condition is proved.

Suppose now that f possesses a series g_n^n, $n > 0$. Since the dimension is n, the series is complete. Let π be an ordinary place not fixed for the series. The divisors of g_n^n containing π form a g_{n-1}^{n-1}. By repeated application of this argument if $n > 1$ the existence of a g_n^n is shown to imply that of a g_1^1. Assume then $n = 1$, and let the series be generated by $P^\lambda = \lambda_0 P_0 + \lambda_1 P_1$. Then

$$\rho\lambda_0 = P_1(x), \quad \rho\lambda_1 = - P_0(x) \tag{8.2}$$

is a rational transformation T of the curve f onto the line KP^1. If M^λ is the point (λ_0, λ_1) of the line, there corresponds to M^λ a divisor D^λ of g_1^1 consisting of a single place π and the center N^λ of π is the inverse $T^{-1}M^\lambda$. Hence T is of degree one, and so it is birational. Therefore the curve f is rational.

(8.3) *Application. The following irreducible plane curves of degree m are rational:* (a) *curves with a point of multiplicity* $(m - 1)$; (b) *curves with the maximum number* $N = (m - 1)(m - 2)/2$ *of double points with distinct tangents.*

Since a line is rational one may assume $m > 1$. Regarding (a), the lines through the $(m - 1)$-tuple point are linearly independent absolutely and also mod f since their degree $< m$. Their intersection divisors each contain one variable point. Hence the lines generate a g_1^1 and so (a) follows. In particular then irreducible conics are rational. Regarding (b), we may then assume $m > 2$. By (4.6) f contains a g_n^n, hence it is rational.

(8.4) *Rational involutions.* If the curve f possesses a rational involution I_μ there is a related rational transformation T of f onto a line l. If l is the line KP_λ^2, T is given by relations (8.2) and the divisors of I_μ are the variable divisors of g_μ^1 generated by $P^\lambda = \lambda_0 P_0 + \lambda_1 P_1$. The converse is obvious. Hence:

(8.5). *The rational involutions on a curve f are merely the collections of divisors of its one dimensional linear series.*

(8.6) Another fruitful approach to rational involutions is as follows. If X is an affine coordinate for the line l then K^f is algebraic over $K(X)$, and hence K^f is a simple extension $K(X, Y)$. If $F(X, Y) = 0$ is the irreducible equation satisfied by Y, F is an affine birational model of f and in this model the divisors of I_μ in the affine plane are the intersections with F of the lines $X =$ const. Thus F is of degree μ in Y. The converse is obvious.

As an application of (8.5) one will prove readily:

(8.7) *Conics and cubics carry an infinity of rational involutions of degree two.*

9. Hyperelliptic curves. We have just shown (8.6) that f possesses a rational I_2 when and only when it is reducible to the type

(9.1) $$F = A(X)Y^2 + 2B(X)Y + C(X) = 0; \qquad A, B, C \in K[X].$$

A further reduction is obtained by means of the birational transformation

$$X \to X, \quad A(X)Y + B(X) \to Y$$

to the form

(9.2) $$Y^2 = F_q(X), \quad F \in K[X] \text{ and of degree } q.$$

Suppose that $F = G^2H$ where the factors are in $K[X]$ and H has no square factors. Then the birational transformation $Y \to G(X)Y$, $X \to X$ operates the reduction to the same form (9.2) but so that F has no square factors. Suppose $q = 2r$, and let F have the root α. The birational transformation

$$X \to \frac{1}{X} + \alpha, \quad Y \to \frac{Y}{X^r}$$

will operate the reduction to the form (9.2) with q odd.

Upon combining with (8.5) we have then:

(9.3) *A necessary and sufficient condition in order that the curve f possess a rational involution I_2 is that it be birationally equivalent to a curve of type*

$(9.4)_p$ $$Y^2 = F_{2p+1}(X)$$

where F has no square factors. The involution is then the g_2^1 cut out by the lines $X =$ constant.

The conics ($p = 0$) and cubics ($p = 1$) have already been discussed. The conics are rational. The curves reducible to the type $(9.4)_1$, are known as *elliptic*, and those reducible to the type $(9.4)_p$, $p > 1$, are known as *hyperelliptic*. We shall see later that p is a birational character: the *genus*, so that curves corresponding to distinct values of p are birationally distinct.

§ 5. Adjoint Curves and Series

10. Let us adopt henceforth as birational model a curve f which has no other singularities than double points with distinct tangents. An *adjoint* to the curve is a curve that passes through the double points. An adjoint of order q will be denoted by φ_q. We recall that if there are δ double points then

$$p = \frac{(m-1)(m-2)}{2} - \delta$$

is non-negative (4.5). The number p is known as the *genus* of the curve f. We shall show that p is a birational invariant of the curve and its importance will manifest itself presently.

Let us suppose that adjoints φ_q do exist. Referring to the proof of (4.5) this is certainly true for $q = m - 2$, and hence for every $q \geq m - 2$, when $m > 2$. In point of fact adjoints φ_q exist provided that

$$\delta = \frac{(m-1)(m-2)}{2} - p \leq \frac{q(q+3)}{2}$$

which clearly holds if $p \geq 1$ for $q = m - 3$. Thus for $p \geq 1$ there exist adjoints of order $m - 3$. Let $D_1, \cdots, D_\delta$ be the double points and let π_{2i-1}, π_{2i} be the two places of center D_i. Set also $\Delta = \Sigma\pi_j$. If the adjoints φ_q exist each φ_q intersects f in a divisor $\Delta + G$, G effective. We say that G is *cut out by* φ_q. The totality of the divisors G constitutes a linear series $g^{r_q}_{n_q}$, *the series cut out by the adjoints* φ_q. If $G = G_1 + G_2$, G_i effective, we say that G_2 is *cut out by the adjoints* φ_q *through* G_1, and $|G_2|$ is the linear series cut out by the adjoints φ_q through G_1. The divisor G_2 is also said to be a *residue* of G_1 relative to the series cut out by the φ_q.

The following is the basic property of the adjoints:

(10.1) **Max Noether's residue theorem.** *Let G, G' be equivalent effective divisors and let there exist an adjoint φ_q cutting out $G + H$, H effective. Then there exists likewise an adjoint φ'_q cutting out $G' + H$.*

For the proof we require three preliminary lemmas. As before the curve f is assumed of order m.

(10.2) **Lemma.** *If a line l cuts f in m distinct points $B_1, \cdots, B_m$ and the curve g contains each B_i then $g = lg_1$* mod f, *where of course $l, g, g_1 \in K_H[x]$.*

Select a triangle of reference $A_0A_1A_2$ none of whose vertices are on f and such that l is the line x_0. Thus the B_i are on A_1A_2 and distinct from A_1 and A_2. Since f is regular in x_2 we may divide g by f as to x_2 and obtain $g = hf + g'$, where $g' \in K_H[x]$ and is of degree $< m$ in x_2. Thus $g' = x_0g_1 + g''(x_1, x_2)x_1^k$, where g'' is of degree $< m$, and $g', g''x_1^k$ vanish at the points B_i. Since $x_1 \neq 0$ at the B_i it follows that g'' vanishes at the m points. Thus the curve g'' of degree $< m$ intersects $l = x_0$ in m points. Hence $g'' = 0$, $g = x_0g_1$ mod f, i.e. $g = lg_1$ mod f.

(10.3) **Lemma.** *If l intersects f in the double point D and in $m - 2$*

further points $B_1, \cdots, B_{m-2}$ *and if* g *contains the* B_i *and has a double point in* D *then again* $g = lg_1 \bmod f$, *where as before* $l, g, g_1 \in K_H[x]$.

Select the triangle of reference so that A_1 is D, the B_i are on x_0 and the vertices A_0, A_2 are not on f. The same relations will take place as before so that:

$$g = hf + x_0 g_1 + g''(x_1, x_2)x_1^k, \quad k > 0.$$

This time since g and f have a double point in A_1 they are of degree ≥ 2 in x_0, x_2. Hence this must also hold for g''. Thus $g'' = x_2^2 g'''(x_1, x_2)$. Now g''' of degree $< m - 2$ must intersect x_0 in the $m - 2$ distinct points B_i. Hence $g''' = 0 = g''$ and the conclusion is the same as before.

(10.4) **Lemma.** *Let* π, π' *be the two places whose center is the double point* D. *If* $g \in K_H[x]$ *has a zero of order at least two in both* π *and* π' *then it has at least a double point in* D.

Take a triangle of reference with $A_0 = D$ and A_0A_1, A_0A_2 not tangent to f at D. Passing to affine coordinates we will have

$$F = \alpha(Y - m_1X)(Y - m_2X) + \cdots, \quad \alpha m_1 m_2 \neq 0, \quad m_1 \neq m_2;$$

$$G = a_1(X, Y) + a_2(X, Y) + \cdots,$$

where a_i is a form of degree i. The two places π, π' of center A have then representations (V, 14.5)

$$\pi\colon\ Y = m_1X + \cdots; \qquad \pi'\colon\ Y = m_2X + \cdots.$$

Since G is of order at least two in each we must have $a_1(1, m_1) = a_1(1, m_2) = 0$. Since $a_1(1, z)$ is of degree one with two distinct roots, $a_1(1, z) = 0$, hence $a_1(X, Y) = 0$ and G has multiplicity at least two at D.

Proof of the residue theorem. Since $G \sim G'$ there is an element $R = P/Q$ of the function field K^f whose divisor is $G' - G$. Let $M_1, \cdots, M_s$ be the zeros of Q and choose coordinates so that the triangle of reference $A_0A_1A_2$ bears no special relation to f, P, Q. More explicitly the A_i are not to be on fPQ, not on a line joining two double points, nor on any tangent at a point M_i or issued from a point M_i, and each side of the triangle is to intersect f in m distinct points. Since Q and f are regular in x_2 upon taking their resultant as to x_2 we obtain a relation

$$Af + BQ = \Pi(\alpha_i x_0 + \beta_i x_1)^{\sigma_i}; \qquad A, B \in K_H[x]; \quad \alpha_i, \beta_i \in K.$$

Since the lines $l_i = \alpha_i x_0 + \beta_i x_1$ are the lines A_2M_i they are not tangent to f and do not intersect on the curve. Multiplying then both P and Q by B the function R will be determined by a quotient of forms of type:

$$\frac{P}{\Pi l_i^{\sigma_i}}. \tag{10.5}$$

Let now φ be an adjoint cutting out a divisor $G + H$, H effective. Upon setting $S = P\varphi$, we find that instead of (10.5) R will be likewise determined by a quotient

$$\frac{S}{\varphi \Pi l_i^{\sigma_i}}. \tag{10.6}$$

Let now M be one of the intersections of l_i with f and let π be a place of center M. Given any form $g \in K_H[x]$ we denote by $\omega(g)$ its order at π. If A is any divisor then $\eta(A)$ will designate the coefficient of π in A.

Since l_i is not tangent to f at π, and π like all places of f is linear we have $\omega(l_i) = 1$. We also have:

$$\omega(S) = \omega(P) + \omega(\varphi) = \omega(P) + \eta(G) + \eta(H) + \eta(\Delta).$$

Now on the one hand the order of π as a pole of R is at most $\eta(G)$; on the other hand it is $\sigma_i - \omega(P)$ since the l_j do not intersect on f. Hence $\sigma_i - \omega(P) \leq \eta(G)$. Hence

$$\omega(S) \geq \sigma_i + \eta(\Delta).$$

We have now two possibilities: (a) M is not a double point. Then $\eta(\Delta) = 0$, hence $\omega(S) \geq \sigma_i$. Therefore if $\sigma_i > 0$, S contains the point M. (b) M is a double point. Then $\eta(\Delta) = 1$, $\omega(S) \geq \sigma_i + 1$, hence if $\sigma_i > 0$, S is of order at least two at π. Thus S is of order at least two at each of the two places of center M and therefore (10.4) M is a double point for S.

We conclude that if $\sigma_i > 0$ then by reference to (10.2) and (10.3) S fulfills all the conditions for divisibility by $l_i \bmod f$.

Beginning then with l_1 one may replace S/l_1 by another form still called S at the cost of replacing σ_1 by $\sigma_1 - 1$ throughout. The orders of S at the intersections of l_1 with f will merely have been lowered by one unit, and those at the intersections with l_i, $i > 1$, will remain the same. Hence we will have (10.2) and (10.3) save that σ_1 will have been replaced by $\sigma_1 - 1$. The same process may be continued until all the σ_i are reduced to zero. At the end we shall have a determination of R by a quotient ψ/φ, where φ is the same adjoint as before. Since the divisor of R is $G' - G$ and the divisor of zeros of φ is $G + H + \Delta$, the same for ψ is $G' + H + \Delta$. Hence ψ is an adjoint of the same order q as φ and the theorem is proved.

11. (11.1) *Given any effective divisor G let H be a residue of G as to the adjoints φ_q. Then the complete series $|G|$ determined by G is cut out by the adjoints φ_q through H.*

(11.2) *The adjoints φ_q through a given divisor H cut out a complete linear series.*

In particular for $H = 0$:

(11.3) *The adjoints φ_q cut out a complete linear series.*

If the curve f has no singularities all the curves of the plane are adjoints. Hence:

(11.4) *If f has no singularities all the curves of a given degree cut out on f a complete linear series.*

As an application we will prove a special case of a classical result on cubic curves:

(11.5) *Let f, f_1 be two plane cubics where one, say f, is non-singular. Suppose that the two curves intersect in nine distinct points $M_1, \cdots, M_9$. Then any cubic passing through eight of the points also passes through the ninth.*

Let π_i be the place of center M_i and let $H = \pi_1 + \cdots + \pi_8$. The cubics φ through H have a variable intersection divisor D such that the collection $\{D\}$ is a complete series. Since the full intersection divisor of φ is of degree 9 and has a fixed part of degree 8 the series is a g_1^r. Thus $r \leq 1$. If $r = 1$ then f is rational and all its complete series must be of type g_n^n (8.1). Now the forms x_0, x_1, x_2 are linearly independent mod f. Hence the series which they generate is a g_3^2 and it is complete since it is the series cut out by all the lines. Hence f is not rational. It follows that $r = 0$ and so φ generates a g_1^0, i.e. all its places are fixed. Since f_1 is a special φ, π_9 is in the intersection divisor of φ with f. Hence if φ contains H, i.e. it passes through $M_1, \cdots, M_8$ it also contains π_9, i.e. it passes through M_9.

As a matter of fact (11.5) is true even when f has a double point or is singular or even reducible, but this is not readily proved by means of linear series. On the other hand our argument holds whatever the fixed part H, of degree 8, of the intersection divisor of f_1, and it asserts that if φ contains H then its intersection divisor is the same as that of f_1.

The following interesting property is an immediate consequence of (11.5). Let $A_1A_2A_3$ and $B_1B_2B_3$ be two sets of collinear points of f, where the six points are distinct and the lines A_iB_i are not tangent to f. Then A_iB_i intersects f in a third point C_i and $C_1C_2C_3$ are collinear. The restrictions as to distinct points and non-tangency are of course readily removed.

Let us also recall finally that (11.5) with the irreducibility restriction removed implies Pascal's theorem. For these and other related properties of cubics the reader will profitably consult Robert Walker [1], p. 191 and van der Waerden [2], p. 87.

§ 6. The Theorem of Riemann-Roch

12. This fundamental theorem deals with the difference $n - r$ for a complete g_n^r. In view of (11.1) it is natural to calculate first the difference $n_q - r_q$ for the complete series $g_{n_q}^{r_q}$ generated by the adjoints φ_q. If δ is the number of double points then the divisor Δ, sum of the places whose centers are the double points, is of degree 2δ. Hence

$$n_q = mq - 2\delta.$$

Among the adjoints a central role is played by those of order $m - 3$. The curves and the adjoint series which they generate are known as *canonical curves* and *canonical series.*

It turns out to be convenient to set $q = m - 3 + s$, where $s \geq 0$. That is to say only adjoints φ_q, $q \geq m - 3$, are to be considered. We have then:

(12.1) $$n_q = n_{m-3+s} = m(m - 3 + s) - 2\delta = ms + 2p - 2.$$

In particular the degree of the canonical series is

(12.2) $$n_{m-3} = 2p - 2.$$

Hence its dimension $\leq 2p - 2$.

A divisor G and the complete series $|G|$ are said to be *special* whenever there exists a canonical curve φ_{m-3} through G. Let G be special and let H be a residue of G relative to the canonical series. Set also

$$|G| = g^r_n, \quad |H| = g^{r'}_{n'}, \quad n + n' = 2p - 2.$$

Then $|G|$ may be generated by all the φ_{m-3} through H and $|H|$ by all the φ_{m-3} through G. By Noether's theorem G may be replaced by any $G' \in |G|$, and H by any $H' \in |H|$. Hence in particular r' is a character of $|G|$. The number $\sigma = 1 + r'$ is known as the *speciality-index* of g^r_n. It is the maximum number of linearly independent adjoints φ_{m-3} through any divisor G of the series. When g^r_n is not special its speciality-index is $\sigma = 0$. We may now state:

(12.3) **Theorem of Riemann-Roch.** *Let σ be the speciality-index of a complete g^r_n. Then*

(12.3a) $$n - r = p - \sigma.$$

In particular if the series is non-special

(12.3b) $$n - r = p.$$

Since for $n > 2p - 2$, g^r_n is certainly non-special, (12.3b) holds for n sufficiently large. Thus as a consequence of the theorem:

(12.4) *p is the maximum of $n - r$ for any complete linear series g^r_n, and this maximum is actually reached.*

Since complete linear series have birational character, a consequence of the theorem of Riemann-Roch is

(12.5) *The genus p is a birational invariant.*

Owing to this property one refers sometimes to p as the genus of the function field K^f.

13. For the proof of the Riemann-Roch theorem we shall require:

(13.1) **Lemma.** *Let ψ be a curve of degree n and $M_1, \cdots, M_s$ points of the plane. Then for $n \geq s$ the conditions expressing that ψ passes through the s points M_i are linearly independent.*

Let t be any integer $\leq s$. It is sufficient to show that there is a curve of degree n passing through any t of the points M_i, say $M_1, \cdots, M_t$ but not through the rest. To that end take t lines $l_1, \cdots, l_t$ where l_i contains M_i, but no other M_j and a curve ψ_{n-t} containing no point M_j. The product curve $l_1, \cdots, l_t\psi_{n-t}$ answers the question.

We shall now proceed with the proof of the Riemann-Roch theorem essentially along lines laid down by Max Noether.

Let again δ be the number of double points. The number of terms in a form of order q is

$$\alpha_q = \frac{(q+1)(q+2)}{2}.$$

If the form is to vanish at the δ double points, then the coefficients satisfy δ linear relations which are linearly independent when q exceeds δ. Hence the adjoints φ_q make up a linear family among which $\alpha_q - \delta + \varepsilon_q$ are linearly independent where $\varepsilon_q = 0$ for q sufficiently high. The family contains a linear subfamily composed of adjoints divisible by f, i.e. of form fH_{q-m}. Among these there are α_{q-m} linearly independent and no more where $\alpha_{q-m} = 0$ for $q < m$. Hence for q sufficiently great there are $\alpha_q - \alpha_{q-m}$ curves φ_q linearly independent mod f. Under the circumstances the dimension r_q of the complete series cut out by the φ_q is, with $q - m - 3 + s$:

$$r_q = \alpha_q - \alpha_{q-m} - \delta - 1 + \varepsilon_q + \beta_q = ms + p - 2 + \varepsilon_q + \beta_q$$

where $\beta_{m-3} = 1$ and $\beta_q = 0$ for $q > m - 3$. Therefore the adjoints of order $q = m - 3 + s$ sufficiently high cut out a complete series $g^{ms+p-2}_{ms+2p-2}$. Thus for the complete series $g^{r_q}_{n_q}$ cut out by the curves φ_q, q above a certain value, we have

$$n_q - r_q = p$$

i.e. the theorem of Riemann-Roch holds.

Bearing in mind that for q arbitrary one may have to replace α_q by $\alpha_q + \varepsilon_q + \beta_q$ we have

$$(13.2) \qquad \begin{cases} n_q - r_q = p - \varepsilon_q, & q > m - 3, \\ n_{m-3} - r_{m-3} = p - 1 - \varepsilon_q. \end{cases}$$

In particular $r_{m-3} = n_{m-3} - (p-1) + \varepsilon = p - 1 + \varepsilon$, $\varepsilon = \varepsilon_{m-3}$. Hence:

(13.3) *The canonical series exists for $p \geq 1$ and it is a $g^{p-1+\varepsilon}_{2p-2}$.*

Both (13.2) and (13.3) are temporary since the theorem of Riemann-Roch asserts that the numbers ε are all zero.

(13.4) Consider now any complete g_n^r whatsoever and let G be a divisor of the series. By (13.2) one may choose q so high that r_q exceeds the degree of G. Then by (4.2) some φ_q contains G. Let H be the residue of G as to φ_q. Thus H is of degree $n_q - n$. Since g_n^r is cut out by the φ_q containing H its dimension $r \geq r_q - (n_q - n)$. Hence $n - r \leq n_q - r_q$ and therefore $n - r \leq p$.

(13.5) Notice that at this stage it is already known that for any complete series $n - r \leq p$, and that the maximum p is reached. That is to say (12.4) is already proved and the genus p shown to be birationally invariant. In particular if f contains a g_n^n it is rational (8.1) and so $p = 0$ as for a line.

14. Further progress in the proof of the Riemann-Roch theorem will rest upon:

(14.1) **Max Noether's reduction lemma.** *If G is a special divisor, for almost all places π the complete series $G + \pi$ contains π as a fixed place.*

Let $\{\varphi_{m-3}^i\}$ $i = 0, \cdots, s$ be a maximal linearly independent set of canonical curves through G. They are also linearly independent mod f since $m - 3 < m$. Hence the fixed intersections of $\Sigma\lambda_i\varphi_{m-3}^i$ with f make up a divisor $H + \Delta$, H effective. Take a place π_0 not in $H + \Delta$. In particular then the center A_0 of π_0 is not a double point.

The excluded choices for π_0 are manifestly finite in number. Since π_0 is not in $H + \Delta$ there is a φ_{m-3} containing H but not π_0. Since A_0 is not a double point we may pass a line l through A_0 meeting f in m distinct points $A_0, A_1, \cdots, A_{m-1}$. Thus A_i is the center of one and only one place π_i. Now $l\varphi_{m-3}$ is a φ_{m-2} containing $\pi_0 + G$ with residue $H + H'$, $H' = \pi_1 + \cdots + \pi_{m-1}$. Hence the complete series $|\pi_0 + G|$ is cut out by all the curves φ_{m-2} through $H + H'$. Since such a curve meets l in $m - 1$ distinct points φ_{m-2} is divisible by l and so the divisor which it cuts out as a residue to $H + H'$ contains π_0. Thus π_0 is a fixed place of $|\pi_0 + G|$ and the lemma is proved.

15. The proof of the theorem of Riemann-Roch will now follow rapidly.

(15.1) *A complete g_n^r, hence any g_n^r such that $n - r < p$ is necessarily special.*

Suppose $n - r < p$. If $p = 0$ we have $n < r$ which is ruled out. If $p = 1$ the series is a g_n^n, hence f is rational and so $p = 0$ (13.5), a contradiction. Thus $p > 1$.

Let then $p > 1$, and suppose $n \leq p - 1$. Then certainly $n - r < p$ and so the condition is satisfied. Let G be a divisor of the series. Since the canonical series is of dimension $\geq p - 1$, there is a φ_{m-3} containing G. If H is the residual divisor of G as to φ_{m-3}, g_n^r is generated by the canonical curves through H. Thus (15.1) holds whenever $n \leq p - 1$. We may therefore suppose $n \geq p$ and use induction on n. Supposing then (15.1) true for $n - 1 \geq p - 1$ we shall prove it for n. Since $n - r < p$, necessarily $r > 0$. Take a place π not in Δ nor fixed for g_n^r. There is a divisor $G \in g_n^r$ containing π. If G is special the same reasoning as above will prove g_n^r special. Suppose then G non-special. Since π is not fixed for g_n^r, $|G - \pi|$ is a g_{n-1}^{r-1} and since $(n - 1) - (r - 1) < p$, this g_{n-1}^{r-1} is special. Since the φ_{m-3} through $G - \pi$ do not contain π and π is not in Δ, the reduction theorem may be applied as between $G - \pi$ and π (14.2). Hence $g_n^r = |(G - \pi) + \pi|$ has π as fixed place. This contradiction proves (15.1).

Since $n - r \leq p$ for every g_n^r we may state:

(15.2) *If g_n^r is complete non-special $n - r = p$. That is to say all complete non-special series are of type g_n^{n-p}. This holds in particular for the series cut out by adjoints φ_q, $q > m - 3$. Thus if $q = m - 3 + s$, $s > 0$, the series is of type $g_{ms+2p-2}^{ms+p-2}$.*

The result just stated is the so-called Riemann part of the Riemann-Roch theorem. Roch's complement is the statement regarding the dimension of complete special series to which we now turn our attention.

Let g_n^r have the speciality-index $\sigma > 0$. Thus if G is any divisor of g_n^r there exist σ linearly independent canonical curves and no more through G. If π is not a fixed place of the linear series which they generate, nor in Δ, by the reduction theorem $|G + \pi|$ is a g_{n+1}^r and its speciality-index is $\sigma - 1$. Proceeding thus we shall obtain finally a complete $g_{n+\sigma}^r$ of speciality-index zero, i.e. non-special. By (15.1) $r = n + \sigma - p$, $r - \sigma = n - p$. This is precisely the Riemann-Roch theorem whose proof is now complete.

16. Some noteworthy complements follow:

(16.1) **Law of reciprocity of Brill-Noether.** *Let the complete series g_n^r, $g_{n'}^{r'}$ have for sum the canonical series. Then*

$$n - n' = 2(r - r').$$

Let G be a divisor of g_n^r. By Noether's residue theorem $g_{n'}^{r'}$ is cut out by the φ_{m-3} through G. Hence $r' + 1$ is the speciality-index of g_n^r and $r + 1$ that of $g_{n'}^{r'}$. Consequently $r - r' = n - p - 1$, $r' - r = n' - p - 1$ from which to (16.1) is but a step.

(16.2) *The canonical series is a g_{2p-2}^{p-1}; it is without fixed places and it is the only complete g_{2p-2}^{p-1} of f. Hence the canonical series is a birational invariant.*

We have seen that the canonical series is a $g_{2p-2}^{p-1+\varepsilon}$. Since its speciality-index $\sigma = 1$, we have $p - 1 + \varepsilon - 1 = 2p - 2 - p$, and hence $\varepsilon = 0$. Thus the series is a g_{2p-2}^{p-1}. Suppose that there existed another complete series γ of dimension $r = p - 1$ and degree $n = 2p - 2$. Since $n - r = p - 1 < p$, γ is special. Since its n is the same as for the canonical series the two must coincide.

Suppose now that the canonical series has a fixed place π. Then $|g_{2p-2}^{p-1} - \pi|$ is a complete g_{2p-3}^{p-1}. Its $\sigma = 1$ and so we must have $2p - 3 - (p - 1) = p - 1$ which is false. Hence the canonical series has no fixed places.

(16.3) *The adjoints φ_q, $q \geq m - 3$ cut out series without fixed places.*

This is already true for $q = m - 3$. Consider any $f_s\varphi_{m-3}$. The only fixed divisor of the curves of this type is Δ. Hence this is also true for all the φ_{m-3+s}.

VII. Abelian Differentials

Historically speaking abelian integrals came first and arose as the natural generalization for the complex field of trigonometric and elliptic integrals. However for a general field one may only consider differentials, since integration in such fields is at best not a simple matter. On the other hand the differentials provide us with additional and very powerful means for a direct attack on birational geometry. Our present program is to develop the general theory of the differentials and to discuss some applications. As in the preceding two chapters the groundfield is assumed algebraically closed and of characteristic zero.

§1. Preliminary Questions

1. The abelian differentials of an irreducible curve f are merely the elements of the vector space $\mathfrak{B}$ of the differentials of the field K^f. Since $\dim f = 1$, $\mathfrak{B}$ is spanned by any differential dR of a transcendental element R of K^f. Thus an abelian differential of f is reducible to the form RdS, R and $S \in K^f$, S not in K.

(1.1) Since the abelian differentials are defined in terms of the function field K^f alone they have birational character. Hence we may choose for our curve any convenient birational model. Unless otherwise stated the model selected will be the same as before: a curve f of degree m in KP_x^2 which is not a line through a vertex of the triangle of reference. In particular since $f \neq x_0$ we will be able to pass freely to the affine model $F(X, Y) = f(1, X, Y)$. Moreover for a general point the ratios x_1/x_0 and x_2/x_0, i.e. X and Y, will be transcendental. This property is decidedly convenient when dealing with differentials.

(1.2) Let the x_i and hence also X, Y be the coordinates of a general point of f. Since X is transcendental at a general point, one may write

$$du = R(X, Y)dX. \tag{1.3}$$

In homogeneous coordinates the related form is

$$du = R(x_0, x_1, x_2)\,\frac{x_0 dx_1 - x_1 dx_0}{x_0^2} \tag{1.4}$$

which is homogeneous and of degree zero in the x_i, dx_j combined.

It should be noted that in one or the other form du is merely a convenient standard designation for the abelian differential and it does not imply that u is an element of K^f such that $du = RdS$. In the background there is the fact that when K is the complex field and R, S are considered as analytic functions say of X then there exists always an analytic function $u(X)$ such that $du(X) = R(X)dS(X)$. However, as the example of $R = 1/X$, $S = X$ shows, it may not always be possible to choose $u(X) \in K^f$.

At a general point

$$\Sigma f_{x_i} \cdot x_i = 0, \qquad \Sigma f_{x_i} \cdot dx_i = 0.$$

Since a general point is not multiple, the f_{x_i} are not all zero. Hence the preceding relations yield

$$x_{i+2}dx_{i+1} - x_{i+1}dx_{i+2} = \rho f_{x_i} (i = 0, 1, 2,; x_{i+3} = x_i). \tag{1.5}$$

Under our hypotheses the ratios x_i/x_j, $i \neq j$ are all transcendental. Hence one may replace x_0, x_1 in (1.4) by any pair x_i, x_{i+1}. Since the f_{x_i} are not all zero one may choose a pair x_i, x_{i+1} such that $f_{x_{i+2}} \neq 0$. At the cost of renumbering the coordinates we suppose $f_{x_2} \neq 0$. Hence we may write

$$du = \frac{A(x)}{B(x)} \frac{x_0dx_1 - x_1dx_0}{f_{x_2}} \tag{1.6}$$

where A, B are forms of $K_H[x]$ and the ratio A/B is of degree $m - 3$.

Let $C(c_0, c_1, c_2)$ be any point strictly in KP^2, i.e. let the c_i be elements of K which are not all three zero. Then

$$\Sigma c_i f_{x_i} \neq 0.$$

For otherwise the general point (x) would be one of the finite intersections of f with the first polar of C and the ratios x_i/x_j would be in K.

In view of (1.5)

$$\frac{x_0dx_1 - x_1dx_0}{f_{x_2}} = \frac{D(x_0, \cdots, dx_2)}{\Sigma c_i f_{x_i}},$$

$$D = \begin{vmatrix} x_0, & x_1, & x_2 \\ dx_0, & dx_1, & dx_2 \\ c_0, & c_1, & c_2 \end{vmatrix}.$$

This yields for du the symmetric form

$$du = \frac{A(x)}{B(x)} \frac{D}{\Sigma c_i f_{x_i}}. \tag{1.7}$$

It is an elementary matter to verify that under a projective transformation the second fraction, and hence also du, preserves its form. That is to say du may be written in the form (1.7) in any coordinate system whatever. Herein lies the advantage of the form (1.7).

(1.8) Let π be a place of f and let

$$x_i = \varphi_i(t), \quad i = 0, 1, 2$$

be a normal irreducible representation of π. The parametric point $M_t(\varphi(t))$ is a general point of f and hence the function field K^f is isomorphic with $K_H(\varphi(t))$, i.e. with a subfield of the power series field $K((t))$. As a consequence the "natural" differentiation of $K((t))$ induces one in K^f, and its space of differential vectors is differentially isomorphic with the one of K^f itself. We define

$$(du)_\pi = (RdS)_\pi = R(t)S'(t)dt.$$

Notice that a regular transformation $t \to tE(t)$ induces a differential automorphism in the space of differentials. To be precise it sends $R(t)S'(t)dt$ into $R(tE(t))S'(tE(t))E_1(t)dt$. It turns out that such a transformation will not affect certain elements which the representations all have in common and which alone matter.

2. Our freedom in the selection of a birational model for the basic curve will be utilized by taking one f in KP^2_x distinct from x_0 and having no other singularities than double points with distinct tangents. The order of the curve is still m and its divisor of double points (sum of the places with a double point for center) is denoted by Δ. However even then we may wish to use an additional degree of freedom in the selection of f.

We recall in fact that f possesses a non-singular birational model Γ in KP^3. A model such as described above may then be obtained by projection onto a plane from a center O which is exterior to a certain surface Φ. We assert now the following complement:

(2.1) *The birational model f described above may be so selected that a given finite set of places $\pi_1, \cdots, \pi_s$ is disjoint from Δ.*

In fact assuming the π_i in Γ let $M_1, \cdots, M_s$ be their centers.

The secants of Γ through M_i are on a cone Φ_i. All that is necessary then is to take the projection center O exterior not only to Φ but also to the surfaces Φ_i and the desired result will be accomplished.

Once the model f is selected one may take convenient coordinates for this or that purpose. In particular:

(2.2) *The coordinates may be so chosen that the tangents from* $(0, 0, 1)$ *each have contact of order one (i.e. intersection order two at the contact), and that none of the tangents is the line x_0 nor goes through a double point.*

The contacts of the tangents from a point $C(c_0, c_1, c_2)$, not a double point, are at the intersections with f of the first polar $\Sigma c_i f_{x_i}$ of the point. Now if n is the class of the curve the first polars cut out on f a series g^2_n without fixed places. Hence one may select C not on f so that its first polar cuts out a simple divisor G (besides Δ) which has no place with center on a tangent from a double point. All that is required now is to select coordinates with $C = A_2$ and x_0 not a tangent and (2.2) will hold.

§ 2. The Divisors of the Differentials. Differentials of the First Kind

3. Let du be a differential, π any place and t a parameter in an irreducible representation for π. We have

$$(du)_\pi = t^\omega(a + bt + \cdots)dt, \; a \neq 0.$$

It is seen at once that a regular transformation $t \to tE_1(t)$ does not affect ω. Hence ω depends solely upon π and du. It is known as the *order* of du at the place π, written $\omega(du, \pi)$.

(3.1) $\omega(du, \pi) = 0$ *at almost all places.*

Since X is transcendental at the general point (X, Y) one may write $du = R(X, Y)dX$. Now at almost all places π one may take as parameter $t = X - a$, $a \in K$. Thus $dt = dX$ and hence $\omega(du, \pi) = 0$ at all places where R and $R^{-1} \neq 0$ and where one may choose t as above. Since the excluded places are in finite number (3.1) follows.

By virtue of (3.1): $H(du) = \Sigma\omega(du, \pi)\pi$ is a divisor of f. It is known as the *divisor of the differential du.*

Consider two differentials

$$du = RdX, \qquad du_1 = R_1dX.$$

At π we will have

$$du = R(t)X'(t)dt, \qquad du_1 = R_1(t)X'(t)dt.$$

If ω, ω_1, ω_0 are the orders of R, R_1 and $X'(t)$ at π those of du, du_1 are $\omega + \omega_0$, $\omega_1 + \omega_0$. Hence the coefficient of π in $H(du) - H(du_1)$ is $\omega - \omega_1 =$ the order at π of the element R/R_1 of K^f. Hence $H(du) - H(du_1)$ is the divisor of R/R_1 or $H(du) \sim H(du_1)$. That is to say the divisors of the differentials are all equivalent. Their class $\{H(du)\}$ is the *differential class.* Its effective elements make up a complete linear series called the *differential series.*

(3.2) **Theorem.** *The differential series is the canonical series.*

The proof will come after a further study of the differentials.

4. Let du and π be as before and let $\omega(du,\pi) \neq 0$. We will say that

π is a *zero of order* ω of du when $\omega > 0$,

π is a *pole of order*—ω of du when $\omega < 0$.

A differential which has no poles is said to be of the *first kind* (abridged as *dfk*).

If du, du_1 are *dfk* so is $\lambda du + \lambda_1 du_1$, λ and $\lambda_1 \in K$. Hence the *dfk* are the elements of a vector space $\mathfrak{W}$ with scalar domain K.

It follows at once from the definitions just given that:

(4.1) *A birational transformation sends a dfk into a dfk and transforms*

𝔚 into an isomorphic space. Hence the maximum number of linearly independent dfk is a birational invariant.

We will prove in fact:

(4.2) **Theorem.** *A necessary and sufficient condition for du to* be an *abelian differential of the first kind is that it be reducible to the projective form:*

$$du = \varphi_{m-3}(x_0, x_1, x_2) \cdot \frac{D(x_0, \cdots, dx_2)}{\Sigma c_i f_{x_i}}, \tag{4.2a}$$

where φ_{m-3} is a canonical curve. The cartesian form is

$$du = \frac{\varphi_{m-3} dX}{F_Y}. \tag{4.2b}$$

From this follows at once:

(4.3) *The dimension of the vector space 𝔚 of the differentials of the first kind is equal to the dimension p of the system $\{\varphi_{m-3}\}$. That is to say there can be found p, but no more, linearly independent differentials of the first kind.*

For the complex field this is a classical result due to Abel.

(4.4) *Rational curves have no differentials of the first kind.*

This last result could be proved directly. For when $p = 0$ the differentials are of the form $R(X)dX$, $R \in K(X)$. If R is not constant there are always poles, while dX has $X = \infty$ as a pole.

Proof of (4.2). Referring to the proof of the residue theorem (VI, 10) one may write

$$du = \frac{A(x_0, x_1, x_2)}{l_1 l_2 \cdots l_k} \frac{D}{\Sigma c_i f_{x_i}}$$

where the l_i are lines not tangent to f and do not join two double points of f, and A is a form of degree $m - 3 + k$ since du is of degree zero in the x_i and dx_i. Let l_i intersect the curve f in M. Suppose first that M is not a double point. If π is the place of center M we must have $A(\pi) = 0$ and hence $A(x)$ passes through M. On the other hand if M is a double point and the center say of π_1 and π_2, then $\Sigma c_i f_{x_i}$ and l_i are each of order one on π_j and so A is of order two there. Consequently it has M as double point at least (VI, 10.4).

To sum up then, A passes through all the intersections of l_i with f and if l_i passes through a double point of f, A has at least a double point there. Since l_i is not tangent to f nor joins two of its double points, A is divisible by l_i mod f (VI, 10.2, 10.3).

The same reasoning enables one to suppress the factors l_i one at a time. Thus du will be reducible to the projective type (4.2a) except that so far it is only known that φ_{m-3} is a form of degree $m - 3$, but not necessarily an adjoint.

Returning, however, to the double point M, we have this time the affine from (4.2b). As above F_Y is of order one at π_i, hence the same holds for φ_{m-3}. Hence φ_{m-3} must pass through M and so it is an adjoint. This proves the necessity of the condition of the theorem.

Suppose now du in the projective form (4.2a). Let π be any place of F and let M be its center. Referring to (V, 14.4) when M is not a double point one may put du in the affine form (4.2b) with X as the parameter and $F_Y \neq 0$. Since φ_{m-3} is a polynomial du will not have π as a pole. On the other hand when M is a double point the cartesian form for du may be taken such that on π (one of π_1, π_2 above) X is still the parameter and F_Y is of order one (V, 14.5). Since φ_{m-3} is an adjoint, φ_{m-3} is of order at least one at π and hence once more π is not a pole. Thus du has no poles and so it is of the first kind. This proves the sufficiency condition of (4.2) and hence the theorem.

§ 3. Elliptic and Hyperelliptic Differentials. Canonical Model

5. We have shown (VI, § 4) that curves possessing a rational involution I_2 are characterized by their reducibility to the form

$$Y^2 = F_{2p+1}(X), \qquad F \in K[X], \tag{5.1}$$

where F has no square factors. The curves with $p = 0$ are rational. The elliptic curves correspond to $p = 1$ and the hyperelliptic curves to $p > 1$.

In the projective form (see 5.6 below) the curve is seen to have, for $p > 1$, coincident tangents at the multiple point $N(0, 0, 1)$. Hence the *dfk* and the genus cannot be obtained from our general theory and require a special treatment.

We will suppose that $p \geq 1$ and also that $F(0) \neq 0$. This last condition is not a true restriction, for if it is not fulfilled one may apply an affine transformation $X \to X + a$, $Y \to Y$ where $F(a) \neq 0$. As a result the curve will retain the form (5.1) but we will have $F(0) \neq 0$.

(5.2) **Theorem.** *The curve* (5.1) *has p and no more linearly independent dfk.*

From (5.2) together with (4.3) we conclude:

(5.3) *The genus of the curve* (5.1) *is p.*

Remembering the reduction to the form (5.1) we may deduce from (5.3):

(5.4) *The genus of the curve $Y^2 = F_{2p+2}(X)$, where F has no square factor, is again p.*

Proof of (5.2). It will be by direct reduction of the differentials. Now any abelian differential can be written in the form

$$du = \frac{A(X) + YB(X)}{C(X)} \frac{dX}{Y} \tag{5.5}$$

where A, B, $C \in K[X]$. We shall examine the behavior of du at the various places of the curve. The homogeneous representation of the curve is

(5.6) $$\varphi(x) = x_0^{2p-1}x_2^2 - f(x_0, x_1) = 0,$$

where $\varphi \in K_H[x]$, and $f(1, X) = F_{2p+1}$. Since

$$\varphi_{x_0} = (2p-1)x_0^{2p-2}x_2^2 - f_{x_0}, \quad \varphi_{x_1} = -f_{x_1}, \quad \varphi_{x_2} = 2x_0^{2p-1}x_2,$$

we see that because f has no square factor, the point $N(0, 0, 1)$ is the only multiple point (actually an ordinary point for $p = 1$) and at the same time the only point on x_0 (at infinity).

Thus the ordinary points are all in the affine plane. However if $M(a, b)$ is such a point the representation for the place π of center M will not be the same for $b \neq 0$ and $b = 0 = F(a)$. Thus as regards the representations of the places we have to examine three distinct cases. We shall examine each separately and consider the corresponding behavior of du.

First case. The center of the place π is a point $M(a, b)$ with $b \neq 0$. hence $F(a) \neq 0$. Since M is a simple point and $X = a$ is not the tangent at M, we may take for π the parameter $t = X - a$. Then $b = Y(\pi) \neq 0$ and π can only be a pole if $C(a) = 0$. Suppose then that this holds and let $C(X) = (X-a)^s C_1(X)$, $C_1(a) \neq 0$. One may then have poles at π and at the place $\pi' \neq \pi$ whose center is $(a, -b)$, and $t = X - a$ is a suitable parameter for π' also. It follows that if du is to be of the first kind $A(X) \pm YB(X)$ must be of order $\geq s$ in $t = X - a$. Since the order of Y is zero this requires that both $A(X)$ and $B(X)$ be divisible by $(X-a)^s$. Thus the factor $(X-a)^s$ may be suppressed in A, B, C.

Second case. The center of π is a point $M(a, 0)$. Thus now $F(a) = 0$. This time there is only one place π to be considered. Since a is a simple root of $F(X)$, $F'(a) \neq 0$ and so (5.1) considered as an equation in X has a unique solution $X = a + Y^2E(Y^2)$ in $K[[Y]]$ (V, 4.2). Hence we may take $t = Y$. Thus π has the representation

$$Y = t, \quad X = a + t^2E(t^2).$$

Notice that at π

$$\frac{dX}{Y} = \frac{2dY}{F'(X)}$$

and since $F'(a) \neq 0$, $\dfrac{dX}{Y}$ is of order zero at π. Thus we only need to consider the order of its coefficient in du.

Suppose this time C factorable as before and

$$A(X) = (X-a)^q A_1(X), \quad B(X) = (X-a)^r B_1(X), \quad A_1(a)B_1(a) \neq 0.$$

We are only interested of course in the case $s > 0$.

Let first $q > r$. Then du is of order $2(r-s)+1$ at π and so we must have $r \geq s$, hence $q \geq s$. Thus $(X-a)^s$ may be suppressed as before.

If $q \leq r$, the order of du is $2(q-s)$ and again $q \geq s$ with the same conclusion.

To sum up, if du is a *dfk* then it is reducible to the type

$$du = \{A_q(X) + YB_r(X)\}\frac{dX}{Y} \tag{5.7}$$

where A, B are polynomials of degrees q, r.

Third case. The center of π *is the multiple point* $N(0, 0, 1)$. As we shall see this case reduces essentially to the preceding. Consider the curve

$$Y^2 = G_{2p+2}(X) \tag{5.8}$$

where G has no square factor. At the cost of a possible change of the coordinate X we may assume that $G(0) = 0$. Then the birational transformation,

$$T:\quad X \to \frac{1}{X},\quad Y \to \frac{Y}{X^{p+1}}$$

whose inverse has the same form reduces (5.8) to a curve (5.1) and therefore also (5.1) to the type (5.8) with $G(0) = 0$.

Notice in passing that under T the only points of (5.1) which go to infinity are those on the line $X = 0$. Since by assumption $F(0) \neq 0$, there are exactly two such points and as they are simple for (5.1) we conclude that *the hyperelliptic curve* (5.8) *has two places with centers at infinity.* On the other hand under T the only point of (5.8) imaged into the point at infinity N is the origin. As the latter is a simple point of (5.8) it is seen that *the point at infinity* N *of the curve* (5.1) *is the center of a single place.*

With evident meaning of the symbols T reduces du to

$$du = \left\{\frac{A_q^*(X)}{X^q} + \frac{YB_r^*(X)}{X^{p+r+1}}\right\}\frac{-X^{p-1}dX}{Y} = -\left\{\frac{A_q^*(X)}{X^{q-(p-1)}} + \frac{YB_r^*(X)}{X^{r+2}}\right\}\frac{dX}{Y}.$$

The order must be non-negative at the unique place π of center N'. As in the preceding case a suitable representation is (here $a = 0$):

$$X = t^2E(t^2),\quad Y = t,$$

and we merely need to verify that the bracket is of non-negative order. We must have $B_r^* = 0$, hence $B_r = 0$, since otherwise there is a term of odd negative order. Then the first term is of order $2(p-1-q)$ and as this must not be negative we must have $q \leq p-1$. Hence when du is of the first kind it is reducible to the form

$$du = A_{p-1}(X)\frac{dX}{Y}. \tag{5.9}$$

Conversely when du is in this form, whatever $A_{p-1}(X)$, du has no poles and so it is of the first kind. Notice also that the representation is unique.

For if it were not some $du = 0$, with $A_{p-1}(X) \neq 0$ but $A_{p-1}(X) = 0$ mod $(Y^2 - F_{2p+1}(X))$ which is manifestly ruled out.

To sum up, we have:

(5.10) **Theorem.** *Every dfk of the curve* (5.1) *may be uniquely represented in the form* (5.9) *and conversely every differential* (5.9) *is a dfk for the curve.*

The maximum number of linearly independent *dfk* is then manifestly the number of terms in polynomials $A_{p-1}(X)$, i.e. it is p. This proves theorem (5.2).

(5.11) *Noteworthy special case.* In the elliptic case $p = 1$ and the only *dfk* is, up to a constant factor

$$du = \frac{dX}{Y},$$

and this is the well known Weierstrass differential. When K is the complex field X as a function of u is the Weierstrass elliptic function $\mathfrak{p}(u)$.

(5.12) *Canonical series.* Let us suppose $p > 1$. The divisor $H(du)$ will be merely the divisor of the zeros of du. To find the zeros take du in the form (5.9). Suppose also that $A_{p-1}(X)$ is relatively prime to $F(X)$ and has only simple roots. Let a be such a root. As we are under case I, we may take $X = a + t$. Since $F(a) \neq 0$

$$du = A_{p-1}(a + t)E(t)dt.$$

Hence the place π is a zero of order one and likewise for π'. The sum of the orders of the zeros of du is $2p - 2$, which is the maximum possible. Hence if we write

$$a^{\lambda} = A_{p-1}(x_0, x_1) = \Sigma\lambda_i x_0^i x_1^{p-1-i}$$

upon varying the λ_i the variable intersections generate the full canonical series g_{2p-2}^{p-1} of our hyperelliptic curve.

It may be observed that the lines $\mu_0 x_0 + \mu_1 x_1 = 0$, or in affine coordinates $X =$ const., cut out on our curve a rational involution I_2 with which the canonical series is compounded.

6. A certain amount of classification using the genus and the canonical series is already possible. Unless otherwise stated the curve f is again as in the earlier part of the chapter.

(6.1) *All curves of genus zero are rational, that is to say they are birationally equivalent to the straight line, and hence to one another. This is notably true regarding non-singular conics.*

It is sufficient to point out that when $p = 0$ the adjoints φ_{m-3+s}, s sufficiently high, cut out a g_n^n (VI, 13) making the curve rational (VI, 8.1).

(6.2) *All curves of genus one are elliptic.*

In this case there is a single canonical curve φ_{m-3} and it intersects f in the divisor of the double points Δ. Special case: $m = 3$ and φ_{m-3} is a constant. The adjoints φ_{m-2} cut out a g_m^{m-1}. Those containing $m - 2$

suitably chosen places will cut out a residual series g_2^1. Hence the curve may be reduced to $Y^2 = F_3(X)$, where F_3 has no multiple roots.

(6.3) *All curves of genus two are hyperelliptic.*

For the canonical series is a g_2^1.

(6.4) *A necessary and sufficient condition for a curve f to be hyperelliptic is that its canonical series be composite. The series is then compounded with a rational involution I_2 which is unique.*

Necessity has already been proved (5.12). As for sufficiency suppose that the canonical series g_{2p-2}^{p-1} is $\neq 0$ (hence $p > 1$) and is compounded with an involution I_μ. According to (VI, 7.5) $\mu \leq \dfrac{2p-2}{p-1}$, and since $\mu > 1$ we have $\mu = 2$. Therefore f is hyperelliptic (VI, 9).

Suppose now that there exist two distinct involutions I_2, I_2'. Then the canonical series must be compounded with each. Hence a divisor containing a place π must contain at least two more places. Select now the places $\pi_1, \cdots, \pi_{p-1}$ in succession so that π_{i+1} is not one of the fixed places of the canonical divisors containing the π_j, $j \leq i$. Under our assumption the special divisor containing the π_i contains at least $2p - 2$ more (each counted with its multiplicity). Hence the degree of the series $\geq 3(p - 1)$ which is ruled out unless $p \leq 1$. And in fact

(6.5) *Rational and elliptic curves contain an infinite number of rational involutions I_2.*

Take the curve in the reduced form $Y^2 = X$ for rational curves, $Y^2 = F_3(X)$ for elliptic curves. In the first case the lines through any point M of the plane, in the second the lines through any point N of the curve generate for each M or N the series g_2^1 of an infinite family which gives rise to an infinity of distinct involutions of the asserted type.

7. The canonical model. When f is not hyperelliptic the system

$$\rho y_i = \varphi_{m-3}^i(x), \quad i = 0, 1, \cdots, p - 1, \tag{7.1}$$

where $\{\varphi_{m-3}^i\}$ is a maximal linearly independent set of canonical curves, generates a birational model Γ of f known as the *canonical model* of the field K^f which is a curve of order $2p - 2$ in KP_y^{p-1}. On Γ the canonical series is cut out by the hyperplanes of KP_y^{p-1}. Since the set $\{\varphi_{m-3}^i\}$ is unique to within a linear transformation the canonical model Γ is unique to within a projective transformation. Moreover since the canonical series is complete Γ is normal (VI, 7.8). Let us show that Γ has no singularities. Assume that M is a singular point. The hyperplanes through M cut out a series $g_{2p-4-\varepsilon}^{p-2}$ without fixed points. If $\pi_1, \cdots, \pi_s$ are the places of center M, the hyperplanes cut out in addition a fixed divisor $H = \Sigma\mu_i\pi_i$, where $\Sigma\mu_i = \varepsilon + 2$. Hence one may add to the series a fixed divisor $H' = \Sigma\mu_i'\pi_i$, $0 \leq \mu_i' \leq \mu_i$, $\Sigma\mu_i' = \varepsilon$, so as to produce a special series $g^q_{2p-4} = |H' + g^{p-2}_{2p-4-\varepsilon}|$. This series is of dimension $< p - 1$ and $\geq p - 2$, and so it is a special g^{p-2}_{2p-4}. The residual divisors relative to the canonical series make up a g^s_2 and by Brill-Noether's reciprocity law: $2p - 6 = 2(p - 2 - s)$, hence $s = 1$ and the series is a g^1_2. This is ruled out however since Γ is not hyperelliptic.

To sum up we may state:

(7.2) *Whenever the canonical model exists (i.e. $p > 2$ and non-hyperelliptic case) it is normal, non-singular and unique to within a projective transformation of KP^{p-1}.*

Remark. The simplest canonical models are the plane quartics without singularities. They correspond to $p = 3$ and their canonical series is cut out by the straight lines of the plane.

§ 4. Differentials of the Second and Third Kinds

8. Let $du = RdS$ be an abelian differential with a pole at the place π. If t is a parameter for π we will have

$$(du)_\pi = R(t)dS(t) = \left(\frac{a_n}{t^n} + \cdots + \frac{a_1}{t} + b_0 + b_1 t + \cdots\right) dt.$$

As already observed (3) under the change of parameter $t \to tE(t)$, the order n remains fixed. It is seen at once that the coefficient a_1 is likewise unchanged. Thus both n and a_1 depend solely upon du and π. We refer to a_1 as the *residue* of du at the place π, and whenever $a_1 \neq 0$, du is said to have a *logarithmic singularity* at the place π and π to be a *logarithmic* place of du. The justification of these terms is evident. We now define du as a *differential of the second kind* (abridged as *dsk*) whenever it has no logarithmic places, and as a *differential of the third kind* (abridged as *dtk*) otherwise. In particular differentials of the first kind are also of the second kind. Furthermore:

(8.1) *Under a birational transformation an abelian differential of a given kind goes into one of the same kind.*

9. One may also deal with the differentials from a different point of view. For later purposes we shall take the curve in the affine plane, not a line $X = \text{const.}$,

$$F(X, Y) = 0 \tag{9.1}$$

but otherwise wholly unrestricted. Then if F is of degree m in Y and $a \in K$ there are m roots $Y_1, \cdots, Y_m$ of (9.1) in the field of fractional power series $K\{(X - a)\}$ obtained by means of Puiseux's theorem. The roots break up into a certain number of circular systems of conjugate roots. Let them be so numbered that $Y_1, \cdots Y_q$ is one of the systems. If Y_1 has the expansion

$$Y_1 = b + (X - a)^{k/q}(\alpha_0 + \alpha_1(X - a)^{1/q} + \cdots) \tag{9.2}$$

then the expansion of Y_k, $k \leq q$ is obtained by replacing $(X - a)^{1/q}$ by

$\eta^k(X - a)^{1/q}$, where η is a primitive q-th root of unity in K. To the q roots $Y_1, \cdots, Y_q$ there corresponds a unique place π of F whose center is on the line $X = a$ and which has the representation

$$(9.3) \qquad X = a + t^q, \quad Y = b + t^k(\alpha_0 + \alpha_1 t + \cdots).$$

If one replaces Y_1 say by Y_k, $k \leq q$, then (9.3) is merely replaced by the equivalent representation obtained by the change of parameter $t \to \eta^k t$. Let $\pi = \pi_1, \pi_2, \cdots, \pi_r$ be the distinct places thus obtained.

The value $a = \infty$ may also be included in the above considerations in the following manner. The corresponding places are on the line x_0 in projective coordinates. The projective change of coordinates

$$\rho x_0 = x_1', \quad \rho x_1 = x_0', \quad \rho x_2 = x_2'$$

which yields for the affine coordinates

$$(9.4) \qquad X = \frac{1}{X'}, \quad Y = \frac{Y'}{X'}$$

will bring, relative to X', Y' and $a = 0$ the same situation as before, so that we may now view $a = \infty$ like any other value.

Since the X axis is an irreducible curve without singularities the point $N(a, 0)$ is the center of a single place π^* of the line whatever a. For $a = \infty$, N is merely the point $(0, 1, 0)$. The places $\pi_1, \cdots, \pi_r$ are said to be *over* π^*.

It may be noted that all the places of F fall under the category "over π^*" just considered.

Since X is transcendental every differential may be put in the form $du = RdX$, $R \in K^F$. We have at once

$$(9.5) \qquad \sum_{i=1}^{m} R(X, Y_i) = S(X) \in K(X).$$

With $S(X)$ we associate the differential of the X axis, i.e. of the field $K(X)$

$$(9.6) \qquad dv = S(X)dX.$$

(9.7) *When du, dv are related as above then:* (a) *If du has no pole over π^* then π^* is not a pole of dv:* (b) *the residue of dv at π^* is the sum of those of du at the poles over π^*;* (c) *the sum of all residues is the same for du and dv.*

Let first a be finite and let us return to the solutions Y_i of (9.1) where the first q are grouped in the circular system represented by (9.2). This circular system gives rise to the place π represented by (9.3) and we have

$$(9.8) \qquad R(t) = \frac{\beta_k}{t^k} + \cdots + \frac{\beta_1}{t} + \gamma_0 + \gamma_1 t + \cdots.$$

Hence

$$(du)_\pi = R(t)dX(t) = \left(\frac{\beta_k}{t^k} + \cdots\right) qt^{q-1}dt.$$

Hence du has a pole at π if and only if $k > q - 1$ and the corresponding residue is $q\beta_q$.

On the other hand to the roots $Y_1, \cdots, Y_q$ there corresponds in dv the sum

$$\sigma = [R(X, Y_1) + \cdots + R(X, Y_q)]dX.$$

Now (9.8) yields for $h \leq q$:

$$R(X, Y_h) = \frac{\beta_k}{\eta^{hk}(X - a)^{k/q}} + \cdots.$$

Hence if $k \leq q - 1$, $X = a$ is not a pole of σ, while if $k > q - 1$ it is. The corresponding residue of σ is merely the coefficient $q\beta_q$ of $\frac{1}{X - a}$ or equal to that of du for π. This proves (a) and (b) in the present instance. For $a = \infty$ the transformation (9.4) is applied and leads to the same conclusion relative to

$$dv = S\left(\frac{1}{X'}\right)\frac{-dX'}{X'^2} \tag{9.9}$$

and places on the line $X' = 0$.

Since the behavior of (9.8) at the place of center $X' = 0$ is that of dv at the place of center (0, 0, 1), properties (9.7a) and (9.7b) hold without exception.

Since all the places of F are over some π^*, (9.7c) is a consequence of (9.7b) and (9.7) is proved.

10. Differentials of the third kind. It is more expedient to begin with these. The basic result is:

(10.1) **Theorem.** *Let* $\pi_1, \cdots, \pi_r$ *be given places and* $\alpha_1, \cdots, \alpha_r \in K - 0$. *A n.a.s.c. for the existence of a dtk with the* α_i *as the residues at the places* π_i, *and with no other logarithmic places is that*

$$\Sigma\alpha_i = 0. \tag{10.1a}$$

Select coordinates such that the curve is not a line $X =$ const. so that X is a transcendental element of K^F. Then one may apply (9.7). Accordingly to prove necessity one may replace du by a differential $dv = S(X)dX$, $S \in K(X)$. Breaking S into partial fractions we find

$$S(X) = \Sigma\alpha_j(X - a_j)^{k_j}, \quad \alpha_j \in K,$$

where the sum is finite and the exponents may be positive or negative. Hence it is only necessary to deal with a differential $dv = X^h dX$. Now if $h \neq -1$, dv can only have a residue at infinity. The change of variables (9.4) shows at once that this residue is zero. As for $X^{-1}dX$ it has the residue $+1$ at $X = 0$. The change of variables (9.4) replaces it by $-X'^{-1}dX'$ with residue -1 at $X' = 0$. Thus dv has the two residues $+1, -1$. Hence the necessity of (10.1a) holds for it and therefore in all cases.

To prove the sufficiency of (10.1a) it will be necessary to proceed in a roundabout way. We first treat the following special case:

(10.2) *Given any two places, π, π' there is an abelian differential du with π, π' as poles of order one and no other poles. Furthermore it has residues $+1$ at π and -1 at π'.*

Suppose first $p = 0$ and take $F = Y$, i.e. the curve is the X axis. One may even choose this axis so that the centers of π, π' are $X = \pm 1$. It is then clear that

$$du = \frac{dX}{X-1} - \frac{dX}{X+1}$$

behaves as asserted.

Henceforth we assume $p > 0$. Referring to (2.1) one may choose F such that x_0 intersects the curve in no special way and also such that the centers $M(a, b)$, $M'(a', b')$ are ordinary points, in the affine plane and such that $a \neq a'$, and that the lines $X = a$, $X = a'$ intersect F in points $M_1, \cdots, M_m$, and $M'_1, \cdots, M'_m$ which are all distinct. Consider now the differentials of the form

$$du = \frac{\varphi_{m-1}(X, Y)dX}{(X-a)(X-a')F_Y}$$

where as before φ_k denotes an adjoint of order k. It is readily shown that du has no pole at infinity. Let π_i, π'_i be the (unique) places of centers M_i, M'_i. By the same reasoning as in (4) one will show that the only possible poles of du are the places π_i, π'_i. Since $X - a$, $X - a'$ are suitable parameters for π_i, π'_i one will find that they are poles of order ≤ 1. Hence the divisor of the poles of du is

$$G_p(du) = \Sigma(\nu_i\pi_i + \nu'_i\,\pi'_i);\ \nu_i,\ \nu'_i = 0, 1.$$

Let $H = \pi_2 + \cdots + \pi_m + \pi'_2 \cdots + \pi'_m$, and choose an adjoint φ_{m-1} cutting out H. Observe now that: (a) there are $2m + p - 1$ adjoints φ_{m-1} linearly independent mod F, and hence also absolutely; (b) to impose upon φ_{m-1} to cut out H is to impose upon its coefficients $2m - 2$ linear relations with coefficients in K. Hence there are at least $p + 1 \geq 2$ linearly independent curves φ_{m-1} cutting out H. Among them there are the p linearly independent curves $(X-a)(X-a')\varphi_{m-3}$. Hence there is at least one, and φ_{m-1} is to denote it henceforth, which is not of this type. Let us show that φ_{m-1} does not contain M_1 nor M'_1. Suppose that it contains M_1. Then $X = a$ intersects φ_{m-1} in the m distinct points M_i. Hence $\varphi_{m-1} = (X-a)\varphi_{m-2}$. And now $X = a'$ intersects φ_{m-2} in the $m - 1$ distinct points $M'_2, \cdots, M'_m$. Hence $\varphi_{m-2} = (X-a')\varphi_{m-3}$, and consequently $\varphi_{m-1} = (X-a)(X-a')\varphi_{m-3}$ which is not the case. Hence φ_{m-1} does not contain M_1 and likewise not M'_1.

It follows that du has π, π' for sole logarithmic places. If the corresponding residues are $+\alpha$, $-\alpha$, $\frac{1}{\alpha}du$ behaves in accordance with (10.2).

The sufficiency proof for the condition in Theorem (10.1) is now immediate. Assume (10.1a) and for each $i < r$, let du_i have the logarithmic places π_i, π_r with residues $+1$, -1. Then

$$du = \Sigma\alpha_i du_i$$

has residues α_i at the places π_i, $i < r$ and

$$-(\alpha_i + \cdots + \alpha_{r-1}) = \alpha_r$$

at π_r. This completes the proof of the theorem.

11. Differentials of the second kind. We have first the following important property:

(11.1) *If R is any transcendental element of the function field K^F, then dR is a dsk. Moreover if*

$$G_p(R) = \Sigma n_i \pi_i$$

is the divisor of the poles of R then the divisor of the poles of dR is

$$G_p(dR) = \Sigma(n_i + 1)\pi_i.$$

This shows in particular that dR is not a dfk.

This follows at once from the fact that if π, t is a place and its parameter then

$$R(t) = \frac{a_n}{t^n} + \cdots + \frac{a_1}{t} + b_0 + b_1 t + \cdots$$

$$dR(t) = \left(\frac{-na_n}{t^{n+1}} - \cdots - \frac{a_1}{t^2} + b_1 + 2b_2 t + \cdots\right) dt.$$

One may now ask whether there are any differentials of the second kind which are not of type dR. The answer is found in the following theorem:

(11.2) **Theorem.** *There exist exactly $2p$ dsk $dv_1, \cdots, dv_{2p}$ such that:* (a) *no linear combination $\Sigma\lambda_i dv_i$, $\lambda_i \in K - 0$ is a dR, $R \in K^F$;* (b) *every other dsk dv satisfies a relation*

$$dv = \Sigma\lambda_i dv_i + dR;\ \lambda_i \in K,\ R \in K^F.$$

Moreover the dv_i may be chosen in the following manner: (a) *Given any set of p distinct places $\pi_1^*, \cdots, \pi_p^*$ whose sum is not special, then dv_i, $i \leq p$, has just one pole of order two at π_i^* and no other;* (b) *the dv_{p+i} are p linearly independent dfk.*

(11.3) Suppose first $p = 0$. Let again $F = Y$, so that the curve is the X axis. Thus

$$dv = R(X)dX, \quad R(X) \in K(X).$$

Breaking $R(X)$ into partial fractions yields

$$R(X) = \Sigma\alpha_i(X - a_i)^{n_i},$$

where the $n_i \neq -1$ since dv is of the second kind. Hence

$$dv = d\left(\Sigma\alpha_i \frac{(X - a_i)^{n_i+1}}{n_i + 1}\right)$$

which is a differential of a rational function as it should be when $p = 0$.

(11.4) Henceforth we assume $p > 0$. By (2.1) given any place π_1 of center M_1 one may choose F such that M_1 is an ordinary point of F. The affine axes may be taken with M_1 as the origin and with the X and Y axes intersecting the curve in m distinct points $M_1, \cdots, M_m$, and $M_1, M_2', \cdots, M_m'$, none at infinity. Taking this time

$$du = \frac{\varphi_{m-1}dX}{XY\,F_Y}$$

we show as before that φ_{m-1} may be so chosen that M_1 is the only pole of du and is of order *two*. Its residue is necessarily zero and so du is of the second kind. Thus:

(11.5) *Given a place π of F there exists a dsk having at π a pole of order two and no other pole.*

(11.6) Suppose now that du has a pole of order $k > 2$. We may dispose of the situation so that the place in question is π_1 considered above. Take $k - 1$ distinct lines $l_1, \cdots, l_{k-1}$ in KP^2 through M_1, each intersecting F in m distinct points. Let $H(x_0, x_1, x_2)$ be a form of degree $k - 1$ not passing through any intersection of the l_i with f. Then

$$\frac{H(x_0, x_1, x_2)}{l_1 \cdots l_{k-1}}$$

defines a certain element R of K^f. It is clear that R has π_1 as pole of order $k - 1$ and the places π_{ij} whose centers M_{ij} are the other intersections of the l_i with f as poles of order one. Hence dR has a pole of order k at π_1 and one of order two at π_{ij}. If t is a parameter for π_1 we have then

$$du = \left(\frac{a_k}{t^k} + \cdots + \frac{a_2}{t^2} + b_0 + b_1 t + \cdots\right) dt, \qquad dR = \left(\frac{a_k'}{t^k} + \cdots\right) dt,$$

where the coefficients are all in K and $a_k a_k' \neq 0$. As a consequence $du - d\left(\frac{a_k}{a_k'} R\right)$ has a pole of order $< k$ at π_1. In addition it has acquired new poles of order two but the order of no pole already present has been increased.

By repetition of this operation, i.e. by adding to du, assumed a *dsk*, a suitable dR, one may replace it by a *dsk*, still written du, which has only poles of order two.

12. Select now p distinct places $\pi_1^*, \ldots, \pi_p^*$ whose sum is not a special divisor. This may be done as follows: In accordance with (VI, 4.1) the first $p - 1$ may be chosen such that they belong to just one divisor of the canonical series. Taking then π_p^* not in that divisor will achieve the desired result.

Let now dv_i be a *dsk* with π_i^* as pole of order two and no other pole. Let $dv_{p+1}, \cdots, dv_{2p}$ be p linearly independent *dfk*.

(12.1) *No non-trivial linear combination* $\Sigma\lambda_i dv_i$, $\lambda_i \in K$, *can be a* dR, $R \in K^f - K$.

For if R existed its divisor $G(R)$ would be of the form $H - A$, $A = \Sigma\pi_i^*$. Hence the complete series $|A|$ would have positive dimension. However since A is not special and of degree p, $\dim |A| = 0$, and this contradiction proves (12.1).

To complete the proof of (11.2) it is sufficient to show that if du is a *dsk*, then

$$du = \Sigma\lambda_i dv_i + dR, \qquad \lambda_i \in K, \quad R \in K^f.$$

As shown in (11.6) modulo a suitable dR one may reduce du to a differential still called du whose poles $\pi_1, \cdots, \pi_r$ are all of order two.

We shall now reduce in this same manner du to a differential having no other poles than some of the π_i^* and those of order two. Suppose that π_1 is not a π_j^*. Then $A_1 = \pi_1 + A$ is a divisor of degree $p + 1$ and hence $\dim |A_1| = p + 1 - p = 1$. Therefore there exists an $R_1 \in K^f$ having for divisor $H_1 - A_1$. It has necessarily π_1 as pole since otherwise R_1 would have a divisor $H - A$ and this possibility has already been excluded. If t is a parameter for π_1, we have then

$$du = \frac{\alpha}{t^2} + \beta + \gamma t + \cdots, \qquad dR = \frac{\alpha'}{t^2} + \beta' + \gamma' t + \cdots,$$

where the coefficients are in K and $\alpha\alpha' \neq 0$. Hence $du - (d\frac{\alpha}{\alpha'}R)$ ceases to have π_1 as a pole and has acquired no other poles, if any, than some of the π_i^* with order two. After a finite number of steps then du will have been reduced to the desired type.

Suppose then that du has no other poles than some of the π_i^* and those of order two. If t_i is a parameter for π_i^* we have

$$du = \frac{\lambda_i}{t_i^2} + \mu_0 + \mu_1 t_i + \cdots, \quad dv_i = \frac{\alpha_i}{t_i^2} + \beta_{i0} + \beta_{i1} t_i + \cdots$$

where all coefficients are in K and $\alpha_i \neq 0$. Hence

$$du - \sum_{i=1}^{p} \frac{\lambda_i}{\alpha_i} dv_i = \sum_{i=1}^{p} \lambda_{p+i}\, dv_{p+i}, \quad \lambda_{p+i} \in K$$

since the left hand side has no poles and hence is a *dfk*. This completes the proof of theorem (11.2).

§ 5. JACOBIAN SERIES

13. Let A be a linear series g^1_μ without fixed places. By Bertini's theorem only a finite number of divisors of the series have multiple places, so that the multiple places form a finite set $\pi_1, \cdots, \pi_r$. If π_i is an element of the divisor γ of A, let ω_i be its coefficient in γ. The divisor

$$A_J = \Sigma(\omega_i - 1)\pi_i$$

is known as the *Jacobian divisor* of A. As an example let f have ordinary singularities and let it not pass through the point $(0, 0, 1)$. Let the series A be cut out by the lines $\lambda_0 x_0 + \lambda_1 x_1$ and suppose that the tangents among them have order two (ordinary contact) at the places of tangency $\pi_1, \cdots, \pi_n$. Then the Jacobian divisor $A_J = \pi_1 + \cdots + \pi_n$, and its degree n is the class of the curve. We have then (VI, 6.10): $n = m(m-1) - 2\delta$, $2p = (m-1)(m-2) - 2\delta$. Hence here

$$n = 2(p + m - 1), \tag{13.1}$$

and this is one of the results which we propose to generalize.

Returning to the general case since the Jacobian divisor A_J manifestly has birational character relative to A we may choose any convenient birational model for f. Let f be so chosen that the centers P_i of the π_i are all ordinary points and not on f_{x_2}. Take now two simple divisors γ_0, γ_1 of A and let ψ_0 be an adjoint of some order k cutting out γ_0 but not passing through any point P_i. The residual divisor ε is disjoint from A_J and γ_1 is cut out by an adjoint ψ_1 of order k through ε. Thus A is generated by

$$\psi^\lambda = \lambda_0\psi_0 + \lambda_1\psi_1.$$

Set also $R = \psi_1/\psi_0$. Let finally $\psi^{\lambda_i} = \lambda_0^i\psi_0 + \lambda_1^i\psi_1$ be the curve ψ^λ through P_i. Since $\psi_0(P_i) \neq 0$ the order of ψ^{λ_i} at π_i is the same ω_i as that of $\dfrac{\psi_1}{\psi_0} + \dfrac{\lambda_0^i}{\lambda_1^i}$. Hence $\omega_i - 1$ is the order of dR at π_i and conversely. It follows that the Jacobian divisor A_J is merely the divisor of zeros $G_z(dR)$ of dR. The divisor of poles $G_p(dR) = 2\gamma_0$. Hence if C is the canonical series we have

$$C = |G_z(dR) - G_p(dR)| = |A_J - 2A|$$

and consequently, passing to the complete series

$$|A_J| = |C + 2A|. \tag{13.2}$$

From this follows that if g^r_μ is a complete series without fixed places and A is a one dimensional subseries likewise without fixed places then A_J is a member of a complete series, the *Jacobian series* $J(g^r_\mu)$, given by

$$J(g^r_\mu) = |C + 2g^r_\mu|. \tag{13.3}$$

By comparing degrees there follows for the degree ν of the Jacobian series the relation

(13.4) $$\nu = 2(p + \mu - 1).$$

which is the desired extension of (13.1).

(13.5) *Remark.* To the relation (13.2) there is attached an interesting definition of the canonical series due to Enriques. Let A, B denote linear series of positive dimensions without fixed places. One may prove directly the relations

$$|(A + B)_J| = |A_J + 2B| = |B_J + 2A|.$$

From this follows that if $|A_J - 2A|$ exists, it is a fixed series and it is this series which is to be defined as the canonical series. The parallel with the differential series is patent: the fixed series under the definition of Enriques is merely the fixed series of the divisors $G(dR)$ which are all equivalent members of the class of the divisors of the abelian differentials.

(13.6) Let us return to the place π_i. We may choose coordinates so that its center is neither on x_0 nor on f_{x_2} and then π_i will have a representation

$$\rho x_0 = 1, \quad \rho x_1 = a + t, \quad \rho x_2 = b + t^k E(t).$$

Since ψ_0 is of order zero at π_i the order of dR will be that of

$$(\psi_0 \psi_{1x_1} - \psi_1 \psi_{0x_1}) + (\psi_0 \psi_{1x_2} - \psi_1 \psi_{0x_2}) \frac{dx_2}{dt}.$$

Now by differentiating f we find

$$f_{x_1} + f_{x_2} \frac{dx_2}{dt} = 0.$$

Since $f_{x_2} \neq 0$ at P_i, dR has the same order at π_i as

(13.7) $$(\psi_0 \psi_{1x_1} - \psi_1 \psi_{0x_1}) f_{x_2} - (\psi_0 \psi_{1x_2} - \psi_1 \psi_{0x_2}) f_{x_1}.$$

Consider now the Jacobian

$$J = \frac{D(\psi_0, \psi_1, f)}{D(x_0, x_1, x_2)}.$$

From Euler's relation follows that the order of J at π_i is the same as that of

$$\begin{vmatrix} \psi_0, & \psi_1, & 0 \\ \psi_{0x_1}, & \psi_{1x_1}, & f_{x_1} \\ \psi_{0x_2}, & \psi_{1x_2}, & f_{x_2} \end{vmatrix}$$

i.e. again that of (13.7). In other words the Jacobian divisor is the divisor cut out outside the double points by the Jacobian curve J. It is from this property that there stem the terms "Jacobian divisor" and "Jacobian series."

14. We shall now apply the results obtained so far to the proof of an interesting formula due to Zeuthen.

Suppose that T is a rational transformation of degree μ of an irreducible curve f into another f^*. Let $p, \pi, \cdots$ and the other notations be applied as before to f and let $p^*, \pi^*, \cdots$, be the analogues for f^*.

Referring to (V, 18.1) if $\pi_1^*, \cdots, \pi_n^*$ are the branch places of T then: (a) when π^* is not a π_j^* then $T^{-1}\pi^*$ consists of μ distinct places; (b) $T^{-1}\pi_j^*$ consists of say $k < \mu$ places, $\pi_{j1}, \cdots, \pi_{jk}$. Each π_{ji} is assigned a certain multiplicity $d(\pi_{ji})$ as a member of $T^{-1}\pi_j^*$ and $\mu = \Sigma d(\pi_{ji})$. We assign to π_j^* the branch place multiplicity $\varepsilon_j = \Sigma(d(\pi_{ji}) - 1)$.

In point of fact the number which will matter here is

$$\varepsilon = \Sigma\varepsilon_j. \tag{14.1}$$

It is known as the *number of branch-places*, each being counted with its multiplicity ε_j.

As a consequence of T one may view the function field K^{f^*} as a subfield of K^f. Hence an element R of K^{f^*} is also in K^f. Let R be chosen in the following manner: Let us assume as we may that the curve f^* has only ordinary singularities. By Bertini's theorem almost every first polar of f^* will cut out on f^* a divisor consisting of n^* ordinary distinct places, none centered at a double point and none a π_j^*. One may in particular assume the coordinates such that f^* does not go through $(0, 0, 1)$ and that the first polar of this point behaves as indicated above. This first polar however cuts out the Jacobian group A_J of the $g_{m^*}^1 = A$ cut out by the pencil $\lambda_0 x_0^* + \lambda_1 x_1^*$. We may furthermore assume that the divisor cut out by x_0^* is also free from the π_j^* and we will set $R = x_1^*/x_0^*$. Under the circumstances A_J is merely the divisor of zeros $G_z^*(dR)$, and the divisor of poles $G_p^*(dR)$ is free from the π_j^*.

Let us consider now $G_z(dR)$ on f. Referring to (V, 17) it will be seen that if $T\pi = \pi^*$ and π has multiplicity d among the μ images of $T^{-1}\pi^*$, then the order of R at π is d times the order of R at π^*. From this we conclude that: (a) if π^* is not a branch place π_j^*, i.e. if $d = 1$, then the order of R at π and π^* is the same; (b) if π^* is a π_j^* and $\pi \in T^{-1}\pi_j^*$ has the multiplicity d then $G_z(dR)$ has multiplicity $d - 1$ at π. Hence the Jacobian divisor $G_z(dR)$ on f consists of the following:

the μ places of the inverse of each place of A_J each counted once; the places π_{ji} of $T^{-1}\pi_j^*$, where π_{ji} is to be taken with the multiplcity $d(\pi_{ji}) - 1$.

Since the two sets of places are disjoint

$$G_z(dR) = T^{-1}A_J + B, \quad B = \Sigma(d(\pi_{ji}) - 1)\pi_{ji}.$$

On the other hand if C, C^* denote canonical divisors of f, f^* we have

$$G_z(dR) \sim G_p(dR) + C \sim T^{-1}(2A_1 + C), \quad A_J \sim 2A_1 + C^*, \quad A_1 \in A.$$

Hence

$$G_z(dR) \sim T^{-1}(A_J - C^*) + C \sim T^{-1}A_J + B.$$

From this follows

(14.2) $$C \sim T^{-1}C^* + B.$$

Hence passing to the degrees we find finally

(14.3) $$2p - 2 = \mu(2p^* - 2) + \varepsilon$$

which is Zeuthen's formula.

VIII. Abel's Theorem
Algebraic Series and Correspondences

Abel's theorem is one of the great classics of our subject. The study of algebraic series will provide a converse of the theorem and bring out its role in the comparison with linear series. Algebraic series are followed by the general study of correspondences between two curves, of a curve with itself and of the related fixed point questions.

The general notations and assumptions are the same as in the preceding three chapters.

§ 1. Abel's Theorem

1. (1.1) Let f be a curve of genus $p > 0$ and let $M(\xi)$ be a point whose coordinate ratios are in a field $K(\mu_1, \cdots, \mu_s)$ of transcendency $\leq s$. If $du = RdS$ is an abelian differential then we will understand by $(du)_M$ the differential $R(\xi(\mu))\, dS(\xi(\mu))$ of the field $K(\mu)$.

(1.2) Let now g_n^r be a linear series cut out on f by

(1.3) $$\psi^\lambda = \lambda_0\psi_0 + \cdots + \lambda_r\psi_r.$$

Let us set $\lambda_i/\lambda_0 = \mu_i$. The general divisor of the series, written conveniently D^λ or D^μ, consists of n places $\pi_1, \cdots, \pi_n$, whose centers M_j have their coordinate ratios in a finite algebraic extension L of $K(\mu)$. Since L is a differential field and its space of differentials is spanned by the $d\mu_j$, if du is a dfk, $(du)_{M_j}$ has a meaning. We then have

(1.4) $$\Sigma(du)_{M_j} = \Sigma\alpha_i d\mu_i, \quad \alpha_i \in L.$$

A sum such as in (1.4) will be referred to as an *abelian sum* (understood for a dfk). We may now state:

(1.5) **Abel's theorem.** *The abelian sums taken at the places of a general divisor of a linear series are all zero.*

Let g_n^r be the series. Since $r = 0$ is trivial we assume $r > 0$. Referring to (1.4) we must show that all the α_i are zero. Suppose that any α_i, say $\alpha_1 \neq 0$. We may then choose $\mu_2, \cdots, \mu_r \in K$ and still have $\alpha_1(\mu_1, \cdots, \mu_r) \neq 0$. To disprove this merely requires to prove the theorem for the g_n^1 cut out by $\psi_0 + \mu_1\psi_1 = 0$. Changing slightly our notations and setting, contrary to our general usage $X = \dfrac{\psi_1}{\psi_0} \in K^f$ we must prove the theorem for the g_n^1 cut out by $X = \text{const}$. Since the ψ_i are linearly independent mod f, X is transcendental. Hence there is a $Y \in K^f$ such that $K^f = K(X, Y)$. If $F(X, Y) = 0$ is the irreducible equation relating X and Y, F is a birational model of f and $K^F = K^f$. (We depart here for a moment from our standard meaning for F.) Referring now to (VII, 9) we have

$$(1.6) \qquad dv = \Sigma(du)_{M_j} = R(X)dX, \quad R(X) \in K(X).$$

By (VII, 9.7a) since du has no poles, dv has none on the X line. Hence $R(X)$ has no poles and so $R(X) \in K$. However the change of variables $X \to 1/X$, shows that if $R \neq 0$ then dv has a pole at infinity. Hence $R = 0$, $dv = 0$ and the theorem is proved.

(1.7) *Remark.* If $du = RdS$, R and $S \in K^f$, and with α_i as in (1.4), Abel's theorem is equivalent to

$$\alpha_i = \sum_j R(M_j) \frac{\partial S(M_j)}{\partial \mu_i} = 0, \quad i = 1, 2, \cdots, r.$$

The expression in the sum is conveniently written $\partial u(M_j)/\partial \mu_i$, giving for the theorem the formulation:

$$(1.8) \qquad \sum_j \frac{\partial u(M_j)}{\partial \mu_i} = 0, \ i = 1, 2, \cdots, r.$$

2. As an application let K be the complex field and consider the special cubic in the classical Weierstrass form of elliptic functions:

$$y^2 = 4x^3 - g_2 x - g_3 = g(x), \qquad g_2^3 \neq 27g_3^2,$$

so that the roots of $g(x)$ are distinct. The genus $p = 1$ in the elliptic case, and up to a constant factor there is just one dfk

$$du = \frac{dx}{\sqrt{g(x)}}.$$

Let $(z, \sqrt{g(z)})$, $(t, \sqrt{g(t)})$, $(k, \sqrt{g(k)})$ be three collinear points of the curve, where k is a constant so that the third point is fixed. We have then

$$(2.1) \qquad \begin{vmatrix} z, & \sqrt{g(z)}, & 1 \\ t, & \sqrt{g(t)}, & 1 \\ k, & \sqrt{g(k)}, & 1 \end{vmatrix} = 0,$$

and by Abel's theorem

$$(2.2) \qquad \frac{dz}{\sqrt{g(z)}} + \frac{dt}{\sqrt{g(t)}} = 0.$$

It follows that (2.1) defines a solution with an arbitrary parameter k of the differential equation (2.2). It is therefore the general solution of this equation.

§ 2. ALGEBRAIC SERIES

3. Let $\mathfrak{C}$ be an irreducible correspondence between an algebraic variety V^r in KP_y^q and the curve f and let Φ be the graph of $\mathfrak{C}$ and n the degree of $\mathfrak{C}$ on f.

To a general point N on V^r there correspond n distinct general points $M_1, \cdots, M_n$ of f (III, 17.3) and Φ, hence also the correspondence $\mathfrak{C}$, is uniquely determined by any one of the general points (N, M_i) of Φ. Since M_i is a general point it is the center of a single place π_i of f. Let $D = \Sigma\pi_i$. We refer to $\mathfrak{C}$ as an *irreducible algebraic series.* The numbers n, r are the *degree* and the *dimension* of the series and the latter is conveniently denoted by γ_n^r.

Since together with N any one of the points M_i determines the full correspondence $\mathfrak{C}$, one may say that the pair (N, D) likewise suffices to determine $\mathfrak{C}$.

Consider now a finite set of irreducible algebraic correspondences $\mathfrak{C}_1, \cdots, \mathfrak{C}_s$ between V^r and f and let $D_h, M_{hi}, \cdots$, correspond to $\mathfrak{C}_h$ in the obvious way. Let $\nu_1, \cdots, \nu_s$ be positive integers and set

$$D = \sum_h \nu_h D_h = \sum_{h,i} \nu_h \pi_{hi}. \tag{3.1}$$

The $\mathfrak{C}_h$ may also include exceptionally correspondences whose divisor consists of a single fixed place. The symbol

$$\mathfrak{C} = \Sigma\nu_h\mathfrak{C}_h$$

is called an *algebraic series.* The degree of the series is $n = \Sigma n_h\nu_h$, its dimension is r, and the series is once more written γ_n^r.

It is clear that a g_n^r is an irreducible γ_n^r whose associated variety is a KP^r.

It will be convenient to designate by $K(N)$ the field obtained by adjoining to K the coordinate ratios of N.

We shall be concerned presently with the possibility that the general divisor D of γ_n^r be contained in a divisor of a linear series g_t^s. Suppose that the latter is generated by

$$\psi^\lambda = \lambda_0\psi_0 + \cdots + \lambda_s\psi_s. \tag{3.2}$$

Upon writing that ψ^λ contains $\nu_h D_h$ there is obtained a system of relations

$$\Sigma\lambda_j\chi_{\alpha j}^h(M_{hi}) = 0$$

where $\chi_{\alpha j}^h(x) \in K_H[x]$. Since these relations are symmetrical in the M_{hi}, they may be replaced by an equivalent system

$$\Sigma a_{\alpha j}^h(N)\lambda_j = 0, \quad a_{\alpha j}^h \in K(N).$$

Hence the total system asserting that D is contained in a divisor of g_t^s takes the form

$$\Sigma a_{\beta j}(N)\lambda_j = 0, \quad a_{\beta j} \in K(N), \quad \beta = 1, 2, \cdots, \sigma. \tag{3.3}$$

There is evidently no restriction in assuming that the rank of the system is σ. Then $\sigma \leq s$, since it is known that there is a non-trivial solution in the λ_j.

Upon solving for σ of the λ_j in terms of the rest and substituting in (3.2) there results a system

$$\omega^{\xi}(N; x) = \xi_0\omega_0(N; x) + \cdots + \xi_\rho\omega_\rho(N; x), \tag{3.4}$$

where ω_i is a linear combination of the ψ_j with coefficients in $K(N)$ and $\rho = s - \sigma$. Thus ω^{ξ} generates the complete linear series $|g_t^s - D|$, where D is fixed.

Hereafter we drop the index h and write $M_1, M_2, \cdots$, instead of $M_{11}, \cdots$. It is to be understood that for instance M_{hi} is found ν_h times among the M_j.

4. Since the coordinate ratios of the M_j are in a finite algebraic extension of $K(N)$ they are in a differential field. Hence if du is any *dfk* the abelian sum

$$S(du, D) = \Sigma(du)_{M_j}$$

has a definite meaning.

We propose to prove the following proposition whose second part (sufficiency) is a converse of Abel's theorem.

(4.1) **Theorem.** *A n.a.s.c. for an algebraic series γ_n^r to be contained in a fixed linear series g_n^s is that all the abelian sums $S(du, D)$ of the general divisor D of γ_n^r vanish.*

The theorem holds for $p = 0$ since on the one hand there are then no *dfk*, on the other γ_n^r is contained in the unique g_n^r made up of all the divisors of degree n. We will therefore assume at the outset that $p > 0$.

To prove necessity let ψ^{λ} of (3.2) generate g_n^s. The ψ^{λ} through D make up the ω^{ξ}, and as the system is non-empty ω_0 exists. The curve ω_0 is a certain $\psi^{\lambda'}$ where the $\lambda'_i/\lambda'_j \in K(N)$. Hence $N \to (\lambda')$ defines a rational transformation τ of V^r onto a variety $W \subset KP^s$. Let N^* be the point of KP_{λ}^s whose coordinates are the λ'_i. We may suppose that $\lambda'_0 \neq 0$ and introduce the affine coordinates $\mu_i = \lambda'_i/\lambda'_0$. Similarly we may introduce affine coordinates ν_h for N. The coordinates $\mu_i \in K(\nu) = K(N)$. Now by (1.8):

$$S(du, D) = \sum \frac{\partial u(M_j)}{\partial \nu_h}\, d\nu_h = \sum \frac{\partial u(M_j)}{\partial \mu_i}\frac{\partial \mu_i}{\partial \nu_h}\, d\nu_h = 0,$$

and this proves necessity.

Turning now to sufficiency let ψ^{λ} of (3.2) represent a system of adjoints of order k so high that those through D cut out a complete residual series g_t^s without fixed places and of degree $t > 2p - 2$. Thus g_t^s is non-special and so it is a g_t^{t-p}. Its generating system may be taken to be (3.4). The general divisor, i.e. with the ξ_i indeterminates, consists of t ordinary distinct places. Let us specialize now the point N of V^r to a point N'

such that the linear system (3.3) preserves its rank. The divisor D will become D' and the system (3.4) will become

$$\omega^{\xi}(N'; x) = \xi_0\omega_0(N'; x) + \cdots + \xi_\rho\omega_\rho(N'; x),$$

the $\omega_j(N'; x)$ being now linearly independent over K. The form $\omega^{\xi}(N'; x)$ generates a series $g_t'^{t-p}$ which is the residual of D' as to the series cut out by the adjoints of order k.

By Bertini's theorem almost all the divisors cut out by ω^{ξ} consist of t distinct places. Furthermore almost none have their centers on $x_0 f_{x_2}$. Hence we may select the ξ's with ratios in K such that the centers $M_1', \cdots, M_t'$ of the places of the divisor which they cut out are ordinary distinct points of f, in the affine plane and not in F_Y.

Let $\varphi_{m-3}^j(x)$, $j = 1, 2, \cdots, p$ be a set of p linearly independent canonical curves. Since $\Sigma\pi(M_i')$ is non-special, the matrix

$$\| \varphi_{m-3}^j(M_i') \|$$

is of rank p. One may suppose the M_i' so numbered that the determinant

$$\Delta(M') = | \varphi_{m-3}^j(M_1'), \cdots, \varphi_{m-3}^j(M_p') | \neq 0.$$

Consider now the fixed divisor $H_1 = \Sigma\pi(M_{p+h}')$ and let H be the divisor (of degree p) cut out by the adjoints of order k through $H_1 + D$. If $M_1^*, \cdots, M_p^*$ are the centers of the places of H then

$$\Delta(M^*) = | \varphi_{m-3}^j(M_i^*) | \neq 0; \quad i, j = 1, 2, \cdots, p.$$

For if we specialize the general point N of V^r to N', $\Delta(M^*)$ becomes $\Delta(M')$ and $\Delta(M^*) \neq 0$, hence $\Delta(M^*) = 0$ is ruled out. Furthermore since the M_i' are not in $x_0 f_{x_2}$, i.e. they are in the affine plane and not in F_Y, the same holds for the M_i^*. Hence their coordinates X_i, Y_i exist and $F_{Y_i} \neq 0$. Moreover since they are in $K(N)$ they have differentials.

Since $D + H$ is a divisor of the fixed series cut out by the adjoints of order k through H_1, by the necessity condition of the theorem

$$0 = S(du, D) + S(du, H) = S(du, H).$$

Hence

$$S(du, H) = \Sigma(du)_{M_i^*} = 0$$

which reads here

$$\sum \varphi_{m-3}^j(M_i^*)\frac{dX_i}{F_{Y_i}} = 0.$$

Since $\Delta(M^*) \neq 0$ necessarily $dX_i = 0$, $i = 1, 2, \cdots, p$. Hence the M_i^* are all fixed and D is a divisor of the fixed linear series cut out by the adjoints of degree k through $H + H_1$. This completes the proof of theorem (4.1).

Notice that down to the moment when we utilize the abelian sums what we have said applies to any γ_n^r. Denoting then by γ_p^r the series whose general divisor is H, we have proved the following result useful below:

(4.2) *Corresponding to the algebraic series* γ_n^r *there exists a series* γ_p^r *such that if* D, D^* *are the general divisors of the two series then* D^* *is non-special,* $D + D^*$ *is in a fixed linear series, and hence (necessity of the condition in* (4.1)) *for every differential of the first kind:*

$$S(du, D) + S(du, D^*) = 0.$$

Extension of algebraic series. If we allow in the basic relations (3.1) negative coefficients ν_h, the divisors D may cease to be effective. Whatever they are the new correspondence will be referred to as a *generalized* algebraic series and the same designations as before will be applied to it. Upon replacing "linear series" by "divisor class" Theorem (4.1) still holds. That is to say:

(4.3) *A n.a.s.c. for the divisors of* γ_n^r *to be contained in a fixed divisor class is that every abelian sum* $S(du, D) = 0$.

Suppose that in (3.1) $\nu_i = -\nu'_i < 0$. By (4.2) there exists a γ_p^r with divisor D_i^* such that $S(du, D_i^*) = -S(du, D_i)$. Hence by (4.1) $D_i + D_i^*$ is in a fixed linear series. Therefore as regards (4.3) one may replace D_i by $-D_i^*$ and hence ν_i by $\nu'_i > 0$. By applying the same treatment to all the negative coefficients ν_j, one will reduce the present case to (4.1). Thus (4.3) is a consequence of (4.1).

§ 3. Algebraic Correspondences between Two Curves

5. This topic belongs to one of the most interesting and suggestive parts of algebraic geometry. Especially noteworthy contributions have been made by A. Hurwitz [1] and by F. Severi, (see [5], Ch. VI, where numerous references and historical indications are given). There are many interesting geometric applications. An ample supply will be found in H. G. Zeuthen [1].

We consider then algebraic correspondences between two irreducible curves f and f^*. The first curve is the same as we have dealt with so far. The curve f^* is in $KP^2_{x^*}$ and obeys the same restrictions as f. Elements related to f^* will be denoted by the same letters as the corresponding elements of f but with complementary asterisks. In particular places and parameters are denoted by π, t for f and by π^*, t^* for f^*, and the related representative points by M_t, $M^*_{t^*}$.

Special designations for correspondences will be as follows: The correspondence itself is denoted by $\mathfrak{C}$, its indices by μ and μ^*, its graph (in the product surface $f \times f^*$) by Φ. A place of Φ or of a component of Φ when it is reducible will be denoted by $\bar{\pi}$ and its parameter by θ. The transformations induced by $\mathfrak{C}$ are T: $f \to f^*$ and T^{-1}: $f^* \to f$.

Consider now a correspondence $\mathfrak{C}$ which is irreducible, i.e. its graph Φ is an irreducible curve of the surface $f \times f^*$, and non-degenerate, i.e. Φ is not a curve $A \times f^*$, or $A^* \times f$, where A and A^* are points of f and f^*. This means that neither Tf nor $T^{-1}f^*$ is a single point.

If (M, M^*) is a general point of the graph Φ then M and M^* are general points of f and f^* associated under the correspondence $\mathfrak{C}$ and conversely. There are also two rational transformations $S: \Phi \to f$, $S^*: \Phi \to f^*$, defined by $S(M, M^*) = M$, $S^*(M, M^*) = M^*$. The degrees of S and S^* are μ^* and μ.

By the definition of the indices μ, μ^*, TM consists of μ^* distinct general points of f^* and $T^{-1}M^*$ of μ distinct general points of f.

The operations S and S^* cause isomorphic imbeddings of the function fields K^f and K^{f^*} as subfields of the function field K^Φ of the graph Φ. The degrees relative to K^Φ are μ^* for K^f and μ for K^{f^*}.

As in the case of rational transformations the correspondence $\mathfrak{C}$ is extended to the places. Let $\bar{\pi}$ be a place of the graph Φ and θ its parameter. The representative point $\mathfrak{M}_\theta$ of $\bar{\pi}$ is of the form (M_θ, M_θ^*) and M_θ and M_θ^* are parametric points of two places π and π^* which are associated under $\mathfrak{C}$. We have then $M_\theta = S\mathfrak{M}_\theta$, $M_\theta^* = S^*\mathfrak{M}_\theta$. Let d^* and d be the local degrees of S and S^* on π and π^*. If t, t^* are parameters for the two places we have then

$$t = \theta^{d^*}E(\theta), \quad t^* = \theta^d E^*(\theta). \tag{5.1}$$

If we make the regular change of parameter on $\bar{\pi}$: $\theta E^{*1/d}(\theta) \to \theta$ or $\theta \to \theta E_1(\theta)$, (5.1) assumes the simpler form

$$t = \theta^{d^*}E(\theta), \quad t^* = \theta^d. \tag{5.2}$$

The correspondence is now extended to the places by pairing off π and π^* under $\mathfrak{C}$. The place $\bar{\pi}$ of the graph is then considered as one of the images of the pair π, π^*. For it is not ruled out that the same pair π, π^* may have several images in the graph.

Let $E(\theta)$ of (5.2) satisfy

$$\theta^{d^*}E(\theta) = \alpha\theta^{d^*} + \beta\theta^e + \cdots . \tag{5.3}$$

The numbers d, d^*, e, $\cdots$ have no common factor. For if c were one θ could be replaced by $\theta^{1/c}$, hence d, d^*, e, $\cdots$ by d/c, d^*/c, e/c, $\cdots$. As a result d, d^* would not be the local degrees of S^*, S at $\bar{\pi}$.

6. We must now assign multiplicities to π and π^* as elements of $T^{-1}\pi^*$ and $T\pi$.

Let M_t and $M_{t^*}^*$ be the representative points of π and π^*. Given π^*, and therefore $M_{t^*}^*$, there correspond to it as many distinct points $\mathfrak{M}_\theta$ associated with the same place π in relation to $\bar{\pi}$ as there are values of θ obtainable from (5.2). These values are

$$\theta = \eta^k t^{*1/d}, \quad k = 1, 2, \cdots, d \tag{6.1}$$

where η is a primitive dth root of unity in K. To (6.1) there corresponds the point M_t whose parameter t is given by

$$t = \eta k d^* t^{*d^*/d} E(\eta^k t^{*1/d}). \tag{6.2}$$

Since d, d^*, e, $\cdots$ of (5.2), (5.3) have no common factor, the points M_t thus obtained are all distinct. We assign then naturally to π the multiplicity d in relation to $\bar{\pi}$ and we denote it henceforth by $d(\bar{\pi})$. Similarly the place π^* is assigned the multiplicity $d^* = d^*(\bar{\pi})$ as place of $T\pi$, in relation to $\bar{\pi}$.

7. Let the birational models of f and f^* still called f, f^*, be so chosen that A and A^*, the centers of π and π^*, are ordinary points of f and f^*. Suppose that there are several places $\bar{\pi}_1, \cdots, \bar{\pi}_s$ of the graph Φ with the same center (A, A^*) as π. In particular say $\bar{\pi} = \pi_1$. The total multiplicities δ and δ^* assigned to π and π^* as elements of $T^{-1}\pi^*$ and of $T\pi$ are

$$\delta = \Sigma d(\bar{\pi}_i), \quad \delta^* = \Sigma d^*(\pi_i).$$

Since μ and μ^* are the degrees of S^* and S we will have

$$\mu = \Sigma\delta, \qquad \mu^* = \Sigma\delta^*.$$

8. Branch places and Zeuthen's formula for correspondences. The branch places of the irreducible correspondence $\mathfrak{C}$ on f are the places π such that in $T\pi$ there are places with multiplicity > 1. Let us suppose that π^* is such a place and has been assigned the multiplicity $d^*(\pi)$ in relation to $\bar{\pi}$. Then π is assigned in relation to $\bar{\pi}$ the branch place multiplicity $d^*(\bar{\pi}) - 1$. The total branch place multiplicity of π is

$$\varepsilon(\pi) = \sum_i (d^*(\bar{\pi}_i) - 1)$$

extended this time to all the places $\bar{\pi}_i$ with center (A, A^*) such that A is the center of π. Thus for a given π there may now be several points (A, A^*), and several places π^*, each bringing its contribution to $\varepsilon(\pi)$. Notice that if π is not a branch place then $\varepsilon(\pi) = 0$. Thus $\varepsilon(\pi)$ is defined for all places π of f. The total number of branch places on f, each counted with its multiplicity is by definition

$$\varepsilon = \Sigma\varepsilon(\pi).$$

That this number is finite will appear at once.

Consider in fact the rational transformation S: $\Phi \to f$ of (5). The multiplicity of $\bar{\pi}$ as element of $S^{-1}\pi$ is the H.C.F. $d(\pi)$ of the orders of the elements of K^f on π and it is the same as the $\bar{\pi}$-multiplicity of π^* as element of $T\pi$. From this follows that $\bar{\pi}$ contributes the same amount to the branch place multiplicity of π relative to S as π^* does relative to $\bar{\pi}$ and the correspondence $\mathfrak{C}$ itself. Therefore ε is also the number of branch places of S as defined in (VII, 14). Since the number of distinct branch places of S is finite and each has a finite multiplicity the number ε is finite.

Needless to say there is a number ε^* of branch places for f^* and it has the same properties as ε, with f^*, S^* in place of f, S.

The analogues of B of (VII, 14) for S and S^* are the divisors of Φ given by

$$B = \Sigma(d^*(\bar{\pi}) - 1)\bar{\pi}, \quad B^* = \Sigma(d(\bar{\pi}) - 1)\bar{\pi},$$

where the sums are extended to all the places $\bar{\pi}$ of Φ. If C, C^* and C_0 are canonical divisors of f, f^* and Φ (VII, 14.2) yields on Φ:

(8.1) $$C_0 \sim S^{-1}C + B \sim S^{*-1}C^* + B^*.$$

By comparing degrees this yields Zeuthen's formula for irreducible correspondences

(8.2) $$\varepsilon + \mu^*(2p - 2) = \varepsilon^* + \mu(2p^* - 2).$$

For a rational transformation $f \rightarrow f^*$ of degree μ, i.e. a $(\mu, 1)$ irreducible correspondence $f \rightarrow\rightarrow f^*$, $\varepsilon = 0$, $\mu^* = 1$ and the formula reduces to (VII, 14.3). The ε of that formula is the same as the present ε^*.

9. Correspondences between rational curves. As one would expect when the two curves f, f^* are rational one may proceed much more directly. Let the models of the curves be the projective lines KP_x^1 and $KP_{x^*}^1$ referred to the coordinates x_0, x_1 and x_0^*, x_1^*. Take again for $\mathfrak{C}$ an irreducible non-degenerate (μ, μ^*) correspondence. The field $K(x_1^*/x_0^*)$ is now algebraic over $K(x_1/x_0)$ and hence there is a relation

(9.1) $$\varphi(x_0, x_1 ; x_0^*, x_1^*) = 0, \quad \varphi \in K_H^2[x; x^*],$$

where φ is irreducible. The graph is merely the curve φ. If $M(x_0, x_1)$ is a general point of the line f then the points M^* of TM are those whose coordinates x_0^*, x_1^* satisfy (9.1). Hence φ is of degree μ^* in the x_i^*, and for evident reasons of symmetry it is of degree μ in x_0, x_1. If π, π^* are associated under $\mathfrak{C}$ and have the centers $A(a_0, a_1)$ and $A^*(a_0^*, a_1^*)$ the reader will readily verify that the multiplicity δ^* of π^* as element of $T\pi$ is the multiplicity of $(a_0^* x_1^* - a_1^* x_0^*)$ as factor of the form $\varphi(a_0, a_1; x_0^*, x_1^*)$.

(9.2) *General remark.* One may say that an irreducible non-degenerate correspondence between two lines is completely determined by a single relation, here (9.1). In this case then the ideal $\mathfrak{P}_H$ of the graph is merely the principal ideal of $K_H^2[x; x^*]$ generated by the element φ. Such correspondences may well exist in the general case, namely when the graph Φ is defined by a single irreducible relation $\varphi(x; x^*) = 0$. The ideal $\mathfrak{P}_H$ is then again the principal ideal (φ). One may also characterize this special case by the property that in the product space $KP_x^2 \times KP_{x^*}^2$ the graph Φ is then the complete intersection of the surface $f \times f^*$ with a hypersurface φ.

10. Once multiplicities $\delta^*(\pi_i^*)$ have been assigned to the elements $\pi_i^*, \cdots, \pi_k^*$ of $T\pi$ one may introduce the divisor $D^* = \Sigma\delta^*(\pi_i^*)\pi_i^*$, which we call the *image divisor* of π under T, written $T\pi$. The degree of D^* is $\Sigma\delta^*(\pi_i^*) = \mu^*$. Similarly there is an image divisor $D = T^{-1}\pi^*$ of π^* under T^{-1} and its degree is μ. These divisors will play a central role in the comparison with linear series.

Just as in the case of algebraic series it is of interest to combine irreducible correspondences into composite correspondences. This is done formally as follows: Given the irreducible non-degenerate correspondences $\mathfrak{C}_1, \cdots, \mathfrak{C}_s$ with associated elements $\Phi_i, \cdots$, for $\mathfrak{C}_i$ we define a *reducible correspondence* as an expression

$$\mathfrak{C} = \Sigma\sigma_i\mathfrak{C}_i$$

where the σ_i are arbitrary integers. Intuitively $\mathfrak{C}$ corresponds to the "reducible" graph Φ consisting of the Φ_i taken with the multiplicities σ_i. When the σ_i are all positive they are essentially the multiplicities of the components Φ_i of Φ. When the σ_i are negative however, their geometric interpretation would require the extension of the analogue of the divisor concept to curves on a surface, here the product $f \times f^*$. (See the concept of cycle in the next chapter: IX, 5.)

Pursuing the treatment of a composite $\mathfrak{C}$ the associated transformations are by definition the operations

$$T = \Sigma\sigma_i T_i, \quad T^{-1} = \Sigma\sigma_i T_i^{-1}.$$

If $D_i^* = T_i\pi$, $D_i = T_i^{-1}\pi^*$ we define

$$T\pi = \Sigma\sigma_i T_i\pi = \Sigma\sigma_i D_i^*; \quad T^{-1}\pi^* = \Sigma\sigma_i T_i^{-1}\pi^* = \Sigma\sigma_i D_i.$$

If $\mathfrak{C}$, $\mathfrak{C}'$ are correspondences one defines $-\mathfrak{C}$ and $\mathfrak{C} + \mathfrak{C}'$ in the obvious way. A function $\varphi(\mathfrak{C})$ is said to be *additive* wherever

$$\varphi(\mathfrak{C} - \mathfrak{C}') = \varphi(\mathfrak{C}) - \varphi(\mathfrak{C}').$$

We also say that a property is *additive* whenever if it holds for $\mathfrak{C}$ and $\mathfrak{C}'$ then it holds also for $\mathfrak{C} - \mathfrak{C}'$. Thus the transformations T, T^{-1}, the divisors D, D^*, the indices μ, μ^*, the multiplicities $\delta(\pi)$, $\delta^*(\pi^*)$ of the places are all additive.

The transformation T is said to be *linear* whenever the divisor $D^* = T\pi$ is in a fixed divisor class. If D^* is effective this means also that it is in a fixed linear series of degree μ^*. Similarly for T^{-1} and D. It is clear that linearity is additive.

If both T and T^{-1} are linear $\mathfrak{C}$ itself is said to be linear.

(10.1) *All correspondences between rational curves are linear.*

Owing to the additive property we only need to consider an irreducible correspondence $\mathfrak{C}$. Assuming then f and f^* both rational we are in the situation of (9). With φ as there defined we may write

$$\varphi = \Sigma\lambda_{ij}(x_0^*, x_1^*)x_0^i x_1^j, \quad i + j = \mu.$$

Hence the divisors $D = T^{-1}\pi^*$ are elements of the g_μ^μ cut out on f by the forms

$$\psi^c = \Sigma c_{ij} x_0^i x_1^j, \quad c_{ij} \in K.$$

Thus T^{-1} is linear. Similarly of course for T, and so (10.1) holds.

The central theorem regarding linearity is:

(10.2) **Theorem.** *If one of the transformations T, T^{-1} is linear so is the other. Hence in order that the correspondence $\mathfrak{C}$ itself be linear it is sufficient that one of T, T^{-1} be linear.*

We will assume T^{-1} linear and prove that T has the same property.

Let us set $\sigma_i = \sigma_i' - \sigma_i''$, where both σ_i' and σ_i'' are non-negative. Then

$$A = \Sigma\sigma_i' D_i, \quad B = \Sigma\sigma_i'' D_i$$

are both effective, and $D = A - B$. Under our assumption $A - B$ is in a fixed equivalence class $\{B_1 - A_1\}$ of f where A_1 and B_1 are effective. Thus $A + A_1 \sim B + B_1$ on f. There exists then an $R \in K_H^2(x; x^*)$ such that if $M^*(x^*)$ is a general point of f^*, R has on f the divisor $A - B + A_1 - B_1 = D + C$. We call C and D the *fixed* and *the variable divisors* of R on f.

Suppose that $S \in K_H^2(x; x^*)$ has the same variable divisor D as R. Then S/R has only a fixed divisor H on f. Hence there is an $R_1 \in K_H(x)$ which has H as its divisor on f. Hence S/RR_1 has the divisor zero on f. Since S/RR_1 is a rational function of $L_H(x)$, where $L = \overline{K_H(x^*)}$, it is equal to an element of L on f. Since this element can only be in the intersection of L with $K_H^2(x; x^*)$, it reduces in fact to an element $R^2(x^*) \in K_H(x^*)$ on f. Thus $S = R_1(x)R_2(x^*)R(x, x^*)$. Hence R is unique to within a factor $R_1(x)\, R_2(x^*)$ where $R_1(x) \in K_H(x)$ and $R_2(x^*) \in K_H(x^*)$.

In what follows it will be convenient to put R in the explicit form

$$R(x; x^*) = \frac{P(x; x^*)}{Q(x; x^*)}$$

where $P, Q \in K_H^2[x; x^*]$.

Upon substituting for the x_i^* their expressions $x_i^*(t^*)$ in the representation for π^*, $R(x; x^*)$ becomes an element $R(x; t^*)$ of $(K((t^*)))_H(x)$, and its variable divisor is precisely D. In the same manner we can form $R(t; x^*)$ and to prove that T is linear we merely need to prove:

(10.3) *The variable divisor of $R(t; x^*)$ on f^* is $D^* = T\pi$.*

(10.4) An interesting observation may be made regarding the determination of the fixed divisor C. The problem reduces to the determination of the coefficient ε of a given place π of f in C. Let ξ be an element of K^f of order one at π. Then $S = \xi^{-\varepsilon}R(x; x^*)$ is a function such as S whose fixed divisor does not contain π. Thus the order ε is such that there exists an element $R_1(=\xi^{-\varepsilon})$ of K^f whose product by R suppresses π as part of the fixed divisor. If $R_2 \in K^f$ has the same property then π is not part of the divisor of R_2/R_1, hence R_1 and R_2 have the same order $-\varepsilon$ at π.

(10.5) Let us suppose that the places π, π^* of f, f^* correspond under $\mathfrak{C}_j$.

Upon substituting the $x_i(t)$, $x_i^*(t^*)$ in $R(x; x^*)$ we obtain

$$R(t, t^*) = \frac{P(t, t^*)}{Q(t, t^*)}$$

where we have written $P(t, t^*), \cdots,$ for $P(x_0(t), \cdots; x_0^*(t^*), \cdots), \cdots$.

The numerator and denominator are elements of the ring of formal power series $K[[t, t^*]]$. Upon applying (V, 1.2a) to them one obtains a relation

$$R(t, t^*) = E(t, t^*)t^a t^{*b}\frac{p(t, t^*)}{q(t, t^*)}, \tag{10.6}$$

$$p(t, t^*) = t^r + p_1(t^*)t^{r-1} + \cdots + p_r(t^*), \quad p_r(t^*) \neq 0, \tag{10.7}$$

$$q(t, t^*) = t^s + q_1(t^*)t^{s-1} + \cdots + q_s(t^*), \quad q_s(t^*) \neq 0, \tag{10.8}$$

where p, q are special polynomials in t and relatively prime.

11. Corresponding to the place $\bar{\pi}$ of Φ_i and the associated relations (6.2) introduce the expression

$$\alpha(t, t^*) = \prod_k (t - \eta^{kd^*}t^{*d^*/d}E(\eta^k t^{*1/d})) \tag{11.1}$$

where for the present t, t^* are considered as independent indeterminates. Since the product is symmetric with respect to the $\eta^k t^{*1/d}$, and each term except t^d is of positive degree in $t^{*1/d}$, we have

$$\alpha(t, t^*) = t^d + \alpha_1(t^*)t^{d-1} + \cdots + \alpha_d(t^*),$$

where the right hand side is in $K[[t, t^*]]$ and is a special polynomial in t. Furthermore

$$\alpha_d(t^*) = t^{*d^*}E_1(t^*).$$

Since $\alpha(t, t^*)$ is of degree d^* in t^* the preparation theorem yields

$$\begin{cases} \alpha(t, t^*) = E(t, t^*)\beta(t^*, t), \\ \beta(t^*, t) = t^{*d^*} + \beta_1(t)t^{*(d^*-1)} + \cdots + \beta_{d^*}(t), \end{cases} \tag{11.2}$$

where $\beta(t^*, t) \in K[[t, t^*]]$ and is a special polynomial in t^*.

Now the relation

$$\beta(t^*, t) = 0$$

has a solution in t given by

$$t = t^{*d^*/d}E(t^{*1/d}).$$

Upon solving for t^* in terms of t we see that the special polynomial $\beta(t^*, t)$ in t^* has the d^* conjugate roots in $K\{t\}$:

$$\eta^{*hd}t^{d/d^*}E_1(\eta^{*h}t^{1/d^*}), \qquad h = 1, 2, \cdots, d^*.$$

It has already been observed that these d^* roots are distinct (end of 6 with t and t^* interchanged). Since their number is the degree d^* of $\beta(t^*, t)$ in t^* (degree understood as for polynomials), and since the coefficient of t^* in $\beta(t^*, t)$ is unity we have

$$\beta(t^*, t) = \prod_h (t^* - \eta^{*hd} t^{d/d^*} E_1(\eta^{*h} t^{1/d^*})). \tag{11.3}$$

Thus $\beta(t^*, t)$ is the analogue of $\alpha(t, t^*)$ with the roles of π and π^* reversed.

12. Suppose now that the coefficient σ_j of $\mathfrak{C}_j$ in the expression of $\mathfrak{C}$ is positive. If M_t, $M^*_{t^*}$ designate representative points of π, π^*, then through $\bar{\pi}$ there is found in $T^{-1}M^*_{t^*}$ exactly one general point M_t for each of the d expressions $t(t^*)$ given by (6.2), i.e. for each of the factors of (11.1). Since each of these points is repeated σ_j times, α^{σ_j} is a factor of $p(t, t^*)$. Similarly if $\sigma_j < 0$, α^{σ_j} is a factor of $q(t, t^*)$. Since all the possible points M_t arise in the way just described, $p(t, t^*)$ and $q(t, t^*)$ are the products of the powers α^σ thus obtained.

We have therefore the following situation: Let $\bar{\pi}_1, \cdots, \bar{\pi}_N$ denote all the places of all the graphs Φ_i with the same center (A, A^*), where A and A^* are the centers of π and π^*. For $\bar{\pi}_h$ define s_h as the coefficient σ_j of the particular $\mathfrak{C}_j$ such that $\bar{\pi}_h$ is a place of Φ_j. Let $\alpha_h(t, t^*)$, $\beta_h(t^*, t)$ denote the α, β corresponding to $\bar{\pi}_h$. Then

$$R(t, t^*) = t^a t^{*a^*} E(t, t^*) \prod \alpha_h^{s_h}(t, t^*). \tag{12.1}$$

As a consequence we also have in view of (11.2) for each α_h:

$$R(t, t^*) = t^a t^{*a^*} E_1(t^*, t) \prod \beta_h^{s_h}(t^*, t). \tag{12.2}$$

The degrees of α_h in t and of β_h in t^* are the numbers $d(\bar{\pi}_h)$ and $d^*(\bar{\pi}_h)$. Therefore the coefficient of π in $T^{-1}\pi^*$ is $\Sigma s_h d(\bar{\pi}_h)$ and it is the coefficient of π as a variable place in the divisor D of R for π^* fixed. On the other hand the degree of the product in (12.2) in t^* is $\Sigma s_h d^*(\bar{\pi}_h)$ and this is the coefficient of π^* as a variable place of the divisor D^* of R for π fixed. However this degree is precisely the coefficient of π^* in $T\pi$. Hence $T\pi$ is linear. This proves (10.3) and hence Theorem (10.2).

13. In connection with correspondences Abel's theorem leads to noteworthy relations. Let p^* be the genus of f^* and let $\{du_j\}$ and $\{du_k^*\}$ be sets of p and p^* linearly independent dfk for f and f^*. Suppose first that the correspondence $\mathfrak{C}$ is irreducible and let M be a general point of f and $M_1^*, \cdots M_{\mu^*}^*$ the points of TM. Since the M_h^* are general points of f^* the abelian sums

$$dv_k = S(du_k^*, D^*) = \Sigma(du_k^*)_{M_h^*} \tag{13.1}$$

all have meaning. Since the coordinate ratios of the M_h^* are in a definite algebraic extension of $K(M)$ (the field of the ratios of the coordinates of M), and since the sum in (13.1) is symmetric in the M_h^*, dv_k is in fact a differential of the field $K(M)$, i.e. in the last analysis of the curve f. Now by little more than a paraphrase of the proof of (VII, 9.7) one may show that since du_k^* has no poles the same holds for dv_k. Thus dv_k is a *dfk* of the curve f.

If $\mathfrak{C} = \Sigma\sigma_i\mathfrak{C}_i$ where the $\mathfrak{C}_i$ are irreducible then we define for $\mathfrak{C}$

$$dv_k = \Sigma\sigma_i S(du_k^*, D_i^*)$$

and the conclusion is the same.

Since dv_k is a *dfk* of f we have a linear relation

$$dv_k = \Sigma\lambda_{ki}du_i, \qquad \lambda_{ki} \in K. \tag{13.2}$$

We may consider the system (13.2) as a linear transformation τ of the linear systems of the *dfk* into one another which we will write

$$\tau du_k^* = \Sigma\lambda_{ki}du_i. \tag{13.3}$$

By reversing the roles of the two curves we find likewise a transformation

$$\tau^{-1}du_k = \Sigma\lambda_{ki}^*du_i^*, \qquad \lambda_{ki}^* \in K. \tag{13.4}$$

Here as in the case of T, T^{-1} one must not read into the designations τ, τ^{-1} the usual "inverse transformation" relationship. They are merely convenient notations to underscore their operating in opposite directions.

Let us agree to write $\tau = 0$ if every $\lambda_{ki} = 0$ and likewise for τ^{-1}. According to theorem (4.1) T^{-1} is linear if and only if $\tau = 0$ and likewise for T and τ^{-1}. Hence theorem (10.2) is equivalent to the following:

(13.5) *If one of τ, τ^{-1} is zero so is the other.*

Notice that in the usual sense of linear transformations if τ_i, τ_i^{-1} correspond to τ, τ^{-1} for C_i, then

$$\tau = \Sigma\sigma_i\tau_i, \quad \tau^{-1} = \Sigma\sigma_i\tau_i^{-1}. \tag{13.6}$$

§ 4. Algebraic Correspondences of a Curve with Itself

14. Everything that has been said so far continues to be valid when $f^* = f$, i.e. for correspondences of the curve f with itself. There arises however the interesting problem of determining the number of fixed places of the correspondences, i.e. of the places π which are self-corresponding or such that π is a place of $T\pi$, or equivalently, of $T^{-1}\pi$. We shall only be in position to deal with this problem for certain special correspondences to be defined presently.

Let $\mathfrak{J}$ denote the identity correspondence, i.e. the correspondence consisting merely of all the couples (π, π). The special correspondences $\mathfrak{C}$ alluded to above are characterized by the property that there exists an integer γ such that $\mathfrak{C} + \gamma\mathfrak{J}$ is linear. That is to say the divisors $T\pi + \gamma\pi$ belong to a fixed equivalence class. The integer γ is known as the *valence* of $\mathfrak{C}$ and $\mathfrak{C}$ is referred to as a *valence correspondence*. If $\gamma = 0$, $\mathfrak{C}$ is linear. Henceforth instead of "linear correspondence" we shall say "correspondence with valence zero." This is in keeping with the accepted terminology.

When $\mathfrak{C}$ is the identity correspondence both T and T^{-1} reduce to the identity transformation. Hence according to (8.1) if $\mathfrak{C}$ has the valence γ then $T^{-1}\pi + \gamma\pi$ is likewise in a fixed divisor class. Hence the concept of valence is perfectly symmetrical with respect to T and T^{-1}.

15. It is convenient to apply here also the technique of products and graphs. To that end, assuming as before $f \subset KP^2_x$, we introduce a copy f^* of f in $KP^2_{x^*}$, i.e. f^* is the curve of $KP^2_{x^*}$ represented by $f(x^*) = 0$. The points, places, $\cdots$ of f have then obvious images in f^* and a correspondence $\mathfrak{C}: f \longleftrightarrow f$ gives rise to a correspondence $f \longleftrightarrow f^*$ which we continue to denote for convenience by $\mathfrak{C}$. The graph of an irreducible correspondence $\mathfrak{C}$ is then an irreducible curve $\Phi \subset f \times f^*$.

The transformations τ, τ^{-1} of (13) on the differentials may likewise be introduced here. They are both of course linear transformations of the system $\{du_i\}$ of the *dfk* into itself. Since to $\mathfrak{C} = \mathfrak{J}$ there corresponds the identity transformation I on the *dfk* we may state as a consequence of (13.5):

(15.1) *If one of $\tau + \gamma I$, $\tau^{-1} + \gamma I$ is zero so is the other.*

By means of the differentials we also prove readily:

(15.2) *If the genus p of the curve f is positive and if a correspondence $\mathfrak{C}$ has a valence then this valance is unique.*

For if there are two distinct valences γ, γ' then $(\gamma - \gamma')I = 0$. Hence $(\gamma - \gamma')(du)_\pi = 0 = (du)_\pi$, i.e. $du = 0$. Thus f has no *dfk* and so $p = 0$.

One may state more precisely:

(15.3) *A correspondence $\mathfrak{C}$ of a curve of genus zero with itself may be assigned any valence.*

For by (10.1) $\mathfrak{C}$ has valence zero. Since $\mathfrak{C} + \gamma\mathfrak{J}$ has likewise valence zero one may also assign to $\mathfrak{C}$ the valence γ.

The property just proved indicates that on rational curves valences are immaterial. This will be confirmed when we come to the coincidence and fixed point formulas (see 18 and 20). For in these formulas γ always enters in the combination $p\gamma$, and hence it does not appear when the genus p is zero.

16. Let us turn our attention now to the fixed places. We must first define the fixed place multiplicity of an irreducible correspondence $\mathfrak{C}$. Since on the surface $f \times f^*$ the fixed places are among the intersection places of the graph Φ of $\mathfrak{C}$ with the graph Γ of the identity the multiplicity can only have meaning if Φ is not Γ, i.e. if $\mathfrak{C} \neq \mathfrak{J}$.

Suppose then that the correspondence $\mathfrak{C}$ is not the identity. Let π, π^*, $\bar{\pi}$ be related as usual and let π be a fixed place. Let also f be so chosen that the center A of π is an ordinary point of f. Then the center A^* of π^* will also be an ordinary point of f^* and consequently (A, A^*) will be an ordinary point of $f \times f^*$ (IV, 13.9). Furthermore if t is a parameter for A, i.e. a parameter for π, then t^* (the same as t) will be a parameter for π^* and t, t^* will be parameters for (A, A^*) and $f \times f^*$.

Let us observe now that the graph Γ of the identity is a birational model of f and hence irreducible. For relative to the identity the projection $S: \Gamma \to f$ is a rational transformation of degree unity.

If the irreducible representation of π is

$$\rho x_i = \Sigma a_{ij} t^j$$

that of π^* will be

$$\sigma x_i^* = \Sigma a_{ij} t^{*j}.$$

These represent coordinates of parametric points M_t, $M_{t^*}^*$ of π, π^*. Hence $(M_t, M_{t^*}^*)$ will be a parametric point for the place ω of the graph Γ of the identity centered at (A, A^*). Thus ω is represented in the coordinates t, t^* by the sole relation

$$t = t^*. \tag{16.1}$$

This shows among other things that Γ has a single place ω centered at (A, A^*), its representation in the coordinates t, t^* being (16.1).

The place $\bar{\pi}$ of Φ is represented in the same coordinates by

$$t - \eta^{kd^*} t^{*d^*/d} E(\eta^k t^{*1/d}) = 0,$$

or in $K[[t, t^*]]$ by

$$\alpha(t, t^*) = \prod_k (t - \eta^{kd^*} t^{*d^*/d} E(\eta^k t^{*1/d})) = 0,$$

where $\alpha(t, t^*)$ is the expression thus denoted in (11). Anticipating slightly upon the next chapter (see IX, 3) we attach to ω and $\bar{\pi}$ as intersection multiplicity (in accordance with the scheme of V, 15), i.e. to π as fixed place multiplicity, the number $\nu(\bar{\pi})$ given by

$$\alpha(t, t) = t^\nu E_1(t).$$

It is to be noted that $\alpha(t, t)$ is not identically zero. For if it were Γ and Φ would share the place ω and since they are irreducible they would coincide. Moreover ν is unaffected by a regular transformation of t and so it depends solely upon π and $\bar{\pi}$.

If π is associated in the above manner with several places $\bar{\pi}_1, \cdots, \bar{\pi}_s$ of Φ there is a $\nu(\bar{\pi}_i)$ for each $\bar{\pi}_i$ and the total multiplicity of π as fixed place is defined as $N(\pi) = \Sigma\nu(\bar{\pi}_i)$.

17. (17.1) *If $\mathfrak{C}$ is irreducible and is not the identity, the number of its fixed places is finite.*

The fixed places of $\mathfrak{C}$ are among those of f associated with the intersections of Φ with Γ. Since in this association a single place of f corresponds to each place of Φ, it is sufficient to show that the two curves have a finite number of intersections. Since they are irreducible and distinct the ideal of one, say of Γ, contains an element $g(x; x^*)$ which does not contain Φ. Hence g intersects Φ in a subvariety, i.e. in a finite number of points. Since these include the intersections of Φ with Γ (17.1) follows.

Since the number of fixed places is finite, $N(\pi)$ is zero at all but a finite number of places of f. Hence $U(\mathfrak{C}) = \Sigma N(\pi)\pi$ is a definite divisor of f which is effective or zero. We refer to it as the *divisor of the fixed places* of the correspondence $\mathfrak{C}$.

18. Let now $\mathfrak{C}_1, \cdots, \mathfrak{C}_s$ be irreducible correspondences of f with itself, all distinct from one another and from the identity. Introduce the general correspondence $\mathfrak{C} = \Sigma\sigma_i\mathfrak{C}_i$. Since $\mathfrak{C}_i \neq \mathfrak{J}$ the divisor $U_i = U(\mathfrak{C}_i)$ is defined and so is

$$U(\mathfrak{C}) = \Sigma\sigma_i U_i. \tag{18.1}$$

We define $U(\mathfrak{C})$ as the *divisor of the fixed places* of the general correspondence $\mathfrak{C}$.

Consider more particularly the case where $\mathfrak{C}$ *has valence zero.* We have then the associated rational function $R(x; x^*)$ of (10). It is also known that there are fixed divisors A, A^* such that

$$T\pi + A \sim 0, \quad T^{-1}\pi + A^* \sim 0.$$

Now if π is a fixed place the factorization (10.6) yields here

$$R(t, t) = t^{a+a^*}\Pi\alpha_h^{s_h}(t, t).$$

If N is the fixed point multiplicity of π this relation yields

$$\Pi\alpha_h^{s_h}(t, t) = t^N E(t).$$

Hence the order of $R(t, t)$ at π is $a + a^* + N$. This is the same as the order of π in $U(\mathfrak{C}) + A + A^*$. Hence

$$U(\mathfrak{C}) + A + A^* \sim 0$$

and therefore

$$U(\mathfrak{C}) \sim T\pi + T^{-1}\pi. \tag{18.2}$$

In terms of the U_i we also have

$$\Sigma\sigma_i U_i \sim \Sigma\sigma_i(T_i\pi + T_i^{-1}\pi). \tag{18.3}$$

Let $\mathfrak{C}$ and $\mathfrak{C}_i$ be (μ, μ^*) and (μ_i, μ_i^*) correspondences and let u and u_i be the orders of $U(\mathfrak{C})$ and U_i. We have then

$$\mu = \Sigma\sigma_i\mu_i, \quad \mu^* = \Sigma\sigma_i\mu_i^*$$

and hence from (18.2) and (18.3):

$$u = \mu + \mu^*. \tag{18.4}$$

This is the classical fixed point formula for correspondences with valence zero due to de Jonquières.

As a consequence of (15.3) the formula of de Jonquières holds for all correspondences when f is rational. This may also be verified at once when $\mathfrak{C}$ is irreducible. For if φ is as in (9) the fixed points and their multiplicities are readily shown to correspond to the linear factors of $\varphi(x_0, x_1; x_0, x_1)$. Since this form is of degree $\mu + \mu^*$, (18.4) follows.

19. Suppose now that $\mathfrak{C}$, defined as before has the valence γ. Consider the special irreducible correspondence $\mathfrak{C}_0$ defined in the following manner: If n is the class of f take a point P in the plane of f, exterior to f, and such that there are n distinct tangents to f from P. Given any point M of f we associate with M in $\mathfrak{C}_0$ any point M^* of f such that MM^* goes through P. The correspondence is manifestly $(m - 1, m - 1)$ and with valence $\gamma = 1$. The fixed places are the places $\pi_1, \cdots, \pi_n$ whose centers are the contacts of the tangents from P to f.

Let p_i be the coordinates of P and x_i, x_i^* those of M, M^*. They satisfy the relation

$$D(x; x^*) = \begin{vmatrix} x_0, & x_1, & x_2 \\ x_0^*, & x_1^*, & x_2^* \\ p_0, & p_1, & p_2 \end{vmatrix} = 0.$$

Let π be one of the places π_i. Under our assumptions we may choose the coordinate system so that P is the point (0, 1, 0) and the center of π is (1, 0, 0). Thus π will have a normal representation

$$\rho x_0 = 1, \quad \rho x_1 = t, \quad \rho x_2 = t^2 E(t).$$

Then π^*, the image of π in f^* will have a normal representation

$$\rho x_0^* = 1, \quad \rho x_1^* = t^*, \quad \rho x_2^* = t^{*2} E(t^*).$$

Following our general method we must write down the relation stating that the representative points M_t, $M_{t^*}^*$ of π, π^* correspond under $\mathfrak{C}_0$. It becomes here

$$D(t, t^*) = t^2 E(t) - t^{*2} E(t^*) = 0.$$

If $E(t) = a + bt + \cdots$, then

$$D(t, t^*) = (t - t^*)\{a(t + t^*) + b(t^2 + tt^* + t^{*2}) + \cdots\}.$$

Therefore we have one of the two relations

$$(19.1) \qquad t = t^*, \quad a(t + t^*) + b(t^2 + tt^* + t^{*2}) + \cdots = 0.$$

At this juncture it would be convenient to know that the correspondence $\mathfrak{C}_0$ is irreducible. However one may dispense with this property in the following manner. If $\mathfrak{C}_0$ is reducible then, since for M general, TM consists of $m - 1$ distinct points $\mathfrak{C}_0 = \Sigma\mathfrak{C}_{i0}$, where the $\mathfrak{C}_{i0}$ are irreducible and distinct from the identity. Let Φ_{i0} be the graph of $\mathfrak{C}_{i0}$. Now the first relation (19.1) corresponds to a place π in the graph of the identity, and since every $\mathfrak{C}_{i0} \neq \mathfrak{J}$, this π is not in any graph Φ_{i0}. Thus the second relation (19.1) is the only one corresponding to a place $\bar{\pi}$ in a graph Φ_{i0}. Since $E(0) = a \neq 0$, this relation yields here

$$t = -t^* + \lambda t^{*2} + \cdots = t^* E_1(t^*).$$

Upon combining the two representations of π, π^* in terms of t^* there results an irreducible representation of $\bar{\pi}$. There is only one expression $\alpha_i(t, t^*)$ involved, namely

$$\alpha(t, t^*) = t - t^*E_1(t^*) = t + t^* - \lambda t^{*2} + \cdots.$$

Hence

$$\alpha(t, t) = t(2 - \lambda t + \cdots).$$

Consequently the multiplicity of π as a fixed place of $\mathfrak{C}_0$ is unity. Therefore the degree U_0 of the fixed place divisor of $U(\mathfrak{C}_0)$ is equal to the class of f, or

$$u_0 = n = 2(p + m - 1).$$

Consider now a (μ, μ^*) correspondence $\mathfrak{C}$ with valence γ. Then $\mathfrak{C}' = \mathfrak{C} - \gamma\mathfrak{C}_0$ has valence zero and indices $\mu - \gamma(m-1)$, $\mu^* - \gamma(m-1)$. Hence the degree u' of $U(\mathfrak{C}')$ is given by

$$u' = \mu + \mu^* - 2\gamma(m - 1).$$

Since the degree u of $U(\mathfrak{C})$ satisfies

$$u = u' + \gamma u_0,$$

we have finally

$$u = \mu + \mu^* + 2\gamma p, \tag{19.2}$$

which is the classical fixed point formula for correspondences with valence due to Cailey-Brill.

(19.3) *Remark on the differentials.* There is little more to add to the treatment of (13) save that τ and τ^{-1} are now linear transformations (with coefficients in K) of the system of the *dfk* of f alone into itself. We may also notice that the correspondences with valence γ are characterized by $\tau + \gamma I = 0$, or equivalently by $\tau^{-1} + \gamma I = 0$, where I denotes the identity operating on the *dfk*.

§ 5. PRODUCTS OF CORRESPONDENCES

20. The following remarks are admittedly sketchy. Returning to the situation of §3 with the correspondence $\mathfrak{C}$ between f and f^*, let f^{**} be a third irreducible curve and $\mathfrak{C}_1$ a correspondence $f^* \rightarrow f^{**}$. The associated indices and transformations will be written μ_1, μ_1^* and T_1, T_1^{-1}. If M, M^* are points paired under $\mathfrak{C}$ and M^*, M^{**} are paired under $\mathfrak{C}^*$ then M, M^{**} are paired under a correspondence $f \longleftrightarrow f^{**}$ denoted by $\mathfrak{C}_1\mathfrak{C}$. The related indices and transformations are $\mu\mu_1$, $\mu^*\mu_1^*$ and T_1T, $T^{-1}T_1^{-1}$.

One may also define the *inverse* $\mathfrak{C}^{-1}$ of the correspondence $\mathfrak{C}$ as the correspondence in which the roles of f and f^* and hence of T and T^{-1} are interchanged.

All this is applicable to correspondences of f with itself. The only novel element arises when $\mathfrak{C}$ and $\mathfrak{C}_1$ have valences γ and γ_1. If TM

consists of the points M_i^*, $i = 1, 2, \cdots, \mu^*$ and $T_1 M_i^*$ of the points M_{ij}^{**}, $j = 1, 2, \cdots, \mu_1^*$ and if du is a *dfk* then

$$\gamma(du)_M + \sum_i (du)_{M_i^*} = 0$$

$$\gamma_1(du)_{M_i^*} + \sum_j (du)_{M_{ij}^{**}} - 0$$

and hence

$$-\gamma\gamma_1(du)_M + \sum_{ij} (du)_{M_{ij}^{**}} = 0$$

or also

$$T_1 T - \gamma\gamma_1 I = 0.$$

Thus:

(20.1) *The product of two correspondences with valences* γ, γ_1 *is a correspondence with valence* $-\gamma\gamma_1$.

It is clear also that if $\mathfrak{C}$ has the valence γ then $\mathfrak{C}^{-1}$ has the same valence.

The extension of $\mathfrak{C}_1\mathfrak{C}$ and $\mathfrak{C}^{-1}$ to the places is automatic and requires no special treatment.

(20.2) *Coincidences.* Let $\mathfrak{C}$, $\mathfrak{C}_1$ be correspondences of f with itself. Then the place π of f is said to be a *coincidence* of $\mathfrak{C}$ and $\mathfrak{C}_1$ whenever there exists a place π^* such that π, π^* are paired off in both $\mathfrak{C}$ and $\mathfrak{C}_1$, or equivalently if π is a fixed place of $\mathfrak{C}_1^{-1}\mathfrak{C}$. It is then of course likewise a fixed place of $\mathfrak{C}^{-1}\mathfrak{C}_1$.

Let $\mathfrak{C}$, $\mathfrak{C}_1$ be irreducible with graphs Φ, Φ_1. Then the coincidences are associated with the intersections of Φ and Φ_1. If $\mathfrak{C} \neq \mathfrak{C}_1$, or equivalently if $\Phi \neq \Phi_1$ one may repeat word for word the proof of (17.1) and show that the number of intersections, hence the number of coincidences, is finite. We will agree to count each coincidence with its fixed point multiplicity for $\mathfrak{C}_1^{-1}\mathfrak{C}$ and calculate the number κ of coincidences on that basis.

All this is applicable to reducible correspondences

$$\mathfrak{C} = \Sigma\sigma_i\mathfrak{C}_i, \quad \mathfrak{C}_1 = \Sigma\sigma_{1j}\mathfrak{C}_{1j}$$

where $\mathfrak{C}_i$, $\mathfrak{C}_{1j}$ are irreducible and non-degenerate, provided that the two sets $\{\mathfrak{C}_i\}$, $\{\mathfrak{C}_{1j}\}$ are disjoint.

Suppose now that $\mathfrak{C}$, $\mathfrak{C}_1$ have the valences γ, γ_1. Since $\mathfrak{C}_1^{-1}$ is a (μ_1^*, μ_1) correspondence, $\mathfrak{C}_1^{-1}\mathfrak{C}$ has the indices $\mu\mu_1^*$, $\mu^*\mu_1$. Since its valence is $-\gamma\gamma_1$, the number of coincidences of $\mathfrak{C}$, $\mathfrak{C}_1$ each counted with its multiplicity, as calculated from the Cailey-Brill formula (19.2) is

$$\kappa = \mu\mu_1^* + \mu^*\mu_1 - 2\gamma\gamma_1 p. \tag{20.3}$$

Since this expression is symmetrical in the elements of $\mathfrak{C}$ and $\mathfrak{C}_1$, one could also calculate the number of coincidences from the number of fixed places of $\mathfrak{C}^{-1}\mathfrak{C}_1$ and the result would be the same.

IX. *Systems of Curves on a Surface*

In relation to a surface the curves which it contains are the analogues of the effective divisors of an algebraic curve. The resulting additive system, together with a suitable relation of equivalence, possesses a finite base—a most beautiful result due to Severi. It is also in intimate relation with a certain theorem of Picard (on his number ρ), and as shown by the author with topological homology theory.

Since the statement of Severi's theorem is purely algebraic one will expect that it may be obtained by purely algebraic means, at least for a groundfield of characteristic zero. This is what we propose to show in the present chapter. Part of Severi's treatment being already algebraic, to save space we have merely algebraized the former transcendental part of the argument—the proof of Picard's theorem. The general argument is very close to the one already followed by the author in [2], Note I (see especially p. 145).

The groundfield K is assumed algebraically closed and of characteristic zero.

§ 1. Generalities on the Curves on a Surface

1. Our basic surface Φ will be an irreducible surface of degree m in some KP^r. The projective coordinates in that space will be written x_i and the related affine coordinates are $X_i = x_i/x_0$. We shall also consider a projection F of Φ in a KP^3 and in the associated affine space KA^3. We assume of course that F is not the plane x_0. In KP^3 we still use coordinates x_i. However to facilitate the reading of earlier authors we shall use in KA^3 affine coordinates $x = x_1/x_0$, $y = x_2/x_0$, $z = x_3/x_0$. The equation of the surface is $F(x, y, z) = 0$.

It has been proved by various authors, notably by R. Walker [1] for the complex field and Zariski [3,5] for our general groundfield, that any irreducible surface possesses a birational model free from singularities. In view of this we shall assume at the outset that Φ is a surface without singularities in some KP^r. If $r = 2$ the surface is KP^2 itself. Excluding this case we assume $r \geq 3$. This does not exclude the plane as a surface but if it occurs it is supposed to be a subspace of KP^r.

Since we are assuming Φ without multiple points all its branches are linear. Let $A(a_i)$ be any point of Φ and let the coordinates be so chosen that A is in the affine space. Then two of the coordinate differences

$X_i - a_i$, say $u = X_1 - a_1$, $v = X_2 - a_2$ may be chosen as parameters for A and the linear branch $\mathfrak{B}^2$ of center A will be represented by relations

$$(1.1)\qquad \begin{cases} X_i = a_i + \varphi_i(u, v), & \varphi_i \in K[[u, v]], \\ \varphi_1 = u, \quad \varphi_2 = v. \end{cases}$$

Upon applying a regular transformation to u, v there results a representation (1.1) such that if

$$(1.2)\qquad \varphi_i = \alpha_{i1}u + \alpha_{i2}v + \cdots$$

then $\|\alpha_{i1}, \alpha_{i2}\|$ is of rank two. Hence the two points $A_j(\alpha_{ij})$ are not collinear with A. Thus A, A_1, A_2 determine a plane T through A. It is easily seen that the space of the differentials of Φ at A is the same as that of T and so T is the tangent plane to the surface at A. Thus it is independent of the scheme whereby it has been obtained.

In projective coordinates the branch $\mathfrak{B}^2$ is defined by the system

$$(1.3)\qquad \rho x_0 = 1, \quad \rho x_i = a_i + \varphi_i(u, v)$$

or by any similar system with the x_i interchanged. The projection of a linear branch is readily shown to be linear provided that the tangent plane of the branch does not go through the center of projection.

By arguments wholly analogous to those for curves one may show that almost every projection of Φ into KP^3, i.e. successive projections from almost every center, will yield in KP^3 an irreducible surface F of the same degree m as Φ and possessing as its sole singularity a curve of double points, or *double curve* Δ with the following properties: Almost every point M of the curve Δ is a simple point of Δ and it is a double point of F which is the center of two linear branches $\mathfrak{B}_1^2$, $\mathfrak{B}_2^2$ with distinct tangent planes T_1, T_2. The intersection of the two planes is the tangent to Δ at M. Or, taking M as the affine origin, an equivalent statement is that

$$F = l_1 l_2 + \cdots,$$

where $l_i = 0$ is the equation of the plane T_i, so that $l_1 \neq l_2$.

It is advantageous to use the freedom in the choice of the projection $\Phi \to F$ to fulfil one or the other or both of the following conditions: given a preassigned finite set of points $\{A_i\}$ and irreducible curves $\{C_j\}$ of Φ then: (a) no A_i is projected into Δ and (b) no C_j is projected into a component of Δ.

(1.4) *Remark.* We shall constantly designate the projection in F of a curve C of Φ by the same letter C as the curve itself. This will avoid complicated notations, and whether the curve is in Φ or in F will generally be clear from the context.

2. It will be convenient to have at our disposal in KP_x^3 a pencil Π of planes, i.e. planes through a fixed line l, such that: (a) l meets the surface F in m distinct points; (b) almost all the planes of the pencil intersect F in irreducible curves. To show that such pencils exist we will have recourse to the dual space S of KP_x^3, whose points are in one-one correspondence with the planes of KP_x^3. The correspondence associates the plane $u_0x_0 + \cdots + u_3x_3$ with the point (u) of $KP_u^3 = S$.

According to (III, 20.1) the planes intersecting F in reducible curves are imaged in S in the points of a V^s, $s \leq 2$. Let P be a plane intersecting F in an irreducible curve H and l a line of P meeting F in m distinct points. The planes of the pencil Π defined by l are imaged in S in the points of a line l^*, the *dual* of l. Since l^* contains a point, namely the image of P which is not in V^s, l^* will intersect every component of V^s, hence also V^s itself, in a finite number of points. Hence the pencil Π has the two desired properties (a) and (b).

Let us take the plane P as plane x_0 (plane at infinity) and three lines such as l as the lines $x_0 = x_i = 0$. The upshot will be that in the affine system the three pencils $x =$ const., $y =$ const., $z =$ const., will have both properties (a), (b). This will be assumed in all that follows.

The pencil cut out by the planes $y =$ const., will play a dominant role in the sequel. We shall denote the general curve of the pencil by H_y, the pencil itself by $\{H_y\}$ and the section $y = a$ by H_a. Thus generally H_y is a section on which y has transcendency unity.

Let δ be the degree of the double curve Δ. If the plane of H_y does not intersect F in a reducible curve, is not tangent to Δ nor passes through its multiple points, H_y will have for sole singularities δ double points with distinct tangents. Hence the genus p of H_y will then be

$$p = \frac{(m-1)(m-2)}{2} - \delta.$$

This will be the genus for almost all curves H_y, i.e. for all but a finite number of values of y. It is in fact the genus of the general hyperplane section of the surface Φ, as well as of the general curve H_y.

In order to be in position to apply our general theory of curves it will be convenient to consider H_y as a curve of $\overline{K(y)}P^2$ so that we may freely discuss its places, etc.

A surface G of KP^3 is said to be *adjoint* to F if it contains the double curve Δ.

3. Let A be any point of the surface Φ and let affine coordinates X_i be so chosen that A is in the affine space. Let again a_i be its affine coordinates and u, v two parameters for A. If $L = K(a)$, the values of the polynomials of $K[X]$ on Φ may be represented as elements of $L[[u, v]]$. Let in particular $G(X) \in K[X]$ and not containing Φ thus become $G(u, v)$. We have then a prime power factoring

(3.1) $$G(u, v) \sim \Pi G_i^{\sigma_i}(u, v)$$

(3.2) $$G_i = v^n + \gamma_1(u)v^{n-1} + \cdots + \gamma_n(u)$$

where G_i is an irreducible special polynomial. It is not excluded that $G_i = u$ or v. The solution of $G_i = 0$ by Puiseux's theorem consists of n conjugate values of which any one is

(3.3) $$v = u^{k/n}E(u^{1/n})$$

or exceptionally of $u = 0$. Each G_i corresponds thus to a single place π_i of the intersection of G with Φ centered at A and all such places are obtained in this manner.

If C is a curve on Φ through A and $\mathfrak{a}$ its ideal, then each polynomial of $\mathfrak{a}$ will admit a factoring (3.1). The H.C.F. of all these expressions will assume a similar form

(3.4) $$H(u, v) = \Pi H_i^{s_i}(u,v)$$

with the H_i of the form (3.2) and defining the places ω_i of C centered at A. For a second curve C' there will be a second factoring and places ω_i'. One recognizes here the same situation as in (V, 15) with u, v playing the part of affine plane coordinates. The rules there developed carry over bodily and will determine the intersection multiplicity of C and C', or of C and G(V, 15.4) at the point A.

If C and C' have no common components the sum of the multiplicities of their intersections is referred to as the *number of intersections* of the two curves.

It is hardly necessary to observe that a rational function $R \in K^{\Phi}$ will give rise (by quotient) to a unique factoring (3.1) in which however some of the exponents σ_i may be negative.

Let now C be an irreducible curve of Φ and let A be a general point, and hence an ordinary point of the curve. The corresponding factoring (3.4) will assume the form

(3.5) $$H(u, v) = \alpha(a)u + \beta(a)v + \cdots$$

where $\alpha, \beta, \cdots \in K(a)$ and are not both zero. If we specialize $A(a)$ to almost any point $A^*(a^*)$ (3.5) will hold with a replaced by a^*.

Taking now $R \in K^{\Phi}$, $R \neq 0$, let

$$R(x) = \frac{P(x)}{Q(x)}; \qquad P, Q \in K_H[x].$$

Since PQ is not in the ideal of Φ it intersects Φ in a curve D and D has a finite number of singular points: singular points of its components, or mutual intersections of the components with one another. Since these singular points are strictly in KP^r, the point A is not one of them. It follows that the local factoring of R at A assumes the form

(3.6) $$R(u, v) = E(u, v)H^{\nu}(u, v) \sim (\alpha u + \beta v + \cdots)^{\nu}.$$

The number ν is known as the *order of R at C*, written $\nu(R, C)$. The relation (3.6) does hold at almost all points of the curve C.

4. The order $\nu(R, C)$ may also be obtained in a different manner. We will suppose the affine model F so chosen that the projection of C, still denoted by C, is not a component of Δ and does not pass through any point at infinity on H_y. We will then say that C is *in general position relative to* H_y. This choice of F is certainly compatible with the selection of coordinates adopted in (2).

Let $B_i(\xi_i, y, \zeta_i)$, $i = 1, 2, \cdots, d$ be the intersections of C with H_y. The number d is the degree of the curve C. The B_i are conjugate relative to $K(y)$. If F_x contains one of the B_i it contains them all. Then F_z contains none of the B_i since otherwise they would all be in Δ. However since the B_i contain one transcendental coordinate, namely y, they are all general points of the curve C and so if $B_i \in \Delta$, C must be a component of Δ contrary to assumption. Thus the B_i can only be in at most one of F_x or F_z. Let us assume that they are not in F_z.

Let $B(\xi, y, \zeta)$ be anyone of the points B_i. Since B is not in F_z, it is the center of a single place $\pi(B)$ of H_y and $\pi(B)$ may be parametrized by $t = x - \xi$. If $R \in K^\Phi$ we have then on $\pi(B)$ an expansion

$$R(x, y, z) = R_\nu(\xi, y, \zeta)(x - \xi)^\nu + R_{\nu+1}(\xi, y, \zeta)(x-\xi)^{\nu+1} + \cdots, \quad R_h(\xi, y, \zeta) \in K(\xi, y, \zeta). \tag{4.1}$$

On $\pi(B_i)$ this will become

$$R(x, y, z) = R_\nu(\xi_i\, y, \zeta_i)(x - \xi_i)^\nu + \cdots$$

which we will write

$$R(x, y, z) = [R_\nu(\xi, y, \zeta)(x - \xi)^\nu + \cdots]_i. \tag{4.2}$$

Returning to (4.1) if u, v are parameters for B and since B is an ordinary point for C, we have essentially the factoring (3.5) with $H = x - \xi(y)$, or:

$$x - \xi = \alpha u + \beta v + \cdots,$$

Hence the order of $R(u, v)$ in $\alpha u + \beta v + \cdots$, is the same as its order ν in $(x - \xi)$ in (4.1). In other words the exponent ν of (4.1) is precisely $\nu(R, C)$.

The order $\nu(R, C)$ has the following properties:

$$\nu(RS, C) = \nu(R, C) + \nu(S, C); \tag{4.3}$$

$$\nu(R/S, C) = \nu(R, C) - \nu(S, C). \tag{4.4}$$

We shall also show that:

(4.5) *There is an $R \in K^\Phi$ whose order is one on C, and hence there is an $R \in K^\Phi$ of any preassigned order on C.*

These properties imply essentially:

(4.6) *The assignment $R \to \nu(R, C)$ is a valuation of K^Φ onto the additive group of the integers plus ∞.*

A valuation of this nature attached to the curve C is said to be *one-dimensional* and C is known as its *kernel*. As a matter of fact we shall not require these valuations and so we do not discuss them further.

To prove (4.5) we must construct an element $R \in K^{\Phi}$ such that $\nu(R, C) = 1$. To that end consider the general polynomial $\varphi(x, z; D)$ of degree q sufficiently high with indeterminate coefficients $D_0, D_1, \cdots$. Upon expressing the fact that φ passes through the points B_i of the plane of H_y, there results a system $E(D)$ of linear relations in the D_i. For $q > d$ the polynomials φ thus obtained will not be tangent to H_y at the points B_i. For d lines l_i one through each B_i and not tangent to F anywhere, together with a curve of degree $q - d$ not passing through the B_i, make up a φ not tangent to F in the B_i.

Since the system $E(D)$ is invariant under permutation of the conjugate points B_i, it may be replaced by another system whose coefficients are in $K(y)$, and in fact in $K[y]$. The general solution in the D_i will yield a polynomial $\varphi(x, y, z)$ which for y fixed is of order one at the $\pi(B_i)$. Thus in the expansion (4.2) of φ the exponent ν will be unity, and since it is the order of φ at C, (4.5) is proved.

5. Cycles. Linear systems. Let $C_1, \cdots, C_n$ be irreducible curves of Φ. By a *cycle* of Φ is meant a sum

$$\Gamma = m_1C_1 + \cdots + m_nC_n \tag{5.1}$$

where the m_i are integers. In other words in the domain of curves the cycles are the analogues of the divisors for a single curve. The term "cycle" has been introduced in this connection by A. Weil, perhaps suggested by the true topological cycles attached by the author to subvarieties of complex varieties.

If the m_i are all positive the cycle Γ is *effective* and will again be referred to as a *curve*. The C_i are then the *components* of the curve Γ and the m_i are their multiplicities.

If $R \in K^{\Phi}$, there is a finite set of curves $C_1, \cdots, C_n$ on which the order of R is non-zero. If m_i is its order on C_i then Γ given by (5.1) is the *cycle* of R, written $\Gamma(R)$.

§ 2. Differentials of the Surface Φ

6. In relation to the surface Φ one may consider simple and double differentials.

(6.1) It will be convenient to assume at first that F is obtained in the following unrestricted manner: x, y are any two algebraically independent elements of the function-field K^{Φ}; $z \in K^{\Phi}$ is such that $K^{\Phi} = K(x, y, z)$; $F(x, y, z) = 0$ is the irreducible equation between the three elements.

(6.2) Let A be a point of Φ and let the related notations be those of (3).

Upon expressing the elements of K^{Φ} and the differentials of this field in terms of the local parameters u, v there result isomorphic imbeddings of K^{Φ} into $L((u, v))$ and related spaces of differential forms into the analogues for $L((u, v))$ sending closed or derived differentials into closed or derived differentials. An element $Q \in K^{\Phi}$ thus goes into a $Q(u, v) \in L((u, v))$ and forms

$$\omega_1 = Rdx + Sdy, \quad \omega_2 = Tdxdy$$

into forms

$$\omega_1(u, v) = R^*(u, v)du + S^*(u, v)dv, \quad \omega_2(u, v) = T^*(u, v)dudv.$$

If $Q(u, v) \in L[[u, v]]$, i.e. if $Q(u, v)$ is a power series (and not a quotient of two such series) we will say that Q is *regular* at the point A. Similarly ω_1 or ω_2 are regular at the point A whenever R^* and S^* or T^* are regular at the point.

A differential which is regular at every point of Φ is said to be *of the first kind.*

(6.3) Let again x_i be projective coordinates for the space KP^r of Φ and let R be represented as

$$R = \frac{P(x_0, \cdots, x_r)}{Q(x_0, \cdots, x_r)}; \qquad P, Q \in K_H[x].$$

Since Q is not in the ideal of Φ, it intersects Φ in a finite number of curves $C_1, \cdots, C_s$. It is at once seen that R is of non-negative order at every point of Φ not on a C_i. Thus it is regular at almost all points of Φ. Since the differentials ω_1, ω_2 are regular respectively where $RS(xy)$ or $T(xy)$ are regular, they are likewise regular at almost all points of Φ. The curves where ω_s is non-regular are also called the *polar curves* of ω_s.

Let C be a curve and let $U(x, y, z) \in K(x, y, z)$ be of order one on C. Then there exists an integer ν (it may be zero) such that $U^{-\nu}.\omega_s$ is of order zero. The number ν is the *order* of ω_s on C.

(6.4) It is clear that the various concepts here introduced are independent of the local parameters u, v at the points of Φ, likewise of the special representations of the differentials in terms of x and y.

(6.5) The classification of the differentials into three kinds is essentially simple, and due for dimensions > 1 to Picard. We say that ω_s is *of the second kind at the curve* C whenever there exists an ω_{s-1} such that $\omega_s - d\omega_{s-1}$ is regular at C. That is to say: ω_s is regular at C modulo a derived differential. Then ω_s is said to be *of the second kind* for Φ whenever it is of the second kind at every curve C of Φ. If one defines an ω_0 as merely an element R of K^{Φ}, ω_1 is of the second kind at C if it is regular at C to within a dR, $R \in K^{\Phi}$. This is quite in keeping with the definition for curves.

A differential *of the third kind* is one which is not of the second kind.

We note at once that:

(6.6) *If* ω_s *is of the first kind it is also of the second kind.*

(6.7) $d\omega_{s-1}$ *is of the second kind.*

§ 3. Simple Differentials

7. We are especially interested in closed differentials

$$\omega_1 = Rdx + Sdy, \tag{7.1}$$

$$\frac{\partial R}{\partial y} = \frac{\partial S}{\partial x}. \tag{7.2}$$

The relation (7.2) expresses the fact that ω_1 is closed.

Let C be a non-polar curve of ω_1. Then ω_1 determines on C an abelian differential written $\omega_1(C)$. If C is H_y we shall write however more simply ω_{1y} for $\omega_1(H_y)$.

Let us revert now to the situation of §1 with F as a certain projection of the surface Φ into an affine space with coordinates x, y, z.

Let C be the same irreducible curve as in (4) and let R be the rational function of (4). Suppose explicitly that $\nu(R, C) = -n$, $n > 0$. Then on $\pi(B_i)$:

$$R(x, y, z) = \left[\frac{R_{-n}(\xi, y, \zeta)}{(x-\xi)^n} + \cdots + \frac{R_{-1}(\xi, y, \zeta)}{x-\xi} + R_0(\xi, y, \zeta) + R_1(\xi, y, \zeta)(x-\xi) + \cdots\right]_i, \tag{7.3}$$

$$R_h(\xi, y, \zeta) \in K(\xi, y, \zeta).$$

If $n > 1$ and we set

$$V_n = -\frac{1}{n-1}\sum \frac{R_{-n}(\xi_i, y, \zeta_i)}{(x-\xi_i)^{n-1}} \in K(x, y) \tag{7.3a}$$

then $\omega_1 - dV_n$ has an R of the same form as (7.3) but with n replaced by $n-1$. Hence modulo a suitable dW not affecting the kind of ω_1 we may assume that on $\pi(B_i)$

$$R(x, y, z) = \left[\frac{R_{-1}(\xi, y, \zeta)}{x-\xi} + \cdots\right]_i \tag{7.4}$$

where R_{-1} is the same as before. Now on $\pi(B_i)$

$$\frac{\partial R}{\partial y} = \left[\cdots + \frac{\dfrac{dR_{-1}(\xi, y, \zeta)}{dy}}{x-\xi} + \cdots\right]_i$$

where in [$\cdots$] only the term of order -1 has been written. In view of (7.2) the differential of H_y

$$\frac{\partial R}{\partial y}\,dx = \frac{\partial S}{\partial x}\,dx$$

is of the second kind on H_y and so it has no logarithmic place on H_y. Hence its logarithmic residue on $\pi(B_i)$ must be zero, or

$$\frac{dR_{-1}(\xi, y, \zeta)}{dy} = 0$$

at the general point B_i of C, and hence on C. Therefore

$$R_{-1}(\xi, y, \zeta) = \lambda \in K.$$

Thus the logarithmic residues of ω_{1y} at the places $\pi(B_i)$ have the common value $\lambda \in K$. We call λ the *logarithmic residue* of ω_1 relative to the polar curve C. This will be fully justified upon our showing, as we shall do presently, that λ does not depend upon its derivation by means of H_y. At all events upon subtracting a suitable dV our initial ω_1 will assume a form such that on $\pi(B_i)$:

$$(7.5)\quad R(x, y, z) = \frac{\lambda}{x - \xi_i} + [R_0(\xi, y, \zeta) + R_1(\xi, y, \zeta)(x - \xi) + \cdots]_i.$$

We observe now that dR, where R is as in (7.3) is of the form ω_1 but with an R in which there is no term in $(x - \xi_i)^{-1}$. Hence if ω_1 with the R of (7.5) is of the second kind at the curve C we must have $\lambda = 0$, and the converse is obvious. Thus a n.a.s.c. for ω_1 to be of the third kind at C is that the logarithmic residue $\lambda(C) \neq 0$.

Suppose $\lambda \neq 0$ and let U be any element of K^Φ of order unity on C. The closed differential $\lambda dU/U$ of the surface has the same logarithmic residue as the reduced ω_1 with R in the form (7.5), and so $\omega_1 - \lambda dU/U$ is regular at C.

To sum up we may state:

(7.6) *Corresponding to any closed ω_1 and polar curve C of ω_1 and for any U of order unity on C there exists an element $W \in K^\Phi$ such that the closed differential*

$$\omega_1 - dW - \frac{\lambda dU}{U}, \quad \lambda \in K$$

is regular at C. The element $\lambda \in K$ is the logarithmic residue of ω_1 relative to C and depends solely upon ω_1 and C. A n.a.s.c. for ω_1 to be of the second kind at C is that $\lambda = 0$.

The only point to be proved is the uniqueness of λ for given ω_1 and C. This is immediate. For if λ' behaves like λ then $\bar{\omega}_1 = (\lambda - \lambda')dU/U$ has no logarithmic residue as to C and so $\lambda = \lambda'$.

If $\lambda(C) \neq 0$, C is said to be a *logarithmic curve* of ω_1.

Let $C_1, \cdots, C_s$ be the set of logarithmic curves of ω_1 with $\lambda_h = \lambda(C_h)$. Let F be so chosen that the C_h are all in general position as to H_y. If C_h is of degree d_h then ω_{1y} has on H_y the polar places centered at the intersections B_{hi} of C_h with H_y. Since H_y is general all these intersections are distinct. Since the residue of ω_{1y} as to B_{hi} is λ_h and the sum of all residues is zero we have

$$\Sigma d_h \lambda_h = 0.$$

It follows in particular that a closed differential of the third kind has at least *two* logarithmic curves. The complete result is embodied in the following all important:

(7.7) **Theorem of Picard.** *Corresponding to the algebraic surface Φ there exists a number $\rho > 0$, the Picard number of Φ, such that:* (a) *there are sets of ρ irreducible curves $C_1, \cdots, C_\rho$ of Φ which cannot be the logarithmic curves of any closed differential of the third kind of Φ;* (b) *any $\rho + 1$ irreducible curves of Φ are the logarithmic curves of some closed differential of the third kind of Φ* (See Picard-Simart [1], II, p. 241).

The proof of the theorem will be based upon certain properties of the double differentials of the second kind and so we must turn our attention to these.

§ 4. Double Differentials

8. Consider then a double differential

(8.1) $$\omega_2 = R\,dx\,dy, \quad R \in K^\Phi.$$

If we have

$$\omega_1 = U\,dy - V\,dx$$

then

$$d\omega_1 = \left(\frac{\partial U}{\partial x} + \frac{\partial V}{\partial y}\right) dx\,dy$$

and this is the general form of a $d\omega_1$.

(8.2) *The differentials of the first kind, the derived $d\omega_1$, and those of the second kind constitute vector spaces $\mathfrak{B}_1$, $\mathfrak{B}_d$, $\mathfrak{B}_2$ with scalar domain K.*

(8.3) $\mathfrak{B}_1$ *and* $\mathfrak{B}_d$ *are subspaces of* $\mathfrak{B}_2$.

The dimension of $\mathfrak{B}_1$ is known as the *geometric genus* of the surface Φ and generally denoted by p_g. It is the maximum number of linearly independent differentials ω_2 of the first kind. The dimension of $\mathfrak{B}_2$ mod $\mathfrak{B}_d$ is denoted by ρ_0. It is the maximum number of differentials ω_2 of the second kind of which no linear combination is a derived differential. There is a very extensive theory of the differentials of the first kind but we shall not go into it here. Regarding the second kind there is again this basic result due to Picard:

(8.4) **Theorem.** *The number* ρ_0 *is finite* (see Picard-Simart, [1], II, p. 186).

This property (actually only its derivation) will be utilized in proving the theorem on the number ρ and so we proceed to establish it.

9. Let us start with any ω_2, say (8.1) and let C of (3) be one of its irreducible polar curves. With F as in (4) we will have the representation (4.1) on $\pi(B)$. The associated abelian differential of the curve C

$$\Omega_1(C) = R_{-1}(\xi, y, \zeta)dy \tag{9.1}$$

is called the *residue* of ω_2 on C.

(9.2) *A n.a.s.c. in order that a double differential* ω_2 *be of the second kind relative to the irreducible curve* C *is that its residue* $\Omega_1(C)$ *be a derived differential for* C, *that is to say a differential* dS, $S \in K^C$.

If ω_2 is of the second kind relative to C some $\omega_2 - d\omega_1$ is regular at C. Hence ω_2 and $d\omega_1$ have equal residues on C. Assuming $\omega_1 = U\,dy - V\,dx$ let us calculate its residue. We have

$$U = \frac{U_{-h}(\xi, y, \zeta)}{(x - \xi)^h} + \frac{U_{-h+1}(\xi, y, \zeta)}{(x - \xi)^{h-1}} + \cdots,$$

$$V = \frac{V_{-k}(\xi, y, \zeta)}{(x - \xi)^k} + \frac{V_{-k+1}(\xi, y, \zeta)}{(x - \xi)^{k-1}} + \cdots.$$

Hence

$$\frac{\partial V}{\partial x} + \frac{\partial U}{\partial y} = \cdots + \frac{\dfrac{dU_{-1}(\xi, y, \zeta)}{dy}}{x - \xi} + \cdots$$

where the only term written at the right is the term in $(x - \xi)^{-1}$. It follows that the residue of $d\omega_1$ and hence also of ω_2 is $dU_{-1}(\xi, y, \zeta)$, i.e. it is a dS, $S \in K^C$. Thus the condition is necessary.

To prove sufficiency suppose that the residue of ω_2 is $\Omega_1(C) = dS$, $S \in K^C$. With V_n as in (7.3a) we find at once that $\omega_2 + d(V_n dy)$ is such that the corresponding R is of order at least $-(n - 1)$ on $\pi(B)$ and this is achieved by merely augmenting $\Omega_1(C)$ by a dS', $S' \in K^\Phi$. Proceeding in the same way with a $V_{n-1}, \cdots$, and setting $V = V_2 + \cdots + V_n \in K^\Phi$, we will find that $\omega_2 + d(V dx)$ is now an ω_2 whose integrand R is of order (-1) on $\pi(B)$. Therefore we may assume that this holds already for the initial ω_2. By hypothesis

$$R_{-1}(\xi, y, \zeta)dy = dS(\xi, y, \zeta). \tag{9.3}$$

Hence

$$\omega_1 = \sum \left[\frac{S(\xi, y, \zeta)}{x - \xi}\left(dx - \frac{d\xi}{dy}dy\right)\right]_i \tag{9.4}$$

is a differential of K^Φ such that $\omega_2 + d\omega_1$ is regular at C. This completes the proof of (9.2).

10. Consider again the differential ω_2 of (8.1), and let it be of the second kind. Let $C_1, \cdots, C_s$ be its polar curves. We may suppose the projection F so chosen that they are all in general position relative to H_y and that none is a component of the intersection of F_z with F.

Let C_h be identified with the earlier curve C and consider the relation (7.3) relative to C_h. We propose to calculate $R_{-n}(\xi, y, \zeta)$. To that end consider the expression

$$Q(x, y, z) = R \cdot \Pi(x - \xi_i)^n.$$

Notice that since the ξ_i are all finite for y finite their integral symmetric functions are polynomials in y. Hence

$$\Pi(x - \xi_i)^n = \varphi_h^n(x, y) \in K[x, y],$$

where φ_h is the projection of C_h in the xy plane. Evidently Q is of order zero on C_h. We also have

$$\begin{aligned} Q(\xi_i, y, \zeta_i) &= \varphi_h^n(\xi_i, y) \cdot R_{-n}(\xi_i, y, \zeta_i) \\ &= R_{-n}(\xi_i, y, \zeta_i) \cdot \prod_{j \neq i}(\xi_i - \xi_j)^n. \end{aligned}$$

Hence

$$R_{-n}(\xi_i, y, \zeta_i) = \frac{Q(\xi_i, y, \zeta_i)}{\prod_{j \neq i}(\xi_i - \xi_j)^n}.$$

Upon forming now V_n of (7.3a) we see that: (a) all the $Q(\xi_i, y, \zeta_i)$ remain finite for a value y which does not correspond to an intersection of C_h with a C_k, $k \neq h$; (b) all the products in all the denominators of the $R_{-n}(\xi_i, y, \zeta_i)$, and hence V_n itself, remain finite for any y such that the corresponding ξ_i remain distinct. Hence V_n is of the form

$$(10.1) \qquad \frac{M(x, y)}{\varphi_h^{n-1}(x, y)G(y)}; \quad M, G \in K[x, y],$$

where G has no other zeros than those of type (a) or (b). Thus V_n has no other poles than these and possibly also $y = \infty$.

Now $\omega_2 + d[V_n dy]$ behaves like ω_2 relative to C_h but with n replaced by $n - 1$. If $n - 1 > 1$ the same treatment yields a V_{n-1} still of type (10.1) such that $\omega_2 + d[(V_n + V_{n-1})dy]$ behaves like ω_2 relative to C_h but with $n - 2$ instead of n, etc., down to $\omega_2 + d[(V_n + V_{n-1} + \cdots + V_2)dy]$ in which the corresponding n is unity. If $R_{-1}(\xi, y, \zeta)$ still denotes the appropriate coefficient of $(x - \xi)^{-1}$, then since ω_2 is of the second kind a relation (9.3) holds, where again S only has poles of types (a), (b) and ∞. If we set

$$\omega_{1h} = (V_2 + \cdots + V_n)dy + \sum \left[\frac{S(\xi, y, \zeta)}{x - \xi}\left(dx - \frac{d\xi}{dy}dy\right)\right]_i$$

then $\omega_2 + d\omega_{1h}$ is regular on C_h.

11. Let us set

$$\omega_{1h} = V\,dy - U\,dx; \quad U, V \in K^{\Phi}. \tag{11.1}$$

The functions U, V are infinite on the intersection of $\varphi_h(x, y)$ with F, and on certain curves H_y already specified. Thus in addition to C_h and these special H_y they are also infinite on the residual intersection D_h of φ_h with F. We propose to replace ω_{1h} by a similar differential but with D_h eliminated as polar curve.

Applying then almost any affine transformation to coordinates x', y', z' we will have

$$\left\{\begin{aligned} &\omega_{1h} = V'dy' - U'dx', \\ &U' = \frac{A(x', y', z')}{G(x', y', z')}, \quad V' = \frac{B(x', y', z')}{G(x', y', z')}; \\ &A, B, G \in K[x', y', z']. \end{aligned}\right. \tag{11.2}$$

We may furthermore suppose that G is regular in z'. If $G_1(x', y')$ is the resultant of $G(x', y', z')$ and $F(x', y', z')$ as to z' we have

$$\alpha G + \beta F = G_1(x', y'); \qquad \alpha, \beta, G_1 \in K[x', y', z'].$$

Hence multiplying in (11.2) A, B, C by α we will replace G by G_1. Thus we may assume that $G \in K[x', y']$. If $\varphi_h(x', y')$ still denotes the projection of C_h in the plane x', y' then

$$G(x', y') = \varphi_h^n(x', y') \cdot \varphi_h'(x', y')$$

where φ_h and φ_h' are relatively prime. Since x', y', z' is almost any coordinate system φ_h is regular in x'. Let $\xi_1', \cdots, \xi_d'$ be the roots in x' of $\varphi_h(x', y') = 0$. They all remain finite when y' is finite.

We have now the reduction into partial fractions represented by

$$\frac{1}{G(x', y')} = \sum \left[\frac{a_0(\xi', y') + a_1(\xi', y')x' + \cdots + a_{n-1}(\xi', y')x'^{n-1}}{(x' - \xi')^n}\right]_i + \frac{b(x', y')}{\varphi_h'(x', y')} \tag{11.3}$$

where all the new quantities are polynomials with coefficients in K. Let E_h represent the curve $\varphi_h' = F = 0$. Upon multiplying both sides of (11.3) by $(x' - \xi_i')^n$, taking the appropriate derivatives and making $x' = \xi_i'$ we find that $a_j(\xi', y')$ has for only poles those of type (a), (b), ∞, relative this time to y' and to the intersections of C_h with E_h.

Now if we suppress in $1/G$ the term beyond the sum we do not affect the behavior of U', V' relative to C_h. This means that we may replace G in (11.2) by $\varphi_h^n \psi_h(y')$, where $\psi_h(y')$ has zeros of types (a), (b).

Writing again x, y, z for x', y', z', we may sum up the final result as follows: There is a certain curve E_h associated with C_h and a differential

$$\omega_{1h} = \frac{B_h(x, y, z)dy - A_h(x, y, z)dx}{\varphi_h^n(x, y)\psi_h(y)}; \quad A_h, B_h, \psi_h \in K[x, y, z],$$

where ψ_h has no other zeros than those of types (a), (b), relative to the intersections of C_h with E_h, and $\omega_2 + d\omega_{1h}$ is regular on C_h.

12. The same treatment may be applied to all the curves C_h and yields the following result: Let $\beta_1, \cdots, \beta_s$ be the values of y such that the planes $y = \beta_k$ consist of the plane at infinity and of the planes $y =$ const., through the intersections of two curves C_h, E_h, of those tangent to C_h, and of those through place centers with the same projection on the xy plane. There exists an ω_1 such that $\omega_2 + d\omega_1$ is regular at all curves C_h but may have acquired new polar curves H_{β_k}.

Let now $b_1, \cdots, b_r \in K$ be the values of y such that the planes $y = b_i$ consist of the planes $y =$ const. which are tangent to F or to Δ or pass through its multiple points or through the points where the planes tangent to Δ coincide, or finally intersect F in a reducible curve. Referring to (III, 20.1) the number of these last planes is certainly finite if $\{H_y\}$ is almost any pencil of plane sections.

Let us show that for almost no pencil $\{H_y\}$ does a value b_i include a β_j.

First of all one may always choose on Φ the pencil $\{H_y\}$ so that the points projected into the exceptional points on Δ, or the contacts with F of planes $y =$ const., are neither on a C_h nor on an E_h. For with general $\{H_y\}$ all these points have transcendency two, whereas the points on the C_h, E_h have at most transcendency unity. Moreover the planes through the former points do not contain generally an intersection of a C_h with an E_h, and are not tangent to a C_h nor pass through a multiple point of a C_h nor finally through a point of a C_h which has on the plane xy the same projection as another point of the same C_h. Let us show finally that in general the plane $y =$ const. through an intersection A of C_h and E_h does not intersect F in an irreducible curve. Indeed since A is not a multiple point of F it is a point where the tangent plane through F contains the original z axis. Thus A is almost any point of C_h and the plane $y =$ const. (new coordinate y) is merely almost any plane. Hence it intersects F in an irreducible curve.

We conclude then that for a general $\{H_y\}$ and hence for almost every $\{H_y\}$ the values b_i will not include a value β_j.

13. Let us set then as we may for the reduced ω_2

$$\omega_2 = \frac{A(x, y, z)}{B(x, y, z)} \frac{1}{G(y)} \cdot \frac{dx\, dy}{F_z}; \quad A, B, G \in K[x, y, z], \tag{13.1}$$

where G has no other roots than the β_j and A/B has no other polar curves than perhaps H_∞.

In addition to everything else we may evidently assume $F(x, y, z)$ regular in its three variables. Applying then reductions such as those of (VI, 10) we will have on H_y (as curve of $K(y)P^2$)

$$\frac{A}{B} = \frac{D(x, y, z)}{E(y)}, \qquad D, E \in K[x, y, z],$$

and hence one may assume that in (13.1) $B = E(y)$. Now if y_0 is a root of $E(y)$ and its multiplicity is ν, $A(x, y, z)/(y - y_0)^\nu$ is of order zero on H_{y_0}. Hence the quotient is a polynomial mod F. It follows that ω_2 can be put in the form

$$(13.2) \qquad \omega_2 = \frac{P(x, y, z)dx\, dy}{G(y)F_z}, \qquad P, E \in K[x, y, z].$$

Since P/F_z is regular at the intersection places of Δ and general H_y, it is shown as for abelian differentials that P is adjoint to F.

We may now apply certain *strictly* algebraic reductions given by Picard (see Picard-Simart [1] II, pp. 163-181) to the effect that one may subtract from ω_2 a certain $d\omega_1$, where

$$\omega_1 = \frac{L(x, y, z)dy - M(x, y, z)dx}{N(y)F_z}; \quad L, M, N, \in K[x, y, z],$$

where L and M are adjoint to F, and where $\omega_2 - d\omega_1$ is like (13.2) but with $G = 1$ and P of bounded degree. In other words to within a $d\omega_1$ the initial differential of the second kind is reducible to the type

$$(13.3) \qquad \omega_2 = \frac{P(x, y, z)dx\, dy}{F_z}$$

where P is an adjoint polynomial whose degree does not exceed a certain μ.

Since among the differentials of type (13.3) the number of those linearly independent is finite, theorem (8.4) on the finiteness of the number ρ_0 is proved.

14. Strictly speaking Picard's argument is algebraic except where he utilizes property (9.2). Since our proof of (9.2) is algebraic, the whole reduction is algebraic and valid for our general choice of groundfield.

One may observe also that Picard devotes considerable effort to the case where for some root β of $G(y)$ the curve H_β contains a singularity of the curve Δ. Since we have shown that this eventuality may be avoided, this part of Picard's argument may be omitted.

The treatment of Picard leans heavily upon a certain theorem of Castelnuovo. In Castelnuovo's proof (Picard-Simart [1], II, pp. 72-74) continuity considerations play an important part. We shall therefore state the special case of the theorem which is required and give the full algebraic adaptation of Castelnuovo's proof.

(14.1). **Theorem of Castelnuovo.** *Let Γ, Δ be two curves of degrees c, d in KP^3. Let G be a surface going simply through Γ and Π a plane intersecting Γ and Δ in c and d distinct points A_i and B_j, where the A_i are ordinary points of G and G is not tangent to Π in these points. Let $A_i A_i'$ be the intersection lines with Π of the tangent planes to G at the A_i. Then the complete linear system $|\Phi^q|$ of the surfaces of degree q sufficiently high satisfying conditions Λ: they pass through Γ and Δ and are tangent to G along Γ, cuts out on Π the complete linear system $|C^q|$ of the curves of Π of degree q satisfying conditions Λ_0: they pass through the A_i, B_j and are tangent to the lines A_iA_i' at the points A_i.*

15. Notice first that one may extend lemma (VI, 13.1) to curves ψ satisfying Λ_0 as follows: The number of linearly independent conditions on the coefficients of ψ for ψ of sufficiently high degree is merely $2c + d$. All that is necessary is to replace in the proof the lines through some of the A_i by conics which are tangent to the A_iA_i' in some of the points and not in the others.

Setting now $m - 1 = 2c + d$ we will rest the proof upon the following property:

$(15.1)_q$. *The system $|C^q|$, $q > m$, is spanned by a finite number of systems $|C^m| + (q - m)l$, where l is a fixed line (systems consisting of any C^m satisfying Λ_0 plus l taken $q - m$ times).*

The curves $C^m + l$, for all l, span a linear system $|C'^{m+1}|$ and we shall first show that $|C'^{m+1}| = |C^{m+1}|$.

Let ρ_{m-1}, ρ_m, ρ_{m+1} be the dimensions of $|C^{m-1}|$, $|C^m|$, $|C'^{m+1}|$. If l, l' are two distinct lines then the curves C'^{m+1} satisfying Λ_0 through the intersection of l, l' form a linear system of dimension $\rho_{m+1} - 1$. This system contains the subsystems made up of all the $C^m + l$ and of all the $C^m + l'$. Since the two have in common $|C^{m-1}| + l + l'$ we have

$$\rho_{m+1} - 1 \geq 2\rho_m - \rho_{m-1}.$$

From the relations

$$\rho_{m-1} = \frac{(m-1)(m+2)}{2} - (m-1), \quad \rho_m = \frac{m(m+3)}{2} - (m-1)$$

we infer that

$$\rho_{m+1} \geq \frac{(m+1)(m+4)}{2} - (m-1).$$

Since $|C'^{m+1}| \subset |C^{m+1}|$ the last inequality holds also in reverse. Hence $|C'^{m+1}| = |C^{m+1}|$ as asserted. Since $|C'^{m+1}|$ can be spanned by a finite number of systems $|C^m| + l$, $(15.1)_{m+1}$ holds.

16. Proceeding step by step we find that $|C^q|$, $q > m$, is spanned by all the systems $|C^m|$ plus $(q - m)$ distinct fixed lines. To prove $(15.1)_q$ it is sufficient therefore to prove:

(16.1) *The set of all systems consisting of a line of* Π *taken* r *times spans the complete system of the curves of degree* r.

Let Π be referred to coordinates x_0, x_1, x_2 and let E denote the system of all curves $\lambda_1 l_1^r + \cdots + \lambda_\sigma l_\sigma^r$. It is sufficient to show that every monomial $x_0^a x_1^b x_2^c$, $a + b + c = r$ is in E. We have whatever $\alpha_1, \alpha_2 \in K$:

$$(x_0 + \alpha_1 x_1 + \alpha_2 x_2)^r = (x_0 + \alpha_1 x_1)^r + \binom{r}{1} (x_0 + \alpha_1 x_1)^{r-1} \alpha_2 x_2 + \cdots + \alpha_2^r x_2^r \in E.$$

Taking $r + 1$ distinct values of α_2 and writing these relations then solving for the $(x_0 + \alpha_1 x_1)^k \cdot x_2^{r-k}$ we find that they are in E. Thus

$$x_0^k \cdot x_2^{r-k} + \binom{k}{1} x_0^{k-1} \cdot \alpha_1 x_1 \cdot x_2^{r-k} + \cdots \in E.$$

Taking now $k + 1$ distinct values of α_1 and solving for $x_0^j x_1^{k-j} x_2^{r-k}$ we find that it is in E. This proves (16.1) and hence (15.1).

17. We will now take projective coordinates x_i for KP^3 so chosen that Π is x_3. Consider the change of coordinates $x_i \to x_i$, $i \neq 2$, $x_2' = u_0 x_0 + u_1 x_1 - x_2$ where u_0 and u_1 are indeterminates. The plane $x_2' = v x_3$, where v is an indeterminate, intersects Γ and Δ in c and d distinct points M_i and N_j and the tangent planes to the surface G at the M_i in lines $M_i M_i'$. The points M_i, N_j and the lines $M_i M_i'$ depend algebraically upon u_0, u_1 and v. However let us make a curve $\varphi_m(x_0, x_1, x_3)$ vanish at the M_i, N_j and have the tangents $M_i M_i'$ in the M_i. Since these conditions are symmetrical in the M_i the N_j and the tangents $M_i M_i'$ we will have

$$\varphi_m(x_0, x_1, x_3; u_0, u_1, v; c) = \sum_{j=1}^{N} c_j \varphi^j(x_0, x_1, x_3; u_0, u_1, v)$$

where the c_j are indeterminates and φ_m^j is a form of degree m in the x_i with coefficients in $K[u_0, u_1, v]$. Let r be the degree of φ_m in v. Then the surface

$$x_3^r \varphi_m(x_0, x_1, x_3; u_0, u_1, \frac{x_2'}{x_3}; c) = \omega_{m+r}(x_0, x_1, x_2', x_3; u_0, u_1; c)$$

intersects Π in φ_m plus r times the line l: $x_2' = x_3 = 0$. That is to say the surface ω_{m+r} satisfying Λ intersects Π in the general C^m plus r times l.

The number r, the degree of $\varphi_m(x_0, x_1, x_3; u_0, u_1, v; c)$ in v may be lowered only when u_0, u_1 satisfy a certain number of relations. In other words for almost every (u_0, u_1), i.e. for almost every pencil $x_2' = v x_3$, r is fixed.

18. Reverting to the initial coordinates we may suppose that $x_2 = v x_3$ is almost any pencil through Π and we will have

$$(18.1) \qquad \omega_{m+r}(x; c) = \Sigma c_j \omega_{m+r}^j(x).$$

The ω^j are not all divisible by x_3 for then one could lower r to $r - 1$.

Let $\omega^1, \cdots, \omega^{k-1}$ be such that no linear combination is divisible by x_3 and let there exist a linear combination $d_1\omega^1 + \cdots + d_{k-1}\omega^{k-1} + \omega^k$, $d_j \in K$, divisible by x_3^s but not by x_3^{s+1}. One may evidently replace ω^k by

$$\omega'^k = \frac{x_2^s}{x_3^s}(d_1\omega_1 + \cdots + d_{k-1}\omega_{k-1} + \omega_k)$$

and $\{\omega^j(x_0, x_1, x_2, 0); \omega'^k(x_0, x_1, x_2, 0)\}$, $j = 1, 2, \cdots, k-1$ is a linearly independent set. Proceeding thus we shall obtain a set $\omega^1, \cdots, \omega^N$ such that no linear combination is divisible by x_3. More precisely $\{\omega^j(x_0, x_1, x_2, 0)\}$, $j = 1, 2, \cdots, N$ will be a linearly independent set. The associated linear system (18.1) will thus cut out on Π the system $|C^m| + rl$, where l is the line $x_2 = x_3 = 0$.

Taking now ν arbitrary pencils (almost any pencils) through Π we obtain for each $n = 1, 2, \cdots, \nu$, surfaces ω^{nj} which satisfy Λ and cut out on Π the complete system $|C^m| + rl_n$, where l_n is a fixed line. By (15.1) the full set $\{\omega^{nj}\}$, n and j variable, spans a linear system which intersects Π in $|C^{m+r}|$. This proves $(14.1)_{m+r}$.

Suppose now that $(14.1)_q$ has been proved for some $q > m$. Thus $|\Phi^q|$ cuts out $|C^q|$ on Π. If H is any plane and $l = H \cap \Pi$, $|\Phi^q| + H$ cuts out $|C^q| + l$ on Π. By (15.1) then with q in place of m, the set of all $\Phi^q + H$ for all H, cuts out a system which spans $|C^{q+1}|$. Hence a fortiori $|\Phi^{q+1}|$ cuts out $|C^{q+1}|$. Since $(14.1)_{m+r}$ holds it holds for all $q \geq m + r$.

19. For our purpose it is necessary to complement one of the results of Picard. He showed (Picard-Simart [1], II, p. 182) that if in a differential ω_2 of type (13.3) the degree q of the polynomial exceeds a certain μ then one may lower it to μ by subtracting a $d\omega_1$ where

$$\text{(19.1)} \qquad \omega_1 = \frac{U\,dy - V\,dx}{F_z}; \quad U, V \in K[x, y, z].$$

In this reduction one may suppose that the curve at infinity is irreducible and has only ordinary singularities (double points with distinct tangents).

How if H is a non-singular irreducible hyperplane section of the surface Φ one may choose the projection of Φ to a surface F of KP^3 such that H only acquires ordinary singularities. On the strength of this remark we may show that the Picard result is equivalent to the following:

(19.2) *Let H be a non-singular irreducible hyperplane section of Φ and let ω_2 have H as its sole polar curve and to order q. Then there exists a number μ such that if $q > \mu$, there can be found an ω_1 with the sole polar curve H such that $\omega_2 - d\omega_1$ has H as sole polar curve and to order μ.*

The Picard property evidently implies (19.2) with H as the curve at infinity. To prove the converse choose coordinates with H as the curve at infinity and F regular in z. Thus F will be of degree m in z. Then

$$\omega_2 - d\omega_1 = \frac{Q_1(x, y, z)}{Q_0(x, y, z)} \frac{dx\,dy}{F_z}, \quad Q_i \in K[x, y, z], \tag{19.3}$$

where Q_1/Q_0 is of degree μ and is regular except at infinity, and where Q_1 is adjoint to F. As before one may assume that $Q_0 = G(y) \in K[y]$. On the other hand since F is regular in z one may divide Q_1 by F as a polynomial in z, and replace Q_1 by its remainder which is like Q_1 but of degree $< m$ in z.

Let b be a root of $G(y)$. Since $Q_1/(y - b)$ is regular on H_b, $Q_1(x, b, z) = 0$ is a consequence of $F(x, b, z) = 0$. We shall prove in a moment that this last curve has no multiple component. Admitting this property for x an indeterminate, the m roots in z of $F(x, b, z)$ are distinct and they must all be roots of $Q_1(x, b, z)$. Since Q_1 is of degree $< m$, $Q_1(x, b, z) = 0$ identically and hence $Q_1(x, y, z)$ is divisible by $y - b$. It follows that it is divisible by $G(y)$. Hence the relation (19.3) holds with $Q_0 = 1$. That is to say, modulo a $d\omega_1$, ω_2 is equal to a differential of the same form with q replaced by $q - 1$. Hence (19.2) is equivalent to the Picard property.

There remains to show that $F(x, b, z)$ has no square factors. Assuming almost any system of coordinates no tangent to H_x, of the form $y = b$, will be multiple, i.e. will have two or more points of contact and this rules out the eventuality under consideration.

It may be noted that the asserted property of the tangents is equivalent to the following for the dual plane curve Γ of H_x: a general line of the plane of Γ does not pass through a multiple point of the curve.

Returning now to (19.2), and operating in the space of Φ, consider a general hyperplane

$$H = \Sigma u_i x_i$$

of that space. Upon replacing K by $\overline{K_H(u)}$ the irreducibility properties of Φ, H_y, etc. are preserved. Applying now (19.2) we obtain a certain $\mu(H)$ for the hyperplane H. Since the property under consideration is expressible by an algebraic system in the u_i/u_j, $\mu(H)$ preserves its meaning when the general hyperplane H is replaced by almost any other. That is to say

(19.4) *There is a fixed number μ which is related as in* (19.2) *to almost every hyperplane section of* Φ.

We will denote by

$$N = \binom{\mu + 3}{3}$$

the number of coefficients of a form of degree μ in four variables. The importance of this number will appear in a moment.

20. We come now to the crux of the argument on the number ρ. We return to the curve C, of degree d and in general position of (4) and let $L = \overline{K(y)}$. Let us view for a moment H_y as a curve of LP^2. As such it is still irreducible (III, 13.1). Referring to (VII, 10.1) there is a differential of the third kind $- V^*(x, z)dx$ of H_y (as curve of LP^2) whose only poles are the $\pi(B_i)$ and $\pi(A_1)$ and they are all of order one with logarithmic residues $+ 1$ at the $\pi(B_i)$ and $- d$ at $\pi(A_1)$. The coefficient $- V^* \in L(x, z)$, i.e. it is representable as a rational function in x, z with coefficients in an algebraic extension $K(y, \theta)$ of $K(y)$. Thus $V^* \in K(x, y, z, \theta)$. Now if $\theta = \theta_1, \cdots, \theta_h$ are the conjugate values of θ then

$$- Vdx = -\frac{1}{h} \Sigma V^*(x, y, z, \theta_j)dx$$

has the same poles as $- V^*dx$ with equal residues there and $V \in K(x, y, z)$, or more accurately $V \in K^\Phi$. It follows that

$$\frac{\partial V(x, y, z)dx}{\partial y} \tag{20.1}$$

is an abelian differential of H_y which has for sole poles at finite distance the $\pi(B_i)$ and with multiplicity two in each. That is to say (20.1) behaves like a differential of the second kind at finite distance on H_y. The reductions of (VII, 4) (proof of VII, 4.2) are applicable and will yield here a function $U^*(x, z)$ of some field $K(x, y, z, \eta)$, where η is algebraic over $K(y)$, such that

$$\frac{\partial U^*}{\partial x} + \frac{\partial V}{\partial y} = \frac{Q^*(x, z)}{F_z}$$

where $Q^* \in K(y, \eta)[x, z]$ and is adjoint to H_y. Replacing η by its conjugates $\eta_1 = \eta, \eta_2, \cdots, \eta_s$ summing and dividing by s there results finally a relation

$$\omega_2^1 = \left(\frac{\partial U}{\partial x} + \frac{\partial V}{\partial y}\right) dxdy = \frac{Q_1(x, y, z)}{G(y)F_z} dxdy$$

$$U \in K(x, y, z); \quad Q_1, G \in K[x, y, z].$$

We may note here that $\omega_2^1 = d\omega_1$, where ω_1 has for logarithmic curves C with residue $+ 1$ and possibly some hyperplane sections.

Applying now the Picard reduction to ω_2^1, relative to suitable new coordinates x, y, z with $\{H_y\}$ still almost any pencil, there is found an ω_1^* whose polar curves are merely hyperplane sections and such that $\omega_2(C) = d\omega_1(C)$ where $\omega_1(C) = \omega_1 + \omega_1^*$ has no other logarithmic curves than C and some irreducible hyperplane sections, and where $\omega_2(C)$ has a single polar curve H of Φ. Moreover H is almost any hyperplane section of Φ and the order of $\omega_2(C)$ as to H is $\leq \mu$.

21. Consider now any $N+1$ curves $C_1, \cdots C_{N+1}$. We may form $\omega_1(C_i)$, $\omega_2(C_i)$ for each C_i relative to a common H and in a suitable coordinate system

$$\omega_2(C_i) = \frac{P_i(x, y, z)dx\,dy}{F_z} = d\omega_1(C_i)$$

where P_i is adjoint of degree $\leq \mu$ to F. Since there are $N+1$ polynomials P_i, they are linearly dependent. Thus there exist $\lambda_i \in K$ and not all zero such that

$$\Sigma\lambda_i P_i = 0.$$

Hence

$$d(\Sigma\lambda_i\omega_1(C_i)) = 0,$$

and therefore

$$\omega_1 = \Sigma\lambda_i\omega_1(C_i)$$

is a closed differential with the polar curves C_i and logarithmic residues λ_i not all zero. In addition it may have some polar curves $H_1, \cdots, H_s$ which are irreducible hyperplane sections. Let γ_i be the residue as to H_i. If $l = 0$, $l_i = 0$ are the equations of H, H_i in affine coordinates of the space of Φ, then

$$\omega_1(C_1, \cdots, C_N, H) = \omega_1 - \sum \gamma_i \left(\frac{dl_i}{l_i} - \frac{dl}{l}\right)$$

has the sole logarithmic curves $C_1, \cdots, C_N$, H with residues λ_i for C_i and $\lambda = \Sigma\gamma_i$ for H.

Consider now any $N+1$ irreducible curves $C_1, \cdots, C_{N+1}$ whatsoever. We form $\omega_1(C_1, \cdots, C_N, H)$ and $\omega_1(C_1, \cdots, C_{N-1}, C_{N+1}, H)$ as above with residues λ_i, λ for the first and λ_i', λ' for the second. Since the λ_i are not all zero we may always dispose of the situation so that $\lambda_N \neq 0$. If one of λ, λ' is zero we already have a closed differential with some of the C_i alone for logarithmic curves. If both are $\neq 0$, then

$$\lambda'\omega_1(C_1, \cdots, C_N, H) - \lambda\omega_1(C_1, \cdots, C_{N-1}, C_{N+1}, H)$$

has the same property. This completes the proof of Picard's theorem (7.7) and shows that $\rho \leq N$.

§ 5. ALGEBRAIC DEPENDENCE OF CURVES ON A SURFACE ACCORDING TO SEVERI

22. We shall now sketch the relation between the Picard ρ theorem and Severi's all important notion of algebraic dependence of curves on a surface.

It has been proved by Chow and van der Waerden (see van der Waerden [2] p. 157) that there is a one-one correspondence between the curves of a given degree on a surface, here Φ, and the points of a finite set of algebraic varieties $V_1, \cdots, V_q$. The collections of curves corresponding to the points of the same variety V_i are said to form an *algebraic system of curves* of Φ. If C, D are two curves in such a system we write $C = D$. This is Severi's *algebraic* dependence between curves. From this it is but a step to relations of the form

$$\Sigma\lambda_i C_i = 0,$$

where the sum is finite and the λ_i are integers. The maximum number ρ^* of algebraically independent curves on the surface is the *Severi base number*. Its meaning is that there exist ρ^* independent curves $C_1, \cdots, C_{\rho^*}$ which form a base in the sense that given any curve C whatever there takes place a relation

$$\lambda C = \Sigma\lambda_i C_i, \quad \lambda \neq 0. \tag{22.1}$$

In the complex domain it has been proved by Severi that $\rho^* = \rho$, or explicitly (Severi [2]):

(22.2) **Theorem.** *The maximum number of algebraically independent curves on* Φ *is equal to the Picard number* ρ.

More precisely Severi has proved (see Severi [2]):

(22.3) *The relation* (22.1) *is equivalent to the existence of a closed differential* ω_1 *with* C *and the* C_i *as polar curves and with the logarithmic residues* $-\lambda$, λ_i *with respect to them.*

It is understood of course that while ω_1 may have other polar curves, there will be no corresponding logarithmic residues.

The central geometric result here is then the fact that there is a finite base. Actually Severi showed that:

(22.4) *There exists a system of* $\rho + \sigma - 1$ *curves* $C_1, \cdots, C_\rho$, $D_1, \cdots, D_{\sigma-1}$, *such that the* C_i *are independent and that every curve* C *satisfies a relation*

$$C = \Sigma\lambda_i C_i + \Sigma\mu_j D_j. \tag{22.5}$$

This may also be formulated as follows:

(22.6) **Theorem of Severi.** *The additive group of the cycles of the surface* Φ *may be finitely generated.* (Severi [3].)

We may also recall in this connection, that upon turning Φ into a four dimensional manifold (in the sense of topology) then as shown by the author ([2], p. 145):

(22.7) *The Picard number* $\rho = R^2 - \rho_0$ *where* R^2 *is the second Betti number of* Φ. *Hence in particular* $\rho \leq R^2$. *Furthermore if* D_0 *denotes the identity then* $D_0, \cdots, D_{\sigma-1}$ *generate an isomorph of the torsion group of the surface.*

The basis for (22.7) is the author's proposition ([2], p. 81):

(22.8) **Theorem.** *One may associate with each algebraic curve* C *on* Φ *a* *definite two dimensional cycle of Φ in the sense of topology. Then there is complete equivalence between a relation of dependence*

$$\Sigma\lambda_i C_i = 0$$

and the homology (in the sense of topology)

$$\Sigma\lambda_i C_i \sim 0.$$

23. Severi's proof of his central theorem (22.6) rests upon Picard's theorem on the number ρ, the theorem of Chow-van der Waerden and the following property:

(23.1) *Corresponding to any cycle C on F one may calculate a certain function $\chi(C)$ of C (its virtual dimension) with the property that if $\chi(C) \geq 0$, there is some curve (effective cycle) $C' = C$.*

Now (23.1) has been proved by Severi by purely algebraic arguments. We may therefore consider Severi's theorem (22.6) as established for an algebraically closed groundfield of characteristic zero.

24. Let C be a fixed irreducible curve of degree d of the surface Φ and D a complete intersection of Φ with a hypersurface G of degree μ. The sum of the intersection multiplicities of C with D is the same as for C with G, i.e. it is equal to μd. Let it be denoted by $[CD]$. The same result will follow if D_1 is merely the residual intersection of Φ with a hypersurface G of sufficiently high degree through a fixed curve E of Φ and we will thus have a related number $[CD_1]$. It is at once seen that $[CD]$ whenever defined is additive relative to both C and D. From this it is but a step to defining $[CD]$ for all cycles C, D. Now an essential part of Severi's theory may be expressed as:

(24.1) **Severi's equivalence criterion.** *A n.a.s.c. in order that a cycle $\lambda C = 0$, $\lambda \neq 0$, is that $[CD] = 0$ whatever the cycle D.*

(24.2) **Corollary.** *A n.a.s.c. in order that the cycles $C_1, \cdots, C_\rho$ form a base is that the intersection determinant*

$$\Delta = \left| [C_i C_j] \right| \neq 0.$$

From this we may readily deduce with Severi [3]:

(24.3) *A base $\{C_i\}$ for which the integer $|\Delta|$ is minimum has the property that every cycle C satisfies a relation*

$$\lambda C = \lambda\Sigma\lambda_i C_i,\ \lambda \neq 0.$$

In other words $C - \Sigma\lambda_i C_i$ is an element of finite order of the additive group of the cycles. Such a base is said to be minimal.

Noteworthy special case. If $\Delta = \pm 1$ then $\{C_i\}$ is a minimal base.

Let C, C' be any two curves, and let $\{C_i\}$ be a base. Thus

$$\lambda C = \Sigma\lambda_i C_i, \quad \lambda' C' = \Sigma\lambda'_i C_i$$

and therefore

$$\lambda\lambda'[C\,C'] = \Sigma\lambda_i\lambda_j[C_i C_j]$$

where the bilinear form at the right is non-degenerate of rank ρ. From this follows readily:

(24.4) *Let $C_1, \cdots, C_k$ be independent curves so that $k \leq \rho$. One may then find curves $D_1, \cdots, D_{\rho-k}$ such that $\{C_i; D_j\}$ is a base. For any two curves C, C' let*

$$\lambda C = \Sigma \lambda_i C_i + \Sigma \mu_h D_h; \qquad \lambda' C' = \Sigma \lambda'_i C_i + \Sigma \mu'_h D_h.$$

If whatever C, C'

$$\lambda\lambda'[CC'] = \Sigma \lambda_i \lambda'_j [C_i C'_j]$$

then $k = \rho$ and $\{C_i\}$ is a base.

(24.5) *Applications.* I. *Plane.* If l is a line then every curve C is in the multiple $|dl|$, where d is the order of C. Hence $\{l\}$ is a minimal base, there are no cycles of finite order and $\rho = 1$.

II. *Ruled surface.* Let H be a hyperplane section and G a generator of Φ and let as before m be the degree of Φ. Then

$$[H^2] = m, \quad [HG] = 1, \quad [G^2] = 0.$$

That is to say: almost any two distinct hyperplane sections intersect in m points; a hyperplane section and a generator intersect in one point; distinct generators do not intersect. It follows that there is no relation $aH + bG = 0$ with $a, b \neq 0$. For intersection with G yields $a = 0$, and intersection with H: $b = am = 0$. Suppose $\rho(\Phi) > 2$ and let $\{H, G, C_1, \cdots, C_{\rho-2}\}$ be a base. Let

$$C'_i = C_i + \alpha_i H + \beta_i G.$$

We wish to find α_i, β_i such that

$$[C'_i H] = [C'_i G] = 0.$$

This requires that

$$m\alpha_i + \beta_i = -[C_i H], \quad \alpha_i = -[C_i G],$$

which gives a unique solution for the integers α_i, β_i.

It is clear that $\{H, G, C'_1, \cdots, C'_{\rho-2}\}$ is likewise a base.

Let now C, C' be any two curves on Φ. We will have

$$\lambda C = \alpha H + \beta G + \Sigma \gamma_i C'_i; \quad \lambda' C' = \alpha' H + \beta' G + \Sigma \gamma'_i C'_i.$$

If d, d' are the orders of the two curves and δ, δ' the number of their intersections with a generator then

$$\lambda[CH] = \lambda d = m\alpha + \beta, \quad \lambda' d' = m\alpha' + \beta'.$$
$$\lambda[CG] = \lambda\delta = \alpha, \quad \lambda' d' = \alpha'.$$

Now Corrado Segre has given a classical formula according to which $[CC']$ is a bilinear form in d, δ and d', δ'. Hence by (24.4) $\rho = 2$ and $\{H, G\}$ is a base. Since

$$\Delta = \begin{vmatrix} [H^2], [H\,G] \\ [HG], [G^2] \end{vmatrix} = -1$$

$\{H, G\}$ is a minimal base. Hence

$$(24.6) \qquad \begin{cases} \lambda C = \lambda\alpha H + \lambda\beta G, \\ \lambda' C' = \lambda'\alpha' H + \lambda'\beta' G. \end{cases}$$

This time

$$d = m\alpha + \beta, \quad d' = m\alpha' + \beta',$$

$$\delta = \alpha, \quad \delta' = \alpha'$$

$$\lambda C = \lambda\delta H + \lambda(d - m\delta)G,$$

$$\lambda' C' = \lambda'\delta' H + \lambda'(d' - m\delta')G.$$

Hence

$$[CC'] = \delta' d + \delta d' - m\delta\delta'$$

and this is precisely Segre's formula.

Consider in particular a quadric. There are two systems of generators G_1 and G_2 intersecting each in a point. We also have $H = G_1 + G_2$. Let δ_i, δ'_i be the numbers of intersections of C, C' with a G_i. Then

$$d = \delta_1 + \delta_2, \quad d' = \delta'_1 + \delta'_2.$$

Hence the well known formula

$$[CC'] = \delta_1\delta'_2 + \delta'_1\delta_2.$$

Since $\{G, H\}$ is a minimal base so is $\{G_1, G_2\}$.

It may be proved in fact that for a ruled surface the additive group of the cycles has no elements of finite order. Hence in (24.6) $\lambda = \lambda' = 1$.

§ 6. Surface Product of Two Curves. Application to Correspondences

25. Let f, f^* be two irreducible curves and let the situation and notations be those of (VIII, §3). In particular f, f^* are assumed nonsingular in suitable spaces. The general theory which has been developed is not directly applicable to the surface $\Phi = f \times f^*$ but it may be carried over without major modifications. We shall merely outline the various steps omitting most details.

Let A, A^* be points of f, f^* and t, t^* parameters for the places $\pi(A)$, $\pi^*(A^*)$. Since these places are linear one may assume that t, t^* are actually affine coordinates for A, A^* and the point (A, A^*) of Φ. Let X_i, X_j^* be affine coordinates with A, A^* as origins for the space of f, f^*. Together they form affine coordinates for the product space with (A, A^*) as the origin. If ξ_i, ξ_j^* are the elements of K^f, K^{f^*} determined by X_i, X_j^* then $K^\Phi = K(\{\xi_i; \xi_j^*\})$. Since ξ_i, ξ_j^* are ascending power series in t, t^* there is an isomorphic imbedding of $K[\{\xi_i; \xi_j^*\}]$ as a subring of the power series ring $K[[t, t^*]]$. From (IV, 13.9) we infer that there is only one branch $\mathfrak{B}$ of Φ of center (A, A^*) and that it is linear. Thus (A, A^*) is an ordinary point of Φ and so Φ has no singular points.

Since $\Phi = f \times f^*$ there passes through every point (A, A^*) a curve f_A^* and a curve f_{A^*} each merely a copy of f^* and f. There arises thus two "non-linear pencils" of curves $\{f_{A^*}\}$ and $\{f_A^*\}$ such that: (a) there is a unique curve of each pencil through every point of Φ; (b) two distinct curves of the same pencil do not intersect; (c) f_{A^*} and f_A^* intersect in a single point.

Since we have local parameters for Φ we may extend all our intersection and order properties to the curves on Φ. In particular

$$(25.1) \qquad [f_{A^*}^2] = [f_A^{*2}] = 0, \quad [f_{A^*} f_A^*] = 1.$$

The definitions of the differentials of various kinds carry over bodily. Taking the points A and A^* as fixed, reductions wholly similar to those discussed previously yield:

(25.2) *If ω_1 and ω_1^* are both of the first or of the second kind for f and f^* then $\omega_2 = \omega_1 \times \omega_1^*$ is of the same kind for Φ.*

(25.3) *Every ω_2 of the second kind of Φ is reducible modulo a $d\omega_1$ of Φ to a linear combination of products of differentials $\bar{\omega}_1 \times \bar{\omega}_1^*$ where $\bar{\omega}_1$ and $\bar{\omega}_1^*$ are differentials of the second kind of f and f^* and not of the form dR or dR^*, $R \in K^f$, $R^* \in K^{f^*}$. Hence here*

$$(25.3a) \qquad \rho_0 \leq 4pp^*.$$

A treatment essentially like that of (21) may be applied to the curves on Φ but the process is not applicable to curves f_{A^*} and f_A^*. Hence we may only assert that:

(25.4) *ρ is finite and $\leq 4pp^* + 2$.*

26. The application to correspondences is immediate. It follows at once from (24.1) that the curves f_{A^*} and f_A^* are independent. Thus $\rho \geq 2$. Moreover since

$$\Delta = \begin{vmatrix} [f_{A^*}^2], [f_{A^*} f_A^*] \\ [f_{A^*} f_A^*], [f_A^{*2}] \end{vmatrix} = -1$$

if $\rho = 2$ then $\{f_{A^*}, f_A^*\}$ is a minimal base.

The curves f_{A^*} and f_A^* represent degenerate correspondences.

If $\rho > 2$ there exist correspondences $\mathfrak{C}_1, \cdots, \mathfrak{C}_{\rho-2}$ whose graphs $\varphi_1, \cdots, \varphi_{\rho-2}$ are independent cycles of the surface Φ and such that $\{\varphi_i; f_{A^*}, f_A^*\}$ is a base for Φ. If $\mathfrak{C}$ is any correspondence with φ as its graph then there is a relation

$$(26.1) \qquad \lambda\varphi = \Sigma\lambda_i\varphi_i + \nu f_{A^*} + \nu^* f_A^*$$

from which follows

$$\lambda\mathfrak{C} = \Sigma\lambda_i\mathfrak{C}_i.$$

Therefore $\{\mathfrak{C}_i\}$ is a base for the correspondences on Φ.

If $\mathfrak{C}$, $\mathfrak{C}'$ have for graphs φ, φ' then the intersections of the graphs correspond to the couples A, A^* associated under both $\mathfrak{C}$ and $\mathfrak{C}'$ or coincidences of $\mathfrak{C}$ and $\mathfrak{C}'$. Their number is $[\varphi\varphi']$. If φ' satisfies a relation (26.1) with coefficients λ', $\cdots$, then the number of coincidences is given by

$$(26.2) \qquad \lambda\lambda'[\varphi\varphi'] = \Sigma\lambda_i\lambda_j'[\varphi_i\varphi_j'] + \Sigma(\lambda_i\nu^{*\prime} + \lambda_i'\nu^*)[\varphi_i f_A^*] + \Sigma(\lambda_i\nu' + \lambda_i'\nu)[\varphi_i f_{A^*}] + \nu\nu^{*\prime} + \nu'\nu^*.$$

The correspondences with the λ_i not all zero are known as *singular*. If there are none the λ_i, λ_i' are all zero and $\{f_{A^*}, f_A^*\}$ is a minimal base. In this case

$$\lambda\varphi = \lambda\nu f_{A^*} + \lambda\nu^* f_A^*$$

and similarly for φ' with λ', $\cdots$. Hence the number of coincidences assumes the simple form

$$[\varphi\varphi'] = \nu\nu^{*\prime} + \nu'\nu^*.$$

The determination of the number of fixed points may also be reduced to a question of intersections of curves on Φ.

All these results are well known for the complex field and have been obtained long ago by Hurwitz [1]. See also Severi [1]. They are also consequences of our coincidence and fixed point formulas for manifolds (see Lefschetz [3]).

(26.3) *Algebra of correspondences on a curve.* Let us consider only correspondences of a given curve f with itself. If

$$\lambda\mathfrak{C} = \Sigma\lambda_i\mathfrak{C}_i$$

we will agree to write

$$\mathfrak{C} = \Sigma\mu_i\mathfrak{C}_i, \qquad \mu_i = \lambda_i/\lambda.$$

Thus the correspondences form a *finite dimensional* vector space over the rationals whose dimension is $\rho - 1$.

Since a multiplication has been defined for correspondences they form a so-called finite algebra. It has been shown essentially by A. Weil that these algebras do not differ from those of Albert's classification of the algebras of Riemann matrices (see Albert [1]).

§ 7. BIRATIONAL INVARIANCE

27. This is a far knottier question for surfaces than for curves. The difficulties are caused by the fundamental elements and also by the absence of a suitable generalization of the concept of *place* that would be applicable to a surface regardless of its singularities.

To simplify matters let us confine our attention to a pair of birationally equivalent surfaces Φ and Ψ without singularities and let T be a birational transformation $\Phi \to \Psi$. Each surface may contain curves imaged into points by T or T^{-1}. It is not difficult to show that such curves are necessarily rational. Hence every ω_2 of Φ is of the second kind on its fundamental curves and likewise on Ψ. On the other hand if C is not fundamental for Φ and ω_2 is of the second kind on C then its image $T\omega_2$ (in an evident sense) is of the second kind on TC. Hence:

(27.1) *Under T differentials ω_2 of the second kind for Φ go into differentials $T\omega_2$ of the second kind for Ψ.*

Since an ω_1 and $d\omega_1$ go into $T\omega_1$ and $dT\omega_1$ and linearly independent differentials go into linearly independent differentials we have:

(27.2) *The number ρ_0 is invariant under T.*

Let e and e' be the numbers of fundamental curves on Φ and Ψ and let ρ, ρ' be their Picard numbers. Then by examining intersections on the two surfaces one may show that

(27.3) $$\rho - e = \rho' - e'.$$

This type of behavior is expressed by the statement: ρ is a *relative* invariant. On the other hand strict invariance, i.e. such as is expressed by (27.2) is described as: ρ_0 is an *absolute* invariant.

Example. Let Φ be a quadric of KP^3 and let it be projected from a point A of Φ onto a plane Ψ not passing through A. The fundamental curves on Φ are the generators G_1, G_2 through A. The projection images them into two points γ_1, γ_2 and the line $l = \gamma_1\gamma_2$ is the only fundamental curve on Ψ. Here $e = 2$, $e' = 1$, hence $\rho - 2 = \rho' - 1$ which agrees with the known values $\rho = 2$, $\rho' = 1$.

Appendix
On The Characteristic Zero

In the present appendix we propose to show that, in a certain sense, algebraic geometry over a groundfield of characteristic zero may be reduced to complex algebraic geometry. This is without question the deep reason why characteristic zero algebraic geometry presents no new results over and above complex algebraic geometry.

Let then V^r be an irreducible r dimensional variety in KP_x^m, where the groundfield K is algebraically closed and of characteristic zero. Let $\{f_1(x), \cdots, f_q(x)\}$ be a base for the ideal $\mathfrak{p}_H$ of V^r. Thus the variety is represented by the system

$$f_i(x) = 0, \quad i = 1, 2, \cdots, q. \tag{1}$$

Let C_h^i be the coefficients of f_i and let R be the rational field. Consider the q-tuply homogeneous field $L = R_H^q(C^1; \cdots; C^q)$. The field $L = R(u_1, \cdots, u_n, u_{n+1})$ where n of the u_i, say $u_1, \cdots, u_n$ are algebraically independent over R and may be taken to be indeterminates, and where u_{n+1} satisfies an irreducible equation

$$F(u_1, \cdots, u_{n+1}) = 0 \tag{2}$$

where $F \in R[u_1, \cdots, u_{n+1}]$.

Let us replace now the u_i, $i \leq n$, by n complex numbers v_i, $i \leq n$, which are algebraically independent over R. At the same time u_{n+1} is replaced by a root v_{n+1} of

$$F(v_1, \cdots, v_{n+1}) = 0. \tag{3}$$

As a consequence the field L goes over into an isomorphic field L^* which is a subfield of the complex field, and the system (1) goes into a system

$$f_i^*(x) = 0, \quad i = 1, 2, \cdots, q \tag{4}$$

where f_i^* is deduced from f_i by replacing the coefficients C_j^i by the corresponding appropriate elements of L^*. As a consequence the variety V^r goes over into a complex variety V^{*r}. The important fact is that *in the passage from V^r to V^{*r} all the strictly algebraic properties of V^r are preserved.* This is clear since in this passage no new algebraic relations between the C^i are introduced. In particular V^{*r} is still irreducible. We are however at liberty to take full advantage of the imbedding into the complex field to derive various results relative to V^r from known results for V^{*r}. Let us mention a few applications:

I. *Numbers* ρ *and* ρ_0. The results obtained by Picard, Severi and the author carry over bodily to surfaces over any field of characteristic zero.

II. *Algebra of correspondences on a given curve.* In the complex case the rank of the algebra is $\rho - 1$, where ρ is the Picard number of the product surface $f \times f^*$. Moreover $\sigma = 1$ (Severi) and $\rho - 1 \leq 2p^2$. Hence these relations hold for any groundfield of characteristic zero. In particular the fact that $\sigma = 1$ signifies that one may take in (IX, 26.3) a system of basic correspondences $\mathfrak{C}_i$ such that $\lambda = 1$ for every correspondence $\mathfrak{C}$ whatsoever.

III. *Intersections.* Let V^r be a variety without singularities. Then V^{*r} is likewise deprived of singularities. Let V^s, V^t be subvarieties of V^r intersecting in a pure subvariety V^{s+t-r} with components V_i^{s+t-r}, $i = 1, 2, \cdots, n$. Passing now to V^{*r} and the field L^*, we will have V^{*s} and V^{*t} intersecting in a pure V^{*s+t-r} with components V_i^{*s+t-r}, in one-one correspondence with the V_i^{s+t-r}. Now upon turning V^{*r} into a complex $2r$-manifold, still written V^{*r}, oriented as indicated in [4], p. 379, and dealing likewise with V^{*s}, V^{*t} and V_i^{*s+t-r}, we will have a homology (in the sense of topology) of the form

$$V^{*s} \cdot V^{*t} \sim \Sigma \mu_i V_i^{*s+t-r}.$$

Here every $\mu_i > 0$ and μ_i is the multiplicity of V_i^{*s+t-r} as element of the intersection $V^{*s} \,.\, V^{*t}$. The same multiplicity μ_i is to be assigned to V_i^{s+t-r} as element of the intersection of V^s and V^t.

Bibliography

ALBERT, A. A.

[1] *On the construction of Riemann matrices, I and II*, Annals of Mathematics, (2), 35 (1934), 1–28, and 36 (1935), 376–394.

BARSOTTI, I.

[1] *Algebraic correspondences between algebraic varieties*, Annals of Mathematics, (2), 52 (1950), 427–464.

BERTINI, E.

[1] *Introduzione alla geometria proiettiva degli iperspazi*, Bologna, 1907.

BOCHNER, S., and MARTIN, W. T.

[1] *Several Complex Variables*, Princeton University Press, 1948 (Princeton Mathematical Series, 10).

CHEVALLEY, C.

[1] *On the theory of local rings*, Annals of Mathematics, (2), 44 (1943), 690–708.

[2] *Some properties of ideals in rings of power series*, Transactions, American Mathematical Society, 55 (1944), 68–84.

[3] *Intersections of algebraic and algebroid varieties*, Transactions, American Mathematical Society, 57 (1945), 1–85.

[4] *Introduction to the theory of algebraic functions of one variable*, American Mathematical Society, 1951 (Mathematical Surveys, vol. VI).

HODGE, W. V. D.

[1] *The Theory and Applications of Harmonic Integrals*, Cambridge University Press, 1941.

—and PEDOE, D.

[1] *Methods of algebraic geometry*, vol. I (1947), vol. II (1952). Cambridge University Press.

HURWITZ, A.

[1] *Mathematische Werke*, vol. 1, p. 163–188. Basel, Birkhäuser, 1932.

KRULL, W.

[1] *Beiträge zur Arithmetik kommutativer Integritätsbereiche, III*, Mathematische Zeitschrift, 42 (1937), 745–766.

[2] *Dimensionstheorie in Stellenringen*, Journal für die reine und angewandte Mathematik, 179 (1938), 204–226.

LEFSCHETZ, S.

[1] *On certain numerical invariants of algebraic varieties with application to Abelian varieties*, Transactions, American Mathematical Society, 22 (1921), 327–482.

[2] *L'Analysis Situs et la Géométrie Algébrique*, Paris, Gauthier-Villars, 1924 (Collection de Monographies sur la Théorie des Fonctions, pub. sous la direction de É. Borel).

LEFSCHETZ, S.

[3] *Correspondences between algebraic curves,* Annals of Mathematics, (2), 28 (1927), 342–354.

[4] *Topology,* New York, American Mathematical Society, 1930 (Colloquium Publications, vol. 12).

[5] *Algebraic Topology,* New York, American Mathematical Society, 1942 (Colloquium Publications, vol. 27).

NETTO, E.

[1] *Vorlesungen über Algebra,* vol. 2, chap. 2, Vorlesungen 33, 36. Leipzig, Teubner, 1900.

NOETHER, E.

[1] *Ein algebraisches Kriterium für absolute Irreduzibilität,* Mathematische Annalen, 85 (1922), 26–33.

[2] *Eliminationstheorie und allgemeine Idealtheorie,* Mathematische Annalen, 90 (1923), 229–261.

PICARD, É.

[1] *Traité d'Analyse,* 3d ed., vol. 2. Paris, Gauthier-Villars, 1926.

PICARD, É., and SIMART, G.

[1] *Théorie des Fonctions Algébriques de Deux Variables Indépendantes,* Paris, Gauthier-Villars, 1897–1906.

RÜCKERT, W.

[1] *Zum Eliminationsproblem der Potenzreihenideale,* Mathematische Annalen, 107 (1932), 259–281.

SEVERI, F.

[1] *Sulle corrispondenze fra i punti di una curva algebrica e sopra certe classi di superficie,* Memorie, Accademia delle Scienze di Torino, (2), 54 (1903), 1–49.

[2] *Sulla totalità delle curve algebriche tracciate sopra una superficie algebrica,* Mathematische Annalen, 62 (1906), 194–225.

[3] *La base minima pour la totalité des courbes tracées sur une surface algébrique,* Annales, École Normale Supérieure, (3), 25 (1908), 449–468.

[4] *Vorlesungen über Algebraische Geometrie,* tr. by E. Löffler, Leipzig, Teubner, 1921.

[5] *Trattato di Geometria Algebrica,* Bologna, Zanichelli, 1926.

VAN DER WAERDEN, B. L.

[1] *Moderne Algebra,* 2d ed. Berlin, Springer, 1937–40.

[2] *Einführung in die Algebraische Geometrie,* Berlin, Springer, 1939.

WALKER, R. J.

[1] *Reduction of the singularities of an algebraic surface,* Annals of Mathematics, (2), 36 (1935), 336–365.

[2] *Algebraic Curves,* Princeton University Press, 1950 (Princeton Mathematical Series, 13).

WEIL, A.

[1] *Foundations of Algebraic Geometry,* New York, American Mathematical Society, 1946 (Colloquium Publications, vol, 29).

ZARISKI, O.

[1] *Algebraic Surfaces,* Ergebnisse der Mathematik und Ihrer Grenzgebiete, Band 3, Heft 5, Berlin, Springer, 1935.

ZARISKI, O.

[2] *Some results in the arithmetic theory of algebraic varieties*, American Journal of Mathematics, 61 (1939), 249–294.

[3] *The reduction of the singularities of an algebraic surface*, Annals of mathematics, (2), 40 (1939), 639–689.

[4] *Local uniformization on algebraic varieties*, Annals of Mathematics, (2), 41 (1940), 852–896.

[5] *A simplified proof for the resolution of singularities of an algebraic surface*, Annals of Mathematics, (2), 43 (1942), 583–593.

[5] *Foundations of a general theory of birational correspondences*, Transactions, American Mathematical Society, 53 (1943), 490–542.

[7] *Generalized semi-local rings*, Summa Brasiliensis Mathematicae, 1 (1946), 169–195.

ZEUTHEN, H. G.

[1] *Lehrbuch der abzählenden Geometrie*, Leipzig, Teubner, 1914.

List of Symbols Most Frequently Used in the Text

$\supset$ contains; $\subset$ is contained in; $\in$ is a member of; $\cup$ union; $\cap$ intersection; $K =$ the groundfield; $K[x_1, \cdots, x_n]$ ring of polynomials in the x_i with coefficients in K, abridged as $K[x]$; $K(x_1, \cdots, x_n)$ quotient field of $K[x]$, abridged as $K(x)$; $K_H[x_0, \cdots, x_n]$ homogeneous ring of forms in the x_i with coefficients in K, abridged as $K_H[x]$; $K_H(x_0, \cdots, x_n)$ field of the quotients of forms of $K_H[x]$ of the same degree, abridged as $K_H(x)$; $K_H^s(x^1; x^2; \cdots; x^s]$, $K_H^s(x^1; \cdots; x^s)$ homogeneous ring and field in several sets of variables $x_0^1, x_1^1, \cdots; x_0^2, x_1^2, \cdots$; $K[[x_1, \cdots, x_n]]$, $K((x_1, \cdots, x_n))$ ring and quotient field of formal power series in the x_i, abridged as $K[[x]]$, $K((x))$.

The ideals of $K[x]$ are written $\mathfrak{a}, \mathfrak{b}, \cdots$, the prime and primary ideals are written $\mathfrak{p}$, $\mathfrak{q}$. The same for $K_H[x]$ are written $\mathfrak{a}_H, \mathfrak{b}_H, \cdots, \mathfrak{p}_H, \mathfrak{q}_H$.

The subring $K[x_1, \cdots, x_r]$ of $K[x]$ is often written $K^r[x]$, and similarly we write $K^r(x)$, $K_H^r[x], \cdots$, for $K(x_1, \cdots, x_r)$, $K_H[x_0, \cdots, x_r], \cdots$.

If x is an indeterminate then $K\{x\}$ denotes the union of the fields $K((x^{1/n}))$, $n = 1, 2, \cdots$.

KP^m, KP_x^m projective m-space over K, the same with coordinates x_i KA^m, KA_X^m affine m-space over K, the same with coordinates X_i; V algebraic variety, V_A its affine part; V^r, V_A^r the same of dimension r; K^V function field of V. Sometimes the variety is also denoted by W. An algebroid r dimensional variety is written $\mathfrak{B}^r$. A correspondence between V^r and W^s is written $\mathfrak{C}$.

f projective plane curve; F the same referred to affine coordinates; π a place of f; g_n^r linear series of degree n and dimension r; $|A|$ complete linear series generated by the divisor A; *dfk, dsk, dtk* differential of the first, second, third kinds; ω_k k-tuple differential.

Index